FOURTH EDITION

OUR SOCIETY

HUMAN DIVERSITY IN CANADA

FOURTH EDITION

OUR SOCIETY

HUMAN DIVERSITY IN CANADA

Edited by Paul U. Angelini
*Sheridan College Institute of Technology
and Advanced Learning*

NELSON / EDUCATION

NELSON / EDUCATION

Our Society: Human Diversity in Canada, Fourth Edition

Edited by Paul U. Angelini

Vice President, Editorial Director:
Evelyn Veitch

Editor-in-Chief, Higher Education:
Anne Williams

Acquisitions Editor:
Maya Castle

Marketing Manager:
Terry Fedorkiw

Developmental Editor:
Liisa Kelly

Photo Researcher:
Natalie Barrington

Permissions Coordinator:
Natalie Barrington

Production Service:
KnowledgeWorks Global Ltd.

Copy Editor:
Erin Moore

Proofreader:
Jayaprakash

Indexer:
Kevin Broccoli

Senior Production Coordinator:
Ferial Suleman

Design Director:
Ken Phipps

Managing Designer:
Franca Amore

Interior Design Modifications:
Sharon Lucas

Cover Design:
Sharon Lucas

Cover Image:
Anne Bradley/Nelson Education Ltd.

Compositor:
KnowledgeWorks Global Ltd.

Printer:
RR Donnelley

Library and Archives Canada
Cataloguing in Publication Data

Our society : human diversity
in Canada / edited by Paul
U. Angelini. — 4th ed.

Includes bibliographical references
and index.
ISBN 978-0-17-650354-3

1. Multiculturalism—
Canada—Textbooks.
2. Canada—Social conditions—
1991- —Textbooks. I. Angelini,
Paul Ubaldo, 1962–

HN103.5.O97 2011 306.0971
C2010-907717-2

ISBN-13: 978-0-17-650354-3
ISBN-10: 0-17-650354-4

CONTENTS

PREFACE

This fourth edition of *Our Society: Human Diversity in Canada*, like the first, was written for students who have had little or no exposure to the issues surrounding diversity in Canada. As an introductory, topic-oriented text, *Our Society* is designed to give readers a panoramic view of diversity in Canada framed within the dominant theoretical paradigms of the day. For readers who have already examined diversity, this edition provides up-to-date statistics, analyses of recent events, and a bibliography that covers a wide variety of issues in each subject area.

The fourth edition offers a completely new chapter on sexuality in Canada. It is sure to spark debate and critical thinking as it skillfully meanders the history and recent developments in the field of sexuality in Canada. There is also a completely new chapter on the treatment of diversity in Canadian literature. It examines how literature is a voice of and for diversity while answering the question how Canadian writing and storytelling influence our ideas about who we are. New topics in other chapters include the influence of South Asian communities, the outcome of the American financial crash, and Theodor Adorno's model for understanding media.

All postsecondary schools and high schools have at least one course that attempts to explain life in Canada. Courses range from the general, such as Introduction to Canadian Studies, to the specific, such as Race and Ethnic Relations in Canada. Increasingly, students have demanded more comprehensive analyses of life in Canada. For example, the course I teach has evolved from dealing exclusively with race and ethnicity to dealing with many issues in Canadian life, including regionalism, gender, and social stratification. This course, renamed Human Diversity and Interactions in Canada, better reflects the interests of my students.

This text focuses on human diversity in Canada. Diversity in simple terms refers to the differences that set people apart from each other. Therefore, in introducing students to the diversity of Canadian life, the text addresses the following questions: How do Canadians differ from each other? What are the scope and the range of each difference? How have differences evolved over time? How do we as Canadians view diversity? Rather than encouraging uniformity, the authors intend, through careful analysis, to promote tolerance and understanding and to show that differences can and do bring Canadians together. In the end, students will appreciate the differences that characterize Canadian life and will have a fuller understanding of what it means to be Canadian. The more we understand about ourselves and the more comfortable we become with this understanding, the more likely we are to accept others without prejudice. After all, difference should be celebrated, not lamented. Many years ago the most anticipated celebration in Toronto was the Santa Claus parade. Families would travel hours to stand along the parade route to catch a glimpse of the man in red. Today, Gay Pride and Caribana have replaced the Santa Claus parade. People arrive from around the world to experience and revel in these proud celebrations of difference spending millions and millions of dollars on hotels, food, refreshments, and entertainment.

The reasons for preparing this fourth edition are the same as those for the original undertaking in 1997. First, students were vocal in their demands for more comprehensive courses dealing with the differences that characterize and shape life in every corner of Canada. The text, therefore, is student-driven.

Second, few texts dealing with this subject matter are written for the target audience of postsecondary and high-school students. Several features make this book uniquely suited for this target audience:

- The text is learning-centred, meaning that the concerns of students come before those of teachers. The writing style, organization, and level of analysis are introductory, with only the most important conceptual jargon included. Reading this text does not require specific prior knowledge.

- The book is student-friendly. Important terms are bolded and featured both at the end of each chapter as a list of Key Terms, and in the end-of-text Glossary. For this edition, page numbers have been added to these sections for easy reference. Additionally, each chapter contains two types of boxes—approximately four of each—that highlight important or complementary information. Box types include "Have You Heard?," which are more informational in nature, and "Critical Thinking Outside the Box," which encourage students to think constructively and critically.

- The topics covered are truly inclusive. We have tried, as much as possible, to include both those topics demanded by students and those that instructors believed were necessary.

- The text is unabashedly Canadian! It is not an American text with Canadian information added; rather, it is a text written by Canadians, about Canadians, for Canadians, providing students with a balanced introduction to life in Canada.

Additional to the features above, this new edition also contains revised statistics, figures, and tables, updated research and examples, and a fresh new look.

All students—at college or university or in high school—are at a time in their lives when they begin to make definitive assessments about the world around them. This is especially important after the events of 11 September 2001: two illegal invasions of Iraq, the American economic meltdown, the continued presence of Canadian troops in Afghanistan, and the subsequent fallout from these events that continues well into the second decade of this new century. We hope the treatment of the subjects covered in *Our Society: Human Diversity in Canada* will make their decisions informed and responsible ones.

ACKNOWLEDGMENTS

The work involved in putting together this edition was no less arduous than that involved in the previous ones. Again, without the guidance and support of many people, this text would still be just an idea.

We would also like to thank a number of people at Nelson for helping to make the fourth edition a reality. We owe a great debt to Executive Editor Laura Macleod and Acquisitions Editor Maya Castle for their sound advice, expert counsel, and neverending support. A similar debt is owed to Developmental Editor Liisa Kelly, whose cogent editing, knowledge of copyright issues, and exceptional organizational skills kept this project on course and on time! We also appreciate the assistance of Susan Calvert, Director of Content and Media Production; Erin Moore, copyeditor; Jayaprakash, proofreader; and Prasanna, Project Manager.

I would like to thank Paul Saundercook for originally convincing me that a project of this nature was both viable and needed. His understanding of the postsecondary marketplace is second to none. I would also like to thank Hopie Palmer and Victor Montgomery for their research and graphic assistance.

Paul U. Angelini
Hamilton, Ontario
October 2010

PART ONE

AN OVERVIEW OF DIVERSITY IN CANADA

Part I takes a macro approach to diversity in Canada. Using the analogy of a house, these first two chapters are the building blocks, the foundation, the walls, and the roof. Together they provide a structure—they "frame" the discussions that take place in Part II.

Chapter 1 looks at regionalism. It begins with a definition of regionalism and then briefly outlines the different regions in Canada. It finishes by examining how the federal government in Ottawa has increased the tensions between regions and by assessing the actions taken by the same government to lessen regional inequality.

Chapter 2 introduces the reader to the study of demography in Canada. In addition to outlining the terms necessary for the study of demography itself, this chapter examines specific demographic trends critical to understanding developments in Canadian diversity.

CHAPTER 1

Regionalism in Canada: The Forgotten Diversity

Paul U. Angelini

Two things hold this country together. Everybody hates Air Canada coffee and everybody hates Ontario.
— Late New Brunswick Premier Richard Hatfield

Regions usually have some concrete, physical foundation…. But to some extent regions are also a state of mind.
— Political scientist Rand Dyck

Objectives

After reading this chapter, you should be able to

- define regionalism

- appreciate the role of regionalism in Canadian social life

- outline briefly some of the suspected causes of regionalism

- understand the sociopsychological component to regionalism

- understand the role of the federal government in creating and attempting to lessen regional differences, and appreciate the aspects of our political system that intensify regional differences

INTRODUCTION: HOW IS REGIONALISM A FORM OF DIVERSITY?

The purpose of this chapter is threefold: (1) to outline what is meant by **regionalism**, (2) to briefly explain some of the suspected causes of regionalism, and, most importantly, (3) to make the case that there is an important sociopsychological component to regionalism that is seldom acknowledged. Simply put, people have a profound effect on their region and on the world around them.

Let us stress that our purpose here is not to attempt to find the causes of regionalism. These attempts are usually bogged down in theoretical and ideological debates that, in the end, tell us little about the people living in these areas. We will, however, briefly outline what some other writers and researchers consider the causes of regionalism. You will have to assess for yourselves which make the most sense. When in doubt you always have the option of doing more research.

Canada is a country characterized by difference. From coast to coast, there are differences in physical terrain, climate, population, distribution of natural resources, percentage of people living in urban areas, ethnicity, religion, occupation, and income. These are real and identifiable differences—but what about "subjective" differences? How do people living in each region feel about themselves, their region, and their fellow inhabitants? What influences how people answer these questions? These are important considerations, because the answers help us more fully understand what is meant by regionalism, and they help bring the "human" aspect to this study. After all, regions are made up of people and people make regions.

WHAT IS REGIONALISM AND WHY STUDY IT?

Regionalism examines the people living in different areas in Canada and the different feelings they have regarding themselves, the people living in other areas, and the federal and provincial governments. Regionalism, therefore, is most of all an attitude. We can define regionalism as an attitude that reflects a long, deep, certain feeling held by the citizens of a particular geographical area that they have their own, unique identity. Often they feel that they have not been given adequate recognition for their hard work and sacrifices. Their dissatisfaction is focused in three specific areas:

1. They believe that people in the federal and provincial governments have not accurately recognized their contribution to the life of their region.

2. They believe they have not been given due recognition for their contribution to building this country called Canada.

3. They believe that their interests have not been adequately represented by the government in Ottawa and that this is one of the principal reasons why some regions receive far more money from the federal government than others; over the years this has meant that economic differences in regional development have been made worse.

In short, while Ontario and Quebec, the central region of Canada, receive almost everything, the Western and Atlantic regions receive very little. Ontario and Quebec get much of the recognition for building Canada; in comparison, the Western and Atlantic provinces get very little.

Before continuing, however, we must address three problems with regional analysis.

PROBLEMS WITH REGIONAL ANALYSIS

Three central problems exist in discussing regionalism:

1. How are geographical regions defined?
2. Are provinces necessarily regions?
3. Are regions the appropriate tool to study the people living in Canada?

How Are Geographical Regions Defined?

Some dispute exists concerning what physical characteristics should be used to designate a region. Historically, we in Canada have used geography to designate four regions (see Figure 1.1).

Perhaps the best example of dispute is over what is commonly referred to as the "West." Geographically, British Columbia is radically different from the three Prairie provinces because of the Cordilleran mountain system (the Canadian Rockies). As a result, many people in British Columbia do not believe that they should be included in the "Western" region. This belief is reinforced by the fact that the economies of these four provinces are also different: The B.C. economy is not based on farming, but the economies of Manitoba and Saskatchewan are. British Columbia has a huge forest industry and a significant fishing industry, whereas Alberta is the centre of Canada's oil and natural gas industries. Similar economic and physical differences exist within the other regions of Canada, too. This is true of Newfoundland and Labrador; the last province to join Confederation (1949) has always considered itself distinct from the rest of the Atlantic provinces.

Are Provinces Necessarily Regions?

Questions arise about the belief that a province is a region. Within provinces there tend to be different regions that share certain characteristics that make them distinct from

Figure 1.1   Regions of Canada

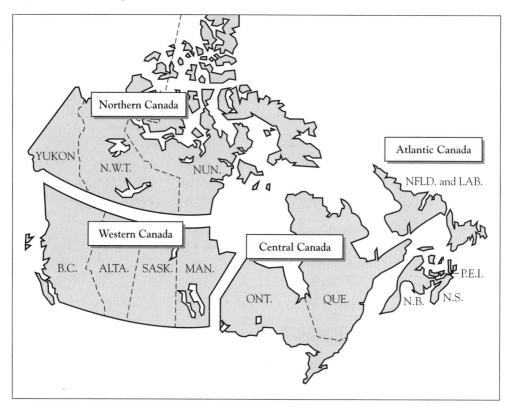

other parts of the province. The best examples of such differences are those between northern Ontario and southern Ontario and between northern Quebec and southern Quebec. In the case of Ontario, the northern part has always differed with respect to economic growth (much slower, if at all), unemployment, per capita income, and types of jobs. Unemployment is one area in which the differences are very visible. Northern Ontario has traditionally experienced higher unemployment rates than the rest of the province, in large part because of the resource focus of industry in northern Ontario, the seasonal nature of such work, and the existence of one-industry towns that shut down when the industry closes. It is not uncommon for unemployment in northern Ontario to be double the provincial average.

In short, the economic prosperity of Ontario is usually only experienced in Metropolitan Toronto, other parts of the **Golden Horseshoe**, which stretches along the coast of Lake Ontario from Niagara Falls to Oshawa, and some parts of south-central

Ontario. A survey by Statistics Canada shows that eight of the top thirteen cities according to median total income (by family type) in Canada are located in Ontario (see Table 1.1).

Are Regions the Appropriate Tool to Study the People Living in Canada?

Because so many questions surround what constitutes regions, issues have arisen regarding the use of regions as an explanatory tool. A wide variety of other tools could be used to explain social life in Canada, including social class, occupation, elites, ethnicity, economic development, and individual choice. Marxists and neo-Marxists stress that analyzing social class and power will best explain the reality of living in Canada. Other writers, such as Richard Simeon, dismiss the use of regions as an analytical tool altogether.[1]

Table 1.1 Median Total Income, By Family Type, By Census Metropolitan Area (all census families)

All Census Families[i]	$ 2002	2003	2004	2005	2006
Ottawa–Gatineau (Ont. part, Ont.–Que.)	73 400	74 500	77 000	80 300	84 000
Calgary (Alta.)	66 700	67 800	71 100	75 400	83 500
Edmonton (Alta.)	63 400	64 800	68 100	72 600	79 300
Oshawa (Ont.)	70 300	72 400	75 000	76 800	78 900
Kitchener (Ont.)	65 900	67 000	69 200	71 100	72 800
Regina (Sask.)	61 500	63 300	66 000	68 500	72 200
Hamilton (Ont.)	63 800	65 200	67 100	69 500	71 600
Victoria (B.C.)	60 400	61 700	64 200	66 900	71 500
Ottawa–Gatineau (Que. part, Ont.–Que.)	61 800	62 800	64 700	68 500	70 900
Windsor (Ont.)	67 100	67 800	68 400	69 700	70 000
Greater Sudbury / Grand Sudbury (Ont.)	58 300	59 200	62 300	66 100	69 700
Thunder Bay (Ont.)	61 800	63 400	64 600	67 200	69 400
Kingston (Ont.)	59 900	61 900	63 700	66 400	69 100

[i]Census families include couple families, with or without children, and lone-parent families.

Source: Adapted from Statistics Canada http://www40.statcan.gc.ca/l01/cst01/famil107a-eng.htm and the CANSIM database http://cansim2.statcan.gc.ca 111-0009, accessed 1 March 2010.

PROVINCES AS REGIONS

With questions surrounding the use of regions as a tool for understanding the Canadian experience, and if provinces are not necessarily regions, can we realistically treat physically and economically different provinces as regions? Our belief is that we can. Specifically, it is important to realize that since 1945, provincial governments have consistently increased their own control over their populations and have continued to challenge the authority of the federal government with respect to the economic and political leadership of their citizens. It is possible that provinces possess the political tools and the will to create a shared regional identity.[2] Our approach does not deny that different regions exist within provinces, and it does recognize provinces as a vital part in the life of the people living in them. As we will see in the section dealing with government actions, Canadian history is full of attempts on the part of the federal government to address provincial demands and to try to bring economic development and prosperity to different parts of the country, with varying degrees of success.

THEORIES ABOUT THE CAUSES OF REGIONALISM

Many explanations have been offered for the causes of regionalism, for why some regions have prospered and others have not, and for the effect this has had on the people who live there. The following is a brief sketch of some of the more prominent of these explanations.[3]

The Natural Resources Approach

The natural resources approach is more often referred to as "staples theory."[4] Generally, this theory asserts that the key to economic prosperity is the availability of natural resources. A short list of such resources includes oil, natural gas, fish, lumber, fur (beavers), coal, and various minerals.

This approach comprises two critical beliefs. The first asserts that some areas in Canada prosper while others do not because of the availability and marketability of their natural resources. In short, how much of a particular resource does your region possess, and does your region have companies or other countries prepared to buy that resource? The second critical belief concerns the external limits on developing your resource. Specifically, how is your resource affected by the fluctuations in price caused by changes in the international marketplace? Some examples will help make this point. How do the oil-producing countries located primarily in the Middle East (e.g., Saudi Arabia, Kuwait, Qatar, and Bahrain) affect the price of oil extracted from oil fields in Alberta? How do changes in world grain prices affect grain growers in Saskatchewan? In large part the prices are beyond the control of the people who produce the product. This helps explain why Western grain farmers and Atlantic fishermen demand compensation and assistance from the federal government in Ottawa to offset international price changes.

To conclude, the staples approach asserts that economic prosperity is largely determined by the availability of natural resources. The problem with this approach is that there is a tendency to exaggerate the likelihood that a region will prosper economically if natural resources are located there in extremely large quantities. Some regions in Canada have an abundance of natural resources yet have not experienced the economic prosperity that the theory would predict. As Ralph Mathews has written, Southern Ontario, for example, has no strong natural resource base, yet it is wealthy. Meanwhile, although the Atlantic provinces have a rich base of iron ore, coal, gold, forests, fish, and hydroelectric power, they have remained poor throughout most of the period since Confederation.[5]

Market Approaches

Market approaches assert that some regions are more prosperous than others because of interference, usually by governments, in the local market that results in market failure. Types of government interference include subsidizing companies that need help to survive and subsidizing the wages of employees.

Market approaches emphasize that for economic development to take place, governments must not interfere with the way the free market functions. Wages should be allowed to fall, taxes collected from companies should be minimal, labour (workers) should move to where jobs are, and money (capital) should not be restricted or penalized if and when it decides to relocate—when companies decide to stop operations, lay off workers, and set up shop elsewhere.

In the 1980s and 1990s market approaches were quite popular as solutions to the problem of regional differences in economic development and as solutions to the economic problems of countries as a whole. The United States and the United Kingdom have vigorously pursued these policies. In Canada, the Progressive Conservative former premier of Alberta, Ralph Klein, and the Progressive Conservative former premier of Ontario, Mike Harris, were both fiercely committed to allowing the free market to operate unmolested by their respective governments. The present Conservative Prime Minister of Canada, Stephen Harper, is similarly committed to the operation of a free market unhindered by government actions.

Interventionist Approaches

Generally, interventionist approaches are based on the belief that some regions have prospered while others have not because of the many political (politicians and government) and economic (the development strategies of companies) forces that have historically favoured some regions at the expense of others.[6] As a general solution, these interventionist approaches regard government involvement as absolutely essential to overcoming regional problems.

Interventionist approaches differ from the staples and market theories in two specific respects. First, staples theory regards regional differences in economic prosperity as natural; interventionist approaches do not. Second, market theories see problems as avoidable if, in large part, governments simply allow the free market to operate. Interventionist approaches do not see the problems as avoidable.

In the post–World War II era, the Canadian federal government has practised interventionism quite extensively. The most visible forms of this intervention are federal government **transfer payments** (worth billions of dollars each year) to the provinces to help the poorer regions of the country (see Table 1.2).

Marxist Approaches

From a Marxist perspective, regional economic inequality is a natural outcome of the class and power differences in a society dominated by capitalism, because the driving force of capitalism is the accumulation of profit. Accumulating profit includes maximizing the value of your company for the shareholders who buy and sell shares in your company and exploiting the people, places, and things used during the production of the goods or services.

Marxism regards regional economic differences as "functional" (i.e., beneficial) to the operation of capitalism for three reasons. First, capitalism uses workers in poorer regions as reserve or surplus labour to hire and lay off whenever the capitalist sees fit. In other words, when times are good, workers from poor regions travel to more prosperous ones to work; when times are bad, these same workers are simply let go, and they return to the region from which they came. Second, underdeveloped regions provide raw materials that are processed in more developed regions. In this way money (capital) is drained from the poor regions to the richer ones. Third, poorer regions provide a market for the goods and services produced in the more developed regions.[7]

Capitalists exploit poorer regions in another way that is usually implicit in Marxist analysis and needs to be reinforced here: capitalists use the existence of poorer regions as a threatening tool to successfully demand concessions from workers

Table 1.2   Major Transfers[i] to Provinces and Territories (billions of dollars) and Per Capita Allocation (thousands of dollars)

Province/Territory	2009–2010	Per Capita	Percent of Total Revenues
Prince Edward Island	490	4 159	34
Yukon	648	21 873	67
Northwest Territories	905	22 797	70
Nunavut	1.0	35 587	85
Newfoundland	1.1	2 389	17
New Brunswick	2.5	3 539	35
Nova Scotia	2.6	3 023	32
Alberta	3.1	987	11
Manitoba	3.4	2 929	26
British Columbia	4.8	1 213	13
Ontario	13.8	1 220	15
Quebec	16.7	2 263	27

[i]All figures comprise Equalization, Territorial Formula Financing, Canada Health Transfer, Canada Social Transfer, direct targeted support, and trust funds.

Note: Equalization payments are especially important to the life of social programs throughout Canada. See Errol Black and Jim Silver, "Equalization: Financing Canadians' Commitment to Sharing and Social Solidarity," Canadian Centre for Policy Alternatives site, March 2004 <www.policyalternatives.ca/documents/Nova_Scotia_Pubs/NSequalization.pdf>, accessed 27 March 2006.

Source: "Federal Support to Provinces and Territories (March 2010)," Department of Finance Canada, available <www.fin.gc.ca/fedprov/mtp-eng.asp>, accessed 1 March 2010. Reproduced with the permission of the Minister of Public Works and Government Services, 2010.

(e.g., to accept less money and fewer benefits) and governments (e.g., to collect less tax money) in wealthier regions. Just as companies threaten to move their operations (including jobs) to the developing world (e.g., Mexico) if unions, workers, and governments do not provide concessions to them, so too do companies threaten to do the same within Canada. In attempts to lure business to their provinces (and out of other provinces) provincial premiers have been known to actively encourage this behaviour.

To conclude, in the above four ways Marxists regard regional imbalance as a normal outcome of capitalism.

FACTORS THAT INTENSIFY REGIONALISM

The Canadian political system operates in ways that intensify regional feelings and economic differences. Two of the most important are federalism and our electoral system.

Federalism

When the Dominion of Canada was created in 1867, a time we refer to as Confederation (see Have You Heard? 1.1), the politicians who wrote the *British North America Act* (since 1982 the *Constitution Act of 1867*) decided that there should be two levels of government to govern the Canadian people. The first level is federal and refers to the national government

---

HAVE YOU HEARD? 1.1

Confederation in Chronological Order

. . . .

Date and Province or Territory	Seat of Government
1 July 1867	
Ontario	Toronto
Quebec	Quebec City
Nova Scotia	Halifax
New Brunswick	Fredericton
15 July 1870	
Manitoba	Winnipeg
Northwest Territories	Yellowknife (originally Winnipeg)
1 July 1871	
British Columbia	Victoria
1 July 1873	
Prince Edward Island	Charlottetown
13 June 1898	
Yukon Territory	Whitehorse
1 September 1905	
Saskatchewan	Regina
Alberta	Edmonton
1 April 1949	
Newfoundland	St. John's
1 April 1999	
Nunavut	Iqaluit

CRITICAL THINKING OUTSIDE THE BOX 1.1

Which theory do you believe best explains regionalism in Canada? Would Canadians in other provinces share your belief? If so, why? If not, why?

located in Ottawa. The second level is provincial and refers to the provinces and territories and their governments.

These same politicians outlined what level of government would be responsible for what area of social life. Section 91 of the Constitution outlines federal responsibilities and section 92 outlines provincial ones. Historically, when disputes arose over a new policy area, such as atomic energy or aviation, the Supreme Court decided which level of government assumed the responsibility for that particular policy area. The federal government was given control of the armed forces, and provincial governments were given control over health care and education. **Federalism** can be defined as a system of government that divides responsibilities between two levels of government, with each level being unable to abolish the other. The two levels of government must cooperate with each other. For roughly the past twenty years, this cooperation has taken the form of meetings between the provincial premiers, their key Cabinet ministers and advisors, and the Prime Minister along with his or her key Cabinet ministers and advisors. The making of political decisions and policies jointly by federal and provincial Cabinet ministers, senior bureaucrats, premiers, and prime ministers is called **executive federalism**.

Executive federalism creates problems. Senior members of government and the bureaucracy make important decisions, and many of those members have the interests of specific regions or other interests at heart, not the interests of Canada as a whole. This is of greater concern when decisions are made behind closed doors without properly informing Canadians of what is going on and without providing Canadians with opportunities for criticism, revision, and input. The **Meech Lake Accord** (1987) was an example of this type of decision making. Then Prime Minister Brian Mulroney thought it would all be a matter of simply "rolling the dice." Canadians were so upset at having been shut out of the negotiations that few tears were shed when three years later (1990) the Accord did not receive the necessary provincial approval in Manitoba, Newfoundland, and New Brunswick to be adopted by the government in Ottawa.

Executive federalism compounds the problems associated with regionalism when some regions feel they are not being represented in Ottawa and when some provinces feel other provinces have too much influence there. This has certainly been the case regarding perceptions of Ontario and Quebec. Both the Western and the Atlantic provinces have always claimed that the two central provinces have far too much representation in Ottawa. Historically, members of Parliament from Ontario and Quebec have dominated important key Cabinet positions, such as foreign affairs, finance, justice, and international trade, as well as senior positions in the bureaucracy and government agencies. Since the election of Stephen Harper's Conservatives in 2004 and 2008, Western grumblings of discontent have been somewhat mute.

The Western provinces have always believed that the citizens of Ontario and Quebec have not adequately recognized their sacrifices and contributions to building Canada. They also believe that their interests have not been vigorously represented in Ottawa. This was especially true during Pierre Trudeau's years as Prime Minister (1968–79 and 1980–84). For the better part of fourteen years, Trudeau's Liberal governments did not have one member elected to Parliament west of the city of Winnipeg, leaving Saskatchewan, Alberta, and British Columbia with virtually no federal political representation in government! Consider how Ontario and Quebec would react if they ever experienced the same lack of representation.

Before the First Ministers' Conference in Victoria, British Columbia, on 1 August 2001, Newfoundland Premier Roger Grimes complained loudly about the return of a per capita funding formula to federal transfers to the provinces. In 1999, at the urging of then Ontario Premier Mike Harris, Ottawa's Canadian Health and Social Transfer (CHST) was calculated using a per capita formula; such a formula benefits the more populous provinces. Premier Grimes put forward the idea that the Atlantic provinces were being asked to put more money into the CHST so that Ontario could expand the services it offered its citizens, which were already beyond what was being delivered in the Atlantic provinces. In effect, the poorer provinces ended up subsidizing the richer ones.

Our Electoral System

The electoral system in Canada contributes to making regionalism worse. Canada's electoral system is a single-member plurality system, or what some call "first past the post." In this system a party receives one seat for every riding it wins. The number of seats in each province depends on its population—the provinces with the most people receive the most seats. We call this **representation by population**. Therefore, the party that wins the most seats wins the election. However, the candidate who wins the riding does not necessarily need more than 50 percent of the votes. To win, a candidate simply needs more than anyone else running against him or her. An example will better illustrate this point.

CRITICAL THINKING OUTSIDE THE BOX 1.2

How would you feel if your province were not represented in the federal government for almost fifteen years? What might be the sociopsychological consequences of such an experience? How did the citizens of Saskatchewan, Alberta, and British Columbia feel and act during Pierre Trudeau's years as Prime Minister? Are there similar feelings in Ontario and Quebec today since the election of Alberta's Stephen Harper as Prime Minister?

Candidate X receives 46 percent of the votes, and Candidate Y receives 30 percent, while Candidate Z receives 24 percent. Candidate X wins, with only 46 percent of the votes (which is not a majority) and in spite of the fact that 54 percent of the people (the total votes of Candidates Y and Z) voted against Candidate X. Now, if this scenario is repeated in riding after riding, the party that Candidate X belongs to will win the election, even though in the election more people voted for other parties. The 40th general election in 2008 and the British Columbia provincial election on 12 May 2009 are vivid examples of this fact (see Have You Heard? 1.2).

Our electoral system contributes to regionalism when the party that wins the election wins because it has won more seats than any other party in Ontario and Quebec. Other regions of the country lose when they do not vote for the same party that wins the most seats in Ontario and Quebec. In the 2008 federal election, the Bloc received only 10 percent of the popular vote, but because these votes were regionally concentrated in the province of Quebec, the Bloc were allotted a whopping 49 seats. Two seats were won by independent candidates (not affiliated with any officially registered party) with meagre 0.6 percent of the popular vote. The NDP received 18.2 percent of the popular vote and only 37 seats, while the Green Party, with a healthy and respectable 6.8 percent of the popular vote, won no seats at all! Of the 308 seats contested during the federal election, 181 belong to Ontario (106) and Quebec (75). The winning political party, therefore, will spend a lot of time, effort, and money pleasing the people and monied interests that elected them. This is inevitable, because the majority of Canada's financial, banking, and manufacturing interests are overwhelmingly concentrated in these two provinces, especially in Ontario. A leisurely drive on the major highways that lead to and from Metropolitan Toronto (Highways 401, 403, 407, and the Queen Elizabeth Way) will certainly confirm this fact.

HAVE YOU HEARD? 1.2

40th General Election, 14 October 2008[i]

Party	Elected Members	Percentage of Popular Vote
Conservative	143	37.7
Liberal	77	26.3
Bloc Québécois	49	10
New Democratic Party	37	18.2
Independent	2	.7
Green Party	0	6.8
Total	**308**	**100.0**

British Columbia Provincial Election, 12 May 2009[ii]

Party	Elected Members	Percentage of Popular Vote
Liberal	49	45.8
New Democratic Party	35	42.1
Other	1	1.8
Green Party	0	8.2
Conservative	0	2.1
Total		

Note: Totals may not add up to 100 percent because of rounding.

Sources: [i]Adapted from "Official Voting Results Fortieth General Election 2008," Elections Canada <www.elections.ca/scripts/OVR2008/default.html>, accessed 1 March 2010

[ii]Adapted from "British Columbia Provincial Election 2013," http://www.electionalmanac.com/canada/britishcolumbia/>, accessed 1 March 2010.

THE REALITY OF REGIONALISM AND ITS OUTCOMES

Perhaps the most visible signs of regionalism and, therefore, of the discontent felt by people living in some regions, are the political parties that were created to represent the interests of a particular region. These parties are a vivid representation of the concerns, expectations, attitudes, and fears of an entire region. Some examples include the rise of the Bloc Québécois in Quebec, the Reform Party (formerly the Canadian Alliance and now known nationally as the Conservative Party) in western Canada, and the Confederation of Regions Party in New Brunswick. These parties were created for at least two reasons. The first concerns the basic similarity between the Liberal and Progressive Conservative parties in terms of ideology, policies, and organization. If the two main parties look the same and sound the same, the concerns of some people are not being addressed. Starting your own party overcomes these problems. Second, belonging to these new parties represents a rejection of the two other parties—it is a protest against the traditional way of doing things. Joining a new party is a way of saying "If you don't listen to us, we will find other ways to voice our discontent and push forward our interests." If you are electorally successful, the other political parties must take you seriously. The Canadian Alliance/Reform Party is an excellent example of this.

The Case of Quebec: Winning Hearts?

Without question the greatest threat to Canadian federalism is Quebec separatism. While other issues may occupy the minds of Canadians on a daily basis, such as racial profiling by police in Toronto, Asian immigration in Vancouver, farming costs in Saskatchewan, the size of fish stocks in the Atlantic provinces, they do not threaten to break up the country. Canadian unity has been at the top of every federal government agenda especially since the Parti Québécois victory in 1977. The federal government has spent billions of dollars trying to win the hearts and minds of all Quebecers. Two of the most visible, divisive, emotional, and symbolic attempts were the 1987 Meech Lake Accord and the 1995–2002 Sponsorship Program.

The Meech Lake Accord (1987) was Prime Minister Brian Mulroney's attempt to have Quebec formally sign the Constitution, something it did not do when the Constitution was repatriated by the Liberal government of Pierre Trudeau in 1982. Quebec City agreed to accept the accord if the Prime Minister and provincial premiers agreed to five key demands (see Have You Heard? 1.3). The most contentious of these was recognition of Quebec as a "distinct society." Accepting the Accord with such a clause was seen by many, including former Prime Minister Pierre Trudeau, as having dire consequences for the survival of Canadian federalism.[8] Trudeau believed a Parti Québécois government intent on separating from Canada could potentially use this clause as "proof" that Quebec was "special" and needed independence from Canada to maintain its "distinctiveness." In spite of the fact that Prime Minister Mulroney and all ten premiers accepted the demands, the Meech Lake Accord died in June 1990 when ratification was delayed in Manitoba by Aboriginal MLA Elijah Harper and when newly elected governments in New Brunswick and Newfoundland and Labrador failed to ratify it.

HAVE YOU HEARD? 1.3

Quebec's Five Demands

• •

- constitutional recognition of Quebec as a "distinct society"
- a role in appointments to the Supreme Court of Canada
- a veto for Quebec on constitutional amendments
- a more influential role in immigration
- limits on federal power in new federal–provincial shared-cost programs—
  the right to opt out, with full financial compensation, from future shared-
  cost programs in areas of exclusive provincial jurisdiction

Source: Marjorie Montgomery Bowker, *The Meech Lake Accord: What It Will Mean to You and to Canada* (Hull, QC: Voyageur Publishing, 1990). For his reaction to the Charlottetown Accord, see Pierre E. Trudeau, *A Mess That Deserves a Big NO* (Toronto: Robertson Davies Publisher, 1992).

The most recent attempt to win the hearts of Quebecers was the $250 million Sponsorship Program and Advertising Activities initiated in 1995. The Program was put together in the wake of Quebec's 1995 sovereignty referendum. The strength of the separatist vote convinced the federal government that something had to be done to weaken separatist feelings in Quebec.

The official purpose of the Sponsorship Program was to raise the profile of the federal government in Quebec by "sponsoring" a number of events and activities across the province. In return for cash, the Canadian flag would be prominently displayed at every event. Such events included but were not limited to the Montreal Grand Prix, hunting and fishing shows, cultural festivals, and television programming. Senior members of the federal Liberal party believed the program was a rational response to the strength of separatist sentiment in Quebec. The public was made aware of potential pecuniary mismanagement when Allan Cutler, a career civil servant in Public Works and Government Services, "blew the whistle" on his bosses. The program became a scandal when in 2002, federal Auditor General Sheila Fraser, recommended the RCMP investigate how advertising money was handed out to different advertising agencies in Quebec (see Have You Heard? 1.4). Slowly, a picture began to emerge of phoney invoices, double billing, and exorbitant fees. Under intense public pressure, Prime Minister Paul Martin established a public inquiry in February 2005 headed by Justice John Gomery.

HAVE YOU HEARD? 1.4

Sponsorship Program and Advertising Activities, 1995–2002

- Put in place after the 1995 Quebec referendum.
- The size of the Program is estimated at $250 million.
- The fund was organized by the Public Works department headed by Alfonso Gagliano, at the time Prime Minister Jean Chrétien's Quebec Lieutenant.
- Senior government officials in Quebec mishandled millions of dollars since 1995.
- Five Crown corporations are involved: the RCMP, VIA Rail, Canada Post, the Business Development Bank of Canada, and the Old Port of Montreal.
- More than $100 million in fees and commissions were paid to different communications agencies.
- In the majority of cases, agencies did little more than hand over cheques.

Note: On 5 May 2006 Jean Brault was sentenced to thirty months in prison and on 6 June 2006 Chuck Guite was convicted of five counts of fraud.

A new sponsorship program was launched on 1 April 2003 with strict new guidelines. See <www.cbc.ca/news/background/auditorgeneral/ag_report2004/20031103ce.pdf>, pp. 32–33.

Source: Adapted from "Auditor General's Report 2004," *CBC News Online*, 11 February 2005, <www.cbc.ca/news/background/auditorgeneral/report2004.html>, accessed 1 March 2010.

The Gomery Report was made public on 1 November 2005. Judge Gomery minced no words and put the blame for the scandal squarely on the shoulders of former Prime Minister Jean Chrétien and his senior advisors, members of Cabinet, and the bureaucracy. The major findings included:

1. Prime Minister Paul Martin was cleared of any personal blame.
2. Former Prime Minister Jean Chrétien was found partly responsible for the Program, while his chief of staff, Jean Pelletier, was blamed for mismanaging it.
3. The Quebec wing of the Liberal party had benefited from financial kickbacks.

4. The Public Works minister at the time, Alfonso Gagliano, was blamed for the fraudulent behaviour of his staff, since he was directly involved in partisan decision making.

5. Public officials had been fearful of going public because of the close relationships between senior civil servants and senior political officials.[9]

In response, Jean Chrétien immediately accused the judge of biased and unfair reporting, and said he would take his claims to the Federal Court and ask for a judicial review of the judge's findings.

Meech Lake and the Sponsorship Program are two items on a long list of attempts by federal governments of all political colours to win the hearts and votes of Quebecers. The Canadair debacle, discussed below, is another.

The Case of Western Canada

Western Canada has always held the belief that its interests are continually undervalued and sometimes simply ignored by the government in Ottawa. The growth of the Reform Party (later the Canadian Alliance, and now the Conservative Party of Canada) is directly linked to this belief. Some of the more prominent examples will demonstrate this point.

The first example goes back to the implementation of the **National Policy** in 1879. The National Policy of Prime Minister John A. Macdonald was an attempt to build a country out of many different geographical regions and to change the very nature of the Canadian economy from one based on extracting natural resources to one based on manufacturing and other nonresource activities.[10] The tool used to begin this change was the *tariff* on imported goods, which caused them to become more expensive than similar goods produced in Canada.

The purpose of the tariff was to protect Canadian manufacturing companies, which were located primarily in central Canada. But the practical consequence of the National Policy was that, for example, Western farmers had to buy their manufactured goods, such as tractors and combines, from more expensive producers in central Canada because the cheaper ones produced in the United States were now even more expensive with the tariff. This cost Western farmers huge amounts of money, and they have never forgotten it. Generally, Westerners believe that they have contributed enormously to Ontario's economic development and prosperity.

The second example concerns the financial institutions, primarily banks, which are located overwhelmingly in Ontario. By jacking up interest rates to control inflation, the actions of these financial institutions have penalized those who live and work outside Ontario. In the 1980s the Bank of Canada attempted to control inflation in Ontario's Golden Horseshoe (its most intensely developed region) by hiking interest rates regardless of how these higher interest rates would negatively affect economic growth in other parts of Canada. This meant that Western grain farmers, Atlantic fishermen, and people outside the Golden Horseshoe would have to pay more, because of the higher interest rates, to work and live (see Figure 1.2). In the early part of the 1980s, interest rates climbed to more than 20 percent! Would you want to borrow money to buy a new tractor or fishing boat at that rate? (Compare with interest rates in 2010.)

The third example concerns the multimillion-dollar maintenance contract for Canada's high-technology CF-18 fighter aircraft. In 1987 three companies submitted bids: Bristol Aerospace of Winnipeg, IMP of Halifax, and Canadair of Montreal. Originally the contract was awarded to Bristol Aerospace of Winnipeg, because it was more technologically capable of handling the sophisticated aircraft and because the bid was between 8 and 12 percent cheaper. When Canadair began to publicly complain and when members of Parliament from Quebec began to put huge pressure on Prime Minister Brian Mulroney by reminding him that Quebec had voted overwhelmingly for his Progressive Conservative

Figure 1.2   Western Perceptions of Their Contribution to Canadian Development

party in the federal election of 1984, Mulroney reversed the decision and awarded the contract to Canadair. The pressure of Quebec MPs was especially intense because another election was just around the corner in 1988. The Prime Minister believed it was more important to keep Quebec happy than Manitoba because Quebec has seventy-five seats in Parliament whereas Manitoba has only fourteen. The people of Manitoba were punished once again when the federal Liberals announced in 1995 that Air Force Headquarters would be moved from Winnipeg to Ottawa in 1996. In fact, during World War II, Industry Minister C.D. Howe established almost fifty Crown corporations in Ontario and Quebec. These industries continued to benefit both economies long after the war ended.

More recent examples of Western dissatisfaction with the federal government are the federal Gun Registry debacle and the Kyoto Accord. The federal Gun Registry was introduced by the Jean Chrétien federal Liberal government in 1993 and became policy in 1995. It was unpopular in the Western provinces, the Northern Territories, and rural areas throughout Canada while large urban centres like Toronto were supportive. Hunters and collectors were particularly upset with being forced to register their guns. Criticism intensified when the cost skyrocketed to over $1 billion. [11] The province of Alberta continues to be concerned with the status of global warming debates generally, and of the Kyoto Accord more specifically. At the Climate Conference in Copenhagen, Alberta fought long and hard to convince the Conservative party that the Tar Sands Project is crucial to Alberta's economy and Canada's energy independence. In the end, Ottawa sided with Alberta by working for, and accepting a deal that is not binding and does not set new targets for the reductions of greenhouse gases. [12]

Perhaps no issue in the new millennium will have a greater impact on Western Canada than what can only be called "the farm crisis." It is virtually unknown outside farming communities and has been consistently ignored by federal and provincial governments. This crisis has hit Western farming communities particularly hard. Put simply, international price fluctuations leading to low commodity prices, corporate agribusiness mergers, high production costs, and poor weather conditions have contributed to a steady decline in the number of farm families and has returned net farm income to Depression-era levels.[13] For example, annual realized net farm income has fallen to those levels for grain and hog producers in Alberta, Ontario, and across Canada.[14] Canadian farmers face the prospect of operating 21st-century farms with Depression-era net incomes.[15] Farm families have resorted to increasing their off-farm income in order to raise overall household income. These concerns continue to exacerbate the historical animosity felt by Western grain farmers towards the federal Wheat Board. Western grain farmers feel the marketing of western grain could be best done by them and not the federal government in Ottawa. Similarly, Alberta heavily criticized the federal government for not working hard enough to get Washington to lift the ban on exporting live Alberta cattle to the United States after the discovery of BSE-bovine spongiform encephalopathy or mad cow disease, in Alberta cattle.

Another example, similar to those above, concerns the Atlantic provinces. The opening of the St. Lawrence Seaway in 1957 was greeted with great fanfare in Ontario and Quebec—but not in New Brunswick and Nova Scotia, to whom the Seaway was simply another way economic interests in central Canada took business away from the entire Atlantic region, especially the port cities of Saint John and Halifax.

Our Northern Experience

No region of Canada has been more universally ignored and misunderstood than the land above the 60th parallel, collectively known as Canada's North. Our northern reaches are so far removed from our daily consciousness that we lack a basic understanding of the land and the people who live there. Here is a quick quiz. (The answers are in Have You Heard? 1.5.) What is the name of the territory that came into existence on 1 April 1999? What is its capital city? How big is the newest territory? What is the name of the dominant ethnic group that lives there? What language do they speak? What does the name of the territory mean in their language? Why is the new territory important to its inhabitants?

HAVE YOU HEARD? 1.5

Nunavut

. . . .

- Nunavut is the territory that came into existence on 1 April 1999.
- Nunavut's capital city is Iqaluit.
- It covers approximately 1 994 000 square kilometres.
- Approximately 80 percent of the population is Inuit.
- Inuktitut is the Inuit language.
- Nunavut means "our land" in Inuktitut.
- The Inuit believe this land is their ancestral home and have always referred to it as Nunavut. A territorial government (a form of self-government) now speaks for the rights, needs, interests, and desires of the people and their ancestral home.

Source: "Basic Facts: The New Territory," Nunavut.com site <www.nunavut.com/basicfacts/english/basicfacts_1territory.html>, accessed 1 March 2010.

Since two-thirds of Canadians live within 320 kilometres of the Canada–U.S. border, any location beyond 320 kilometres is considered "up north." For inhabitants of Winnipeg, Edmonton, and Regina, any journey north is considered to be heading "up north," yet it would take days (depending on the mode of transportation) to reach the 60th parallel, let alone the borders of Nunavut, Yukon, or the Northwest Territories. Perhaps the best example of this southern-centrism is found in southern Ontario. For the inhabitants of the Golden Horseshoe, especially Toronto, driving to cottages located in the Muskoka and Kawartha Lakes is considered going "up north." In fact, some consider Barrie (located in central Ontario) to be "up north." Few Ontarians have any understanding of cities anywhere north of the Horseshoe.

Here is another quick quiz. These answers you must find for yourself. What college is located in Barrie? What are the names of colleges located in the cities of Thunder Bay, Sault Ste. Marie, Sudbury, Timmins, and North Bay? Are there universities located in any of these cities? If so, what are their names? What industries dominate the lives of people living in the northern reaches of Ontario, Quebec, Manitoba, Saskatchewan, Alberta, and British Columbia? What is the meaning and significance of a "one-industry town"? (See Have You Heard? 1.6.)

As Canadians we must make a concerted effort to have an awareness and appreciation of those living in our country's northern reaches.

HAVE YOU HEARD? 1.6

One-Industry Towns: Schefferville, Quebec

· ·

"One-industry town" is the term for Canadian communities whose economic activity is dominated by one particular industry, such as logging, mining, or fishing. The prosperity of each town is directly linked to the prosperity of its major employer. When these companies experience economic troubles or close their doors, the surrounding community suffers accordingly. An example is Schefferville, Quebec. When iron ore mining was operating at capacity, it was the vibrant home of about 4500 people. When the iron ore owners based in Cleveland, Ohio shut down operations, it was reduced to a ghost town of less than 500 people. Can you name any other one-industry towns?

CRITICAL THINKING OUTSIDE THE BOX 1.3

What are the logical consequences of the farm crisis for Canadians? Why is this issue not at the top of all government agendas? Why have the media essentially ignored this issue?

THE ACTIONS OF THE FEDERAL GOVERNMENT

The federal government has always recognized that regionalism does exist. Since Confederation it has spent much time and billions of dollars attempting to reduce the gap between the economically prosperous regions of Canada and those that are not so well off. The federal government has historically attempted to accomplish this in three distinct ways: (1) by reducing physical distances, (2) by instituting programs (spending money), and, perhaps most significantly, (3) by concentrating on sociopsychological phenomena (i.e., attitudes and people's perceptions of each other and of other regions).

Reducing Physical Distances

The early attempts to reduce regional differences and isolation were physical in nature. The first was the construction of the Canadian Pacific Railway (CPR) by Canada's first Prime Minister, John A. Macdonald. The purpose of the railway was to unite the different and far-off regions from the Atlantic Ocean to the Pacific Ocean. Building the CPR was also a precondition for British Columbia joining Confederation; without the railway, there is much doubt that British Columbia would have joined.

The next noteworthy attempt came with the creation of Trans-Canada Airlines (TCA) in 1937, later renamed Air Canada. The creation of TCA was based on the realization by the government that air travel would be the quickest and most efficient way to service the large, outlying, and sparsely populated regions of Canada, in addition to linking the larger metropolitan areas. Private airline companies, it was believed, would not fly to these remote areas because it would not be profitable. This remained the rationale for Air Canada until it was privatized (sold to private investors—the government no longer owns it) in 1989. However, many would argue that Air Canada ceased to operate according to its original mandate long before it was privatized.

Other examples of attempting to physically link the people of Canada were the construction of the Trans-Canada Highway and the creation of Via Rail, a Crown corporation to run railway passenger service, in 1977–78. The vicious budget cuts to Via Rail carried out by the Progressive Conservatives during the mid-to-late 1980s disproportionately penalized Atlantic Canada relative to any other region. Protests of these cuts were widespread, and many believed the cuts to be based on poor research and intentional attempts by the federal government, which continually portrayed Via Rail in a negative fashion, to justify the cuts.[16]

Spending Money

Economically, the federal government has provided money, in many different ways, to the ten provincial governments to help minimize economic differences.[17] In large part the federal government accomplishes this through the use of transfer payments. Transfer payments take place when the federal government collects money through taxation, such as personal income tax, and then hands over or "transfers" a certain percentage of the money collected, as agreed to by the provinces, to the provincial governments. The provinces use this money to help pay for programs such as health care and education. As already mentioned, federal transfer payments are worth billions of dollars every year. It can be argued that transfer payments are more important to the poorer provinces than to the richer ones. A brief look at Table 1.2 shows that on a per capita basis, the poorer provinces receive a greater proportion of transfer payments than the more prosperous ones do. In 2009–2010 Prince Edward Island received total transfer payments of $490 million accounting for about 34 percent of the province's revenues. This works out to be $4159 per person, the highest of any province. Ontario received a total transfer payment of $13.8 billion, which works out to only $1220 per person. Ontario's transfers in 2009–2010 accounted for only 15 percent of Ontario's revenues. On a per capita basis, Alberta's $3.1 billion transfer payment translates to $987 per person, the lowest in Canada. In spite of the federal government's attempts to reduce spending by transferring less money to the provinces, transfer payments are still worth billions of dollars. Without transfer payments, Canada's three territorial governments would be inoperable. In 2009–2010, major federal transfers accounted for about 85 percent of Nunavut's revenues! This works out to an enormous $35 587 per person.

The federal government has also formed and used government departments and agencies, as well as legislation, to study and to help stimulate economic growth in poorer regions. Some of the more notable examples include the *Agricultural and Rural Development Act* (1965), the Fund for Rural Economic Development (1966), the Department of Regional Economic Expansion (1969), the Department of Regional Industrial Expansion (1982), the Department of Industry, Science, and Technology (1987), the Atlantic Canada Opportunities Agency (1987), Western Diversification (1987), Enterprise Cape

Breton (1987), the Canadian Polar Commission (1991), the Canadian Rural Partnership (1998), and the First Nations and Inuit Health Branch of Health Canada (2000).

In 1995 regional representation can be seen in the names given to three federal government departments: Public Works and Atlantic Canada Opportunities Agency, Indian Affairs and Northern Development, and Finance (with responsibility for Quebec regional development). Other departments and agencies with regional responsibilities in 2010 are: the Prairie Farm Rehabilitation Administration, Atlantic Pilotage Authority Canada, the Cape Breton Growth Fund (CBGF), Indian and Northern Affairs Canada, Broadband for Rural and Northern Development, FedNor (Federal Economic Development Initiative in Northern Ontario), Marine Atlantic, the Northern Pipeline Agency Canada, Pacific Pilotage Authority Canada, Fisheries and Oceans Canada-Maritime Region, Fisheries and Oceans Canada-Pacific Region, St. Lawrence Centre, Canada Economic Development for Quebec Regions, Federal Economic Development Initiative for Northern Ontario, Strategic Investments in Northern Economic Development (SINED), and finally, one of the newest established in 2009, Canadian Northern Economic Development Agency or CanNor with its head office in Iqaliut, Nunavut.

Promoting Understanding Among Canadians

The final way the federal government has tried to minimize the differences between regions is by promoting understanding between Canadians. Because of Canada's large physical size (9 970 610 square kilometres) and small population (approximately 31.7 million; see Have You Heard? 1.7) the federal government has taken responsibility for

HAVE YOU HEARD? 1.7			

Canada in a World Perspective

· ·

Country	Area (km²)	Population (2009 estimated)	Population (per km²)
Russia	17 075 400	143 000 000	8.0
Canada	**9 970 610**	**32 800 000**	**3.0**
China	9 556 100	1 328 000 000	136.0
United States	9 529 100	295 000 000	30.7
Brazil	8 511 965	186 000 000	21.8
Australia	7 628 300	20 000 000	3.0

connecting distant regions to each other, emotionally and attitudinally—specifically, by emphasizing what it meant, or means, to be "Canadian" and by educating Canadians about Canada itself, our history, people, places, and attitudes.

The federal government in Ottawa has attempted to educate and inform Canadians about each other by using new technology as it became available (radio and TV) and by the use of **royal commissions**.

In response to new radio technology, the federal government formed the Canadian Broadcasting Corporation (CBC) in 1932. CBC Radio provided an opportunity for Canadians to talk to each other and learn about each other. It also provided Canadian musicians, social commentators, sports broadcasters, newsreaders, and talk show hosts an opportunity to develop their creative talents. Hockey was first broadcast on CBC Radio. In fact, hockey play-by-play commentator Foster Hewitt coined one of the most well-known phrases in all of sport when he described a goal being scored as simply, "He shoots, he scores!" The CBC later did the same when television technology evolved, and in 1952 it formed CBC Television. The purpose of CBC Television was or is to emphasize things that are "Canadian" and to connect people to their community and region. Over the years this has resulted in Canadian programs such as *Hockey Night in Canada, Road to Avonlea, Degrassi High, Rita and Friends, The Beachcombers,* and *Kids in the Hall.* CBC television also gave birth to the regionally oriented newscasts that usually follow the national news.

Before TV, the federal government was already involved in the making of films and documentaries. In 1939 it created the National Film Board (NFB). For decades now NFB documentaries and short films have been seen across Canada, especially in schools. Canadians everywhere are familiar with the 30-second NFB vignettes broadcast between programs on the CBC. The work of the NFB has been awarded many international honours. Overall, the purpose of the CBC and NFB has been to educate and inform Canadians, and the federal government has spent hundreds of millions of dollars over the years to promote this education. There is no better, and perhaps no more ambitious, example of this than the 2001 CBC documentary *Canada: A People's History.* It was an immediate hit with Canadians, averaging 2.5 million viewers for the first six episodes.[18] But CBC-TV producer Mark Starowicz could only entice one company to buy advertising time.[19] CBC proceeded to make the $25 million series in spite of corporate Canada's indifference. It seems Canadians do want to know about each other!

The federal government's heavy involvement in radio, TV, and film is based in part on the belief that what Canadians think, feel, and believe about each other differs from region to region and that this has an important impact on Canadian unity. In fact, in 2006–2007 the federal government spent $3.71 billion on culture (that includes but is not limited to broadcasting, film, video, sound recording, and book and periodical publishing, public archives, historic sites and museums).[20] This belief has prompted the federal government to investigate specific problems in Canada or the likely effects some government policies might have on some regions. The tool used to do this is the royal commission. Royal commissions, headed by a person appointed by the federal government, utilize the expertise of people who work in the public sector or the private sector, academics, and, if necessary, experts outside Canada. They do not implement policy, but simply suggest directions for policy.

To do this, they study, investigate, and accumulate information on important issues or matters of government policy. In the past, there have been two royal commissions concerned with certain aspects of regionalism as they travelled across Canada. The first was the 1937 Royal Commission on Dominion–Provincial Relations, which produced an in-depth study of federal–provincial financial relations—how the federal government transferred money to the provincial governments. The second was the 1981–85 Royal Commission on the Economic Union and Development Prospects for Canada. This Commission was important because it came out in favour of free trade with the United States, in spite of the fact that some experts who presented before the Commission concluded that free trade would be harmful to the poorer regions, especially the Atlantic provinces.

It is not uncommon for the federal government to ignore the recommendations of royal commissions. In 1997, the *Royal Commission Report on Aboriginal Peoples* tabled almost 500 recommendations. The principal recommendation was to increase spending immediately and commit new resources to Aboriginal life in Canada. The Commission suggested spending an average of almost $2 billion per year for the next 20 years. This extra spending would be in addition to the $5 billion to $7 billion already spent annually. Ottawa has yet to implement this principal recommendation. In January 1998, Ottawa announced a $350 million program to deal with the mental and physical damage caused by the residential school program established and partly administered by the federal government between 1867 and 1945.

Royal commissions are popular with the federal government, and it is common for one to last several years. Since 1867 there have been approximately 400 of them[21]—an average of three per year!

THE SOCIOPSYCHOLOGICAL DIMENSION TO REGIONALISM: THE REALITY

Clearly profound economic and social differences exist among the regions in Canada. It is equally clear that there are sociopsychological differences as well. That is, people in different regions do think and feel differently about each other and about the federal government in Ottawa.

What does the **sociopsychological dimension to regionalism** mean? It means more than economic differences between regions with respect to money, companies, investment, income, government policy, elections, and federalism. The sociopsychological dimension is concerned with how individuals living in different regions feel about themselves, their community, other regions, and the federal government. Regional differences in these areas are commonly thought to exist, say, only between the French-speaking majority of Quebec and the English-speaking majority of Quebec and the rest of Canada. Differences, however, go much further than just language and culture. Every year, public opinion polls, quality-of-life surveys, government surveys, and other forms of research indicate that Canadians have different beliefs, opinions, and attitudes about living in Canada and about who benefits the most from government policy. Generally, Ontario and Quebec are considered to be the big winners and Atlantic Canada the big loser. These beliefs have generated much envy. The most recent manifestation of this envy (some would say anti-Ontario attitude) appeared in national headlines before the First Ministers Conference held in Victoria, British Columbia, on 1 August 2001. Nova Scotia Premier John Hamm suggested that the equalization formula be redesigned to put more money in Atlantic coffers. Former Ontario Premier Mike Harris responded by comparing the Nova Scotia Premier to a welfare cheat! University of Moncton Professor Donald Savoie, one of Canada's leading authorities on regional issues, believes the Atlantic provinces got a raw deal with Confederation and that "the region is not doing well because of federal government policy."[22] In fact, he believes that equalization payments are designed to ensure Atlantic Canadians have enough money to buy goods made in Ontario and Quebec—in short, the Atlantic provinces have been kept poor by central Canada.

It is not surprising that people living in different parts of Canada have different attitudes concerning the Canadian experience. These differences are largely because the region you live in, the job you do, and the language you speak all affect the way you think and feel. Our socialization and life experiences have a profound influence on the way we come to understand each other, the federal government, and ourselves. Three examples will illustrate this point: the 2005 flag-lowering protest in Newfoundland and Labrador; the 1995 fishing dispute between Canada and Spain; and the cross-Canada contempt for central Canada and Metropolitan Toronto.

The 2004–2005 Flag Removal in Newfoundland and Labrador

Throughout 2004 and in early 2005 federal–provincial negotiations over oil and natural gas revenues between Ottawa and the Liberal government of Newfoundland and Labrador led by Danny Williams were progressing slowly. The talks centred on sharing offshore oil and natural gas revenues. Sharing revenues has always been a contentious issue in Newfoundland and Labrador. Many in that province believe keeping all or almost all revenues would give the province the base to significantly reduce its reliance on government transfer payments for fiscal survival. In short, Newfoundland and Labrador, a "have not" province, would become more like Alberta, a "have" province.

When talks stalled, Premier Williams ordered all Canadian flags to be removed from government buildings. This contentious move was widely supported across the province. Even Memorial University, traditionally neutral in such disputes, decided to follow the government's lead.[23] Removing the flags was widely discussed in the Atlantic provinces, but it went largely unnoticed outside Atlantic Canada. The premier's actions did lead to a resumption of talks that concluded with a significant victory: the passage of Bill C-43, which allows Newfoundland and Labrador to keep an additional $2.6 billion per year in revenues from offshore oil and natural gas. Regardless of this success, the Churchill Falls Hydro Electric agreement of 1968 still upsets the government. The agreement stipulates that Newfoundland and Labrador must sell hydroelectric power to the province of Quebec at hugely discounted prices until 2041. On two occasions the government has unsuccessfully challenged the agreement in the courts. [24]

The 1995 Fishing Dispute

The 1995 fishing dispute centred on Canadian claims that Spanish fishing vessels waited just beyond Canada's 200-mile (322-kilometre) boundary and fished to excess using illegal nets and taking even the smallest turbot (a species of fish). Earlier, in an attempt to allow fish stocks to replenish themselves, the federal government had banned cod fishing (before the 1992 election), and later it drastically reduced the turbot quotas for Canadian fishermen. Ottawa believed Spanish fishing would eventually lead to the complete collapse of turbot stocks. When Canadian Coast Guard vessels arrested two Spanish fishing vessels, the citizens of the Atlantic provinces, particularly Nova Scotia, were celebrating everywhere, organizing support rallies, carrying signs, and just plain being happy. Finally, the federal government was seen by them as acting on their behalf. The CBC, CTV, *Maclean's*, the *Toronto Star*, and the *Globe and Mail* all reported extensively on the dispute. This attention was heartening for many living in the Atlantic region during these tough times. Barbara Nees from the sociology department of Memorial University in St. John's remarked that it gave people a positive sense of community and a feeling that they were not suffering alone.[25] Nevertheless, the same happiness and pleasure was not shared to the same degree by people living in Toronto, Calgary, Saskatoon, Dryden, Laval, or other cities that do not depend on fishing or fish processing for their livelihood.

The issue for this century for the Atlantic provinces may turn out to be the bulk sale of fresh water to markets in the United States. Atlantic-province governments look upon water as another resource to be exploited—another commodity to be sold in the international marketplace where demand is high, especially in the American southwest.

Former Newfoundland Premier Roger Grimes was at the forefront of this push. The federal government, however, is under increasing pressure from the general population and many environmental groups to do the opposite. A 2001 provincial ministerial report concluded that the cost might be prohibitive, but the option would be open to shrewd entrepreneurs.[26] With economic uncertainty still plaguing the Atlantic fisheries, the bulk sale of fresh water has taken on new importance.

The Contempt for Central Canada, Especially Metropolitan Toronto

Perhaps nowhere is the sociopsychological dimension to regionalism more evident than with respect to the contempt felt by most Canadians for central Canada and Metropolitan Toronto. Rivalries certainly exist between the big cities in Canada, but although there may be intraprovincial rivalries between cities like Calgary and Edmonton or Regina and Saskatoon, and there may be rivalries across provinces between cities like Halifax and Saint John, what all these cities have in common—along with all other cities across Canada—is that they resent the privileged position of Toronto. This resentment is primarily based on central Canada's virtual dominance of economics, politics, and social life. See Have You Heard? 1.8.

HAVE YOU HEARD? 1.8

Even the Supreme Court of Canada?

Canada's highest court is not immune to charges of regional favouritism. Sauvageau, Schneiderman, and Taras report that the notion of the Supreme Court as "objective" and "impartial" is not shared nationally. Those in Quebec regard it as a "Leaning Tower" that always leans in the same direction—a centralist one (thus favouring English Canada). In fact, Guy Laforest saw the introduction of the 1982 Charter of Rights and Freedoms as the "updating of the [English] conquest [of Quebec]." Similar sentiments are found in the Western provinces where Canada's highest court remains a potent "symbol of the entrenched power of the East."

Sources: Florian Sauvageau, David Schneiderman, and David Taras, *The Last Word: Media Coverage of the Supreme Court of Canada* (Vancouver: UBC Press, 2005), pp. 24–25; Guy Laforest, *Trudeau and the End of the Canadian Dream* (Montreal and Kingston: McGill-Queen's University Press, 1995), pp. 180–181, quoted in Sauvageau et al., op. cit., p. 25.

Economic Dominance

The economic dominance of central Canada, especially Metro Toronto, is evident in the overwhelming presence of the head offices of the most dominant corporations in Canada. In 2009, according to the Globe and Mail, 15 of the Top 50 private corporations in terms of profit were located in Ontario and another five in Quebec.[27] A total of 20 of the Top 50 private companies were located in central Canada. Moreover, 15 of the Top 50 are located in the Golden Horseshoe and southwestern Ontario. This number is made more remarkable since the auto manufacturing and parts sectors in Ontario and Quebec have been characterized by slow sales and bankruptcies as a consequence of the massive downturn in the American economy while natural resource companies have been steadily growing, making Calgary a boom town.

Politically, this is reflected in the fact that the first non-Ontarian to occupy the office of Minister of Finance was Jean Chrétien, a Quebec native, in 1979. Can you name another finance minister who did not originate from Ontario or Quebec?

A simple mention of "Bay Street" brings to mind huge office towers, money, and economic power. Again, the economic dominance of the Golden Horseshoe of Ontario is clearly visible with a simple drive along the highways that run through it: the Queen Elizabeth Way and Highways 401, 403, 407, and 427.

Political Dominance

Ontario and Quebec virtually dominate Canada in terms of representation in Parliament, with 181 out of 308 seats and appointments to key Cabinet posts such as the departments of finance, foreign affairs, justice, and international trade. The trend has been for the federal government to choose a finance minister who is a lawyer from Bay Street (who must first be elected, of course). Usually, this lawyer returns to a job on Bay Street at the conclusion of his or her political career.

Cultural and Social Dominance

Culturally, the media outlets of the CBC, Baton Broadcasting, Global TV, and City TV are all located in Metro Toronto. Canada's "national" newspapers, the Globe and Mail and the National Post, and Canada's largest-circulation daily the Toronto Star, are located in Metro Toronto. Metropolitan Toronto is also the centre of publishing and, along with Montreal, the centre of fashion, entertainment, and the arts. In particular, Metro Toronto is the home of the Academy of Canadian Cinema and Television, Air Canada Centre, Rogers Centre (formally SkyDome), BMO Field, the CN Tower, Ontario Place, the Canadian National Exhibition, the Sony Centre for the Performing Arts, Canada's Wonderland, Caribana, the National Ballet of Canada, historic Massey Hall, the Royal Ontario Museum (ROM), the Royal Alexandra Theatre, The Princess of Wales

Have the Western provinces received their share of recognition for helping to build this country? What about the Atlantic provinces? Have Ontario and Quebec received too much?

Theatre, Second City, The Canon Theatre, the Panasonic Theatre, Roy Thomson Hall, Casa Loma, The Hockey Hall of Fame, Paramount Canada's Wonderland, Canadian Opera Company, and countless other sites and exhibits. In fact, the city's website reminds us that Toronto is home to the third largest English-speaking theatre district in the world after New York and London. Toronto remains the only city in Canada to be home to five professional sports teams, three large universities, and four of Canada's largest colleges. For all the reasons mentioned, it is little wonder that other regions of Canada envy and resent central Canada and Metro Toronto in particular.

CONCLUSION

Regionalism is an important diversity in Canada, so important in fact that examining the nature of regionalism is critical if we are to have a complete understanding of social life in Canada. Canadians from different regions are diverse in a great many ways. From a regional perspective, for example, Canadians find themselves different in the areas of geography, climate, income, ethnicity, social class, and attitudes toward each other and toward the federal government. The last two differences confirm for us that regionalism does have an important sociopsychological component.

To what extent does regionalism make Canadians different from each other? Are regional differences more or less important than other differences such as language, social class, gender, sexual orientation, family structure, race, and ethnicity? List what you consider the five most important differences. Why did you choose the differences you did? Would a student in another province choose the same ones? Why or why not?

CRITICAL THINKING OUTSIDE THE BOX 1.6

How do you explain and reconcile the paradox that the federal government created vast regional disparities (economically and sociopsychologically) and later committed itself to reducing the disparities it had created?

What does the future hold for these differences? Probably much of the same. It is extremely unlikely that the nature of the Canadian political system will change any time soon, if at all. This is especially true of federalism and our electoral system, two key elements that intensify regional feelings and differences. As a consequence, it is highly unlikely that the behaviour of the federal government will change. It is equally unlikely that the nature of capitalism will change. As the saying goes, "Money will go where it will get more money." That means money (and jobs) will travel indiscriminately between regions, within regions, and, when necessary, even outside Canada.

These two developments, or lack thereof, do not bode well for the future of Canada. As Canadians, we must be vigilant and insist that all levels of government treat all Canadians living in all regions fairly and equally. If any level of government fails to behave in this manner, it should be reminded that the ballot box is never more than a few years away.

CHAPTER SUMMARY

Understanding regionalism is important to understanding life in Canada. There are economic, political, and sociopsychological components to regionalism. To understand regionalism in its entirety, we must pay particular attention to the sociopsychological component, because it is usually not addressed in the traditional literature. There are many different theories dealing with the causes of regionalism, and it is up to you to decide which of the four dominant theories presented here are best. The federal government has a role in both creating and attempting to minimize regional differences. Finally, we must be aware of and appreciate that certain aspects of our political system—federalism and our electoral system—can and do intensify regional differences.

KEY TERMS

executive federalism, p. 13

federalism, p. 13

Golden Horseshoe, p. 6

Meech Lake Accord, p. 13

National Policy, p. 20

regionalism, p. 4

representation by population, p. 14

royal commission, p. 28

sociopsychological dimension
   to regionalism, p. 30

transfer payments, p. 10

DISCUSSION QUESTIONS

1. What is *regionalism*? Why is regionalism important to understanding the Canadian experience?
2. Briefly outline four theoretical explanations for regionalism. Which do you think makes the most sense? Would Canadians from different provinces choose different explanations? If so, why? If not, why not?
3. How do federalism and our electoral system compound and intensify regional differences?
4. What do we mean by the *sociopsychological dimension* to regionalism?
5. What role(s) has the federal government played in both creating and helping to reduce regional differences? Can you think of any current examples?
6. Is the idea of regionalism "real" to you? If so, why? If not, why?

NOTES

1. See Richard Simeon, "Regionalism and Canadian Political Institutions," in O. Kruhlak, R. Schultz, and S. Pobihushchy, eds., *The Canadian Political Process* (Toronto: Holt, Rinehart and Winston, 1979).
2. See Harry H. Hiller, *Canadian Society: A Macro Analysis* (Scarborough, ON: Prentice-Hall, 1991), p. 11.
3. The explanations of these approaches draw heavily from the following: Ralph Mathews, "Understanding Regionalism as Effect and Cause," in *Social Issues: Sociological Views of Canada*, 4th ed. (Scarborough: Prentice-Hall, 1988), pp. 60–72; Ralph Mathews, *The Creation of Regional Dependency* (Toronto: University of Toronto Press, 1983), pp. 37–55; Janine Brodie, *The Political Economy of Canadian Regionalism* (Toronto: Harcourt Brace Jovanovich, 1990), pp. 21–36; and Donald J. Savoie, *The Canadian Economy: A Regional Perspective* (Toronto: Methuen, 1986), pp. 9–24. The names of some approaches have been altered.

4. This approach is drawn from Mathews, "Understanding Regionalism," pp. 64–65, and Mathews, *The Creation of Regional Dependency*, pp. 45–46.

5. Mathews, "Understanding Regionalism," p. 65.

6. This explanation is based on the one provided by Brodie, *The Political Economy of Canadian Regionalism*, pp. 27–34. The explanation includes Keynesianism, regional science, and developmental approaches.

7. Mathews, "Understanding Regionalism," p. 69.

8. Trudeau went national with his objections, which were published in a short treatise edited by former Cabinet minister Donald Johnston. See Donald Johnston, ed., *With a Bang, Not a Whimper: Pierre Trudeau Speaks Out* (Toronto: Stoddart Publishing, 1988).

9. *Toronto Star*, 2 November 2005.

10. For an excellent explanation of the National Policy, see Desmond Morton, *A Short History of Canada* (Edmonton: Hurtig, 1983), pp. 92–105. This brief history of Canada is both readable and enjoyable. We highly recommend it to anyone interested in the development of Canada.

11. "Gun Registry Cost Soars to 2 billion," *CBC News*, 13 February 2004, <www.cbc.ca/news/story/2004/02/13/gunregistry_rdi040213.html>, accessed 2 March 2010.

12. "Canada Part of Copenhagen Climate Deal," *CBC News*, 18 December 2009, <www.cbc.ca/world/story/2009/12/18/copenhagen-last-day.html>, accessed 2 March 2010. Prior to the Copenhagen climate summit Canada won the infamous "Fossil of the Year" award given to the country that most disrupts climate talks. "Canada's Image Lies in Tatters. It is Now to Climate What Japan is to Whaling," *Guardian*, <www.guardian.co.uk/commentisfree/cif-green/2009/nov/30/canada-tar-sands-copenhagen-climate-deal>, accessed 2 March 2010.

13. Darrin Qualman, *The Farm Crisis and Corporate Power*, Canadian Centre for Policy Alternatives site, p. 13, April 2001 <www.policyalternatives.ca/documents/National_Office_Pubs/farm_crisis.pdf>, accessed 27 March 2006.

14. Statistics Canada, *The Daily*, 4 May 2005.

15. Qualman, op cit., p. 6.

16. For a disturbing account of the decimation of Via Rail, see Jo Davis, ed., *Not a Sentimental Journey: What's Behind the Via Rail Cuts, What You Can Do About It* (Toronto: Gunbyfield Publishing, 1990).

17. For an explanation of the evolution and different types of transfer payments, see Garth Stevenson, *Unfulfilled Union: Canadian Federalism and National Unity*, 3rd ed. (Toronto: Gage, 1988), pp. 124–50.

18. Linda McQuaig, "Just One Sponsor, but Canadians Love CBC *People's History*," StraightGoods.com, 21 December 2000 <http://goods.perfectvision.ca/ViewFeature.cfm?REF=23>, accessed 8 February 2002.

19. Ibid.

20. Statistics Canada, "*Government Expenditures on Culture: Data Tables*," Catalogue no. 87F0001X. <www.statcan.gc.ca/pub/87f0001x/87f0001x2009001-eng.pdf>, accessed 1 March 2010.

21. Keith Archer, Roger Gibbins, Rainer Knopff, and Lesie A. Pal, *Parameters of Power: Canada's Political Institutions* (Toronto: Nelson, 1995), p. 287.

22. "Maritimes Kept Poor by Ontario," *The Hamilton Spectator*, 30 July 2001.

23. Robert Adamec, *Memorial Gazette* 37(9) (27 January 2005).

24. "Churchill Falls Deal Probed," *Montreal Gazette*, 20 December 2005, <www.canada.com/montrealgazette/story.html?id=17f52755-7ede-45a5-8b2f-6a8b7d004957>, accessed 1 March 2010. In fact, in a speech in 1996, then Premier Brian Tobin claimed that Newfoundland and Labrador were generating only $45 000 a day from the agreement while Hydro Quebec was generating $1.4 million.

25. "Conflicting Emotions," *Maclean's*, 27 March 1995.

26. "Export of Bulk Water from Newfoundland and Labrador," *Government of Newfoundland and Labrador*, October 2001, <www.gov.nf.ca/publicat/ReportoftheMinisterailCommitteeExaminingtheExportofBulkWater.PDF>, accessed 1 March 2010.

27. "The Top 1000 Publicly Traded Companies," *Globe and Mail, Report on Business.com* 2009 Edition, <www.v1.theglobeandmail.com/v5/content/tp1000-2009/index.php>, accessed 1 March 2010.

CHAPTER 2

Demographic Trends in Canada

Michelle Broderick

Except in the case of vaccination against small pox ... it is unlikely that immunization or therapy had a significant effect on mortality from infectious diseases before the twentieth century.
—T. McKeown, The Modern Rise of Population

In technologically advanced human societies, virtually every female now survives to reproductive age. This is a biologically novel situation.
—F. Fenner, "Foreword," in The Structure of Human Populations

Objectives
. . . .
After reading this chapter, you should be able to

- understand what the field of demography entails

- identify what kinds of information are used in the demographic study of populations

- understand the methods used by demographers

- appreciate that demographic variation can often account for social, cultural, and economic diversity within a population

- recognize that the study of the demographic history of Canadian populations touches on a wide variety of subjects, from illegitimacy to epidemics

DEMOGRAPHY: AN INTRODUCTION

Demography is the scientific study of human populations. It focuses on the size and composition of a population, which depend on such factors as fertility, nuptiality, mortality, and migration. Demography demonstrates how social and economic factors affect these demographic parameters and, hence, human behaviour. Variations in demographic characteristics can be observed at many different levels, for example, township, city, province, or nation, and they are often linked to social and economic features of these population units. Unique demographic histories experienced by populations in different regions are often the main cause of social, cultural, and economic diversity observed today. By studying the history of populations, we not only learn how they have diversified over time, but also, because of the greater time depth (e.g., several generations), find it easier to link social and economic factors to demographic patterns. This chapter will examine and define the variables used in demography, followed by some examples of contemporary and historical studies on Canadian populations.

Some Important Definitions: Demographic Variables

A **variable** is a characteristic that differs or varies among groups, such as age and religious affiliation. In demographic research, the variables examined are those that affect the growth of a population: fertility, nuptiality, mortality, and migration.

Fertility

Fertility refers to the number of **live births** occurring in a population within a specific period (either one year or aggregates of years). Fertility differs from **fecundity**, which is the maximum number of children that a woman can produce during her lifetime, that is, the potential of childbearing. The figure for fecundity is based on the length of the female reproductive period, usually defined as between the ages of 15 and 44, during which time a woman can produce a maximum of fifteen to twenty children; however, few women ever reach this potential because of the biological and social factors that reduce fertility. For instance, the length of the reproductive period can be affected by the age at which a woman marries—if reproduction does not occur outside of marriage. If a woman marries and has her first child at the age of 25, her reproductive period will be approximately nineteen years. During this time she could produce on average thirteen children. If that same woman married and had her first child at the age of 35 instead of 25, her reproductive period would be shorter, and the number of children she could produce would be considerably lower. Other factors affecting female fertility are the use of contraceptives and abortifacants; by preventing or terminating unwanted births, fewer children are born. Social attitudes toward reproduction can also affect fertility. For instance, if a woman's role in society is that of homemaker, where childbearing is seen as a valuable contribution, women will tend to have more children. Illness and disease can also limit fertility, by either preventing fertilization or by inducing spontaneous abortions (i.e., miscarriages).

Several methods are used to calculate fertility. The easiest method is the **crude birth rate**, which is the number of live births in a given population (see Figure 2.1). This method is "crude" in the sense that it is based on the entire population, not just the women who are capable of reproducing; therefore, this figure can be misleading because the number of women between 15 and 44 years of age can vary among populations. A more refined and accurate method is the use of the **fertility rate**, which is based on the number of women of reproductive age (15 to 44 years).

Nuptiality

Nuptiality, or marriage, is an important variable for two reasons: (1) marriage is related to fertility, in that the age at which marriage occurs can define the length of the female reproductive period and (2) the timing of marriage is affected by social and economic factors. For example, patterns of economic activity, such as farming, coupled with religious restrictions, such as Lent, have in the past resulted in a seasonal pattern of marriage, with most marriages occurring between October and December (i.e., after the harvest

Figure 2.1   Crude Birth Rate in Canada, 2007 (live births per 1000 population)

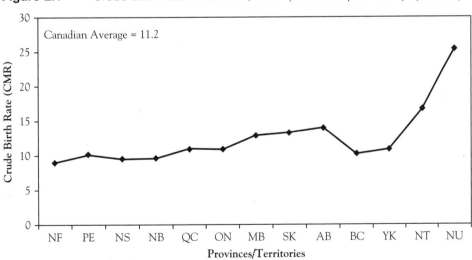

The pattern of fertility is not uniform across Canada. The lowest birth rate was recorded in Newfoundland and the highest in Nunavut. (Nunavut was declared a separate Territory from the Northwest Territories on 1 April 1999.)

Source: Adapted from Statistics Canada, *Births*, Catalogue No. 84F0210X, 2007, September 2009, p. 21, Table 4.

but before religious festivals). Today, this pattern is no longer observed in Canada. It is also common for people to delay marriage until they have achieved economic independence from their parents. The examination of nuptiality not only includes looking at those individuals who marry, but also at those who do not. For instance, if the majority of men and women in a population marry, the potential for population growth through births increases; however, if a large portion of the adult population do not marry, and, hence, may not reproduce, population growth will be slowed. The incidence of **celibacy**, the proportion of individuals in a population who never marry (and presumably, never reproduce), is often related to economics, especially to inheritance practices. For example, in Ireland farmers traditionally passed on their wealth (land) to one son only. The other children (both sons and daughters) either remained on the homestead and did not marry, or they left to seek their fortunes elsewhere.[1] Such a practice would also influence emigration and, hence, the size of the population.

Typical methods used to measure marriage include the **crude marriage rate**, which is the number of marriages recorded in a population (see Figure 2.2), and the **age-specific marriage rate**, based instead on the number of single individuals, who never married, in a given age interval. **Age at first marriage** can also be calculated; it provides, as already

Figure 2.2   Crude Marriage Rate in Canada, 2004 (marriages per 1000 population)

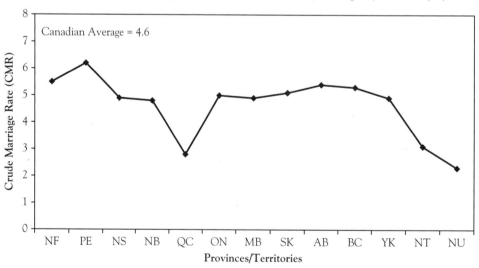

Prince Edward Island, Quebec, the Northwest Territories, and Nunavut deviate the most from the Canadian marriage pattern.

Source: Adapted from Statistics Canada, *CANSIM*, Table 101-1004, available <http://cansim2.statcan.gc.ca/cgi-win/cnsmcgi.exe?Lang=E&CNSM-Fi=CII/CII_1-eng.htm>.

mentioned, information on the length of the female reproductive period (see Figure 2.3). This particular measure has been found to be highly sensitive to economic factors.

Mortality

Mortality refers to the number of people in a population dying in a given period. Two important aspects of mortality are life span and life expectancy. **Life span** refers to the maximum age that a human has ever lived. This figure is currently 122 years: Jeanne Louise Calment was born in Arles, France, on 21 February 1875 and died on 4 August 1997.

As with fecundity, very few humans reach this potential. The **life expectancy** is the age to which most humans can expect to live and is based on the average age at death. In Canada, this figure is 78 years for males and 83 years for females.[2] A variety of biological and social factors can affect mortality. For instance, exposure to disease and toxic substances (such as pollution), nutrition, physical labour or exercise, stress, and access to health care can all affect mortality in a population.

Figure 2.3   Average Age at First Marriage in Canada, 2004

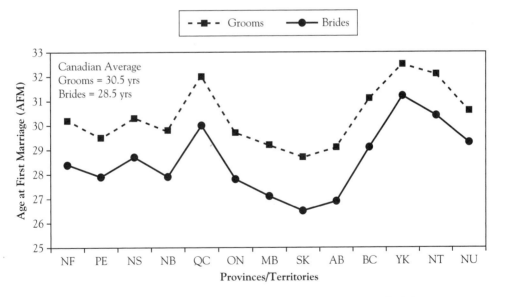

The Canadian pattern of age at first marriage is not unique. It is common to find that men marry at slightly older ages than women. Variation is observed across Canada, with people marrying at younger ages in Manitoba, Saskatchewan, and Alberta, and at older ages in Quebec, British Columbia, and the Yukon and Northwest Territories.

Note: Ontario data is from 2002 (2004 not available).

Source: Adapted from Statistics Canada, *Marriage Database*, Catalogue No. 84F0212XWE, 2004, 15 July 2009, Table 101-1002.

Mortality is measured in a variety of ways, such as the **crude death rate**, which is the number of deaths in a given population (see Figures 2.4 and 2.5). Again, this is a crude method that does not reveal details of the mortality experience. A more detailed picture is achieved by examining mortality in different age groups, that is, **age-specific mortality rates**, and it helps to identify major risk factors affecting different segments of the population. One of the most useful age groups in which to study mortality is of those aged less than one year, that is, the **infant mortality rate** (see Figure 2.6). This measure is extremely useful as an indicator of the general health status of the population, because infants are more susceptible to environmental factors, such as food consumption, medical care, and public sanitation. In other words, the infant mortality rate reflects the standard of living in a population. Infant mortality is also associated with life expectancy. When infant mortality is low, life expectancy is high, and vice versa. For instance, in developed countries life expectancy is much higher than in developing countries, and this reflects the standard of living. Analysis of infant mortality is sometimes divided into two age groups: under six months of age and between six and twelve months. Death under six months tends to be associated with problems that a child was born with, whereas death between six to twelve months is usually related to external or environmental factors, such as disease or nutrition.

Figure 2.4   Crude Death Rate in Canada, 2007 (deaths per 1000 population)

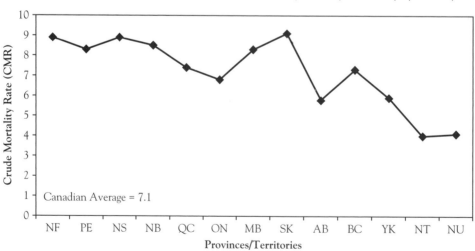

The crude death rate varies across Canada. The highest death rate occurs in Saskatchewan, while the lowest occurs in the Northwest Territories.

Source: Adapted from Statistics Canada, *Deaths*, Catalogue No. 84F0211X, 2007, February 2010, Table 2.

Figure 2.5   Sex-Specific Mortality Rates in Canada, 2007 (deaths per 1000 males and females in the population)

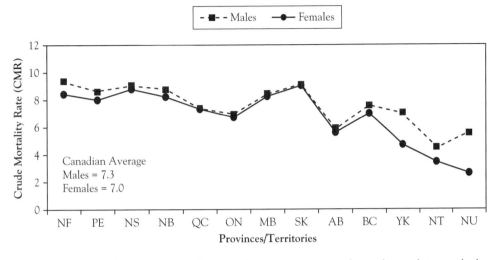

By comparing the crude mortality rates between the sexes, you can see that males are dying at a higher rate than females. This pattern is reflected in their life expectancies, which are 78 years for males and 83 years for females.

Source: Adapted from Statistics Canada, *Deaths*, Catalogue No. 84F0211X, 2007, February 2010, Table 1, p. 20 and Table 1, pp. 68 to 71.

Figure 2.6   Infant Mortality Rates in Canada, 2007 (deaths per 1000 live births)

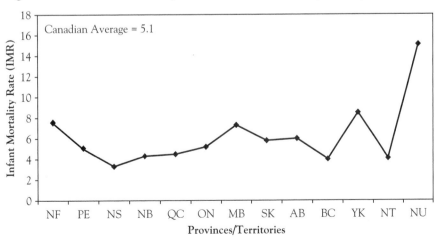

The infant mortality rate also displays a certain amount of variation across Canada. It is at its lowest in Nova Scotia and at its highest in Nunavut.

Source: Adapted from Statistics Canada, *Deaths*, Catalogue No. 84F0211X, 2007, February 2010, Table 4-1, pp. 35 and 37.

Morbidity, the incidence of particular diseases in a population, is also of interest, because this is related to both the social and physical environments. For instance, in Canada we enjoy a temperate climate with warm summers and cold winters. As a result many microorganisms and disease-causing parasites cannot survive year-round, and we do not experience high rates of certain diseases seen elsewhere (e.g., malaria). The age profile of a population will also influence morbidity. In Canada the proportion of the population over the age of 64 almost tripled between 1921 and 2006, increasing from 4.8 percent to 13.7 percent[3] (see Figure 2.7 and Critical Thinking Outside the Box 2.1). This increase is in part the result of lower fertility (fewer children are being born) and of higher life expectancy or survivorship (more people are living longer). Because we have a larger portion of older individuals, we also have an increase in diseases associated with aging, such as cancer and degenerative bone diseases.

Migration

Migration refers to the movement of people into and out of specific geographical areas. There are two types of migration, **immigration**, which is the movement into a specific

Figure 2.7   Proportion of the Population Over the Age of 64 Years, 1951 and 2006

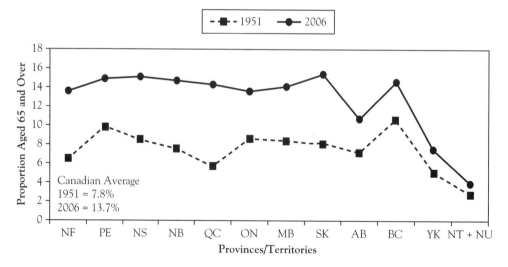

Regional variation in the proportion of the population over the age of 64 is marked. An increase in the number of seniors is also noted over time. This variation across time and space is related to changes in fertility, mortality, and migration. (Data on Nunavut, separate from the Northwest Territories, was not available prior to 1999; therefore, these data were combined.)

Source: Adapted from Statistics Canada, Age, Sex and Marital Status, Data Products: Nation Series: 1991 Census Population, Catalogue No. 93-310, Table 1, 6 July 1992 (for the 1951 data), and from Age & Sex Highlight Tables, 2006 Census, Catalogue No. 97-551-XWE2006002, 17 July 2007.

CRITICAL THINKING OUTSIDE THE BOX 2.1

The Aging of Canada's Population

The **dependency ratio** reflects the proportion of the population who are under the age of 15 and above the age of 64. This group is viewed as being dependent on society, directly or indirectly. The aged are directly supported by our society through the government pension plan and discounted services, whereas children are only indirectly supported, because it is the responsibility of their parents or guardians to care for them.

Whereas the dependency ratio has decreased over time, from 64.4 in 1921 to 31.4 in 2006, the contribution of those over the age of 64 has increased more than threefold, from 12.2 percent to 43.6 percent. This increase reflects the fact that our Canadian population is aging. This trend is likely to continue, and we run the risk of increased poverty and illness among the aged, since our society may not have the resources to support those services needed by the elderly.

Can we begin to plan for this contingency today?

Source: Adapted from Statistics Canada, *Age & Sex Highlight Tables, 2006 Census*, Catalogue No. 97-551-XWE2006002, 17 July 2007.

area, and **emigration**, which is the movement out of a specific area. Both forms of migration occur at the same time. Factors affecting migration can be grouped into three general categories: (1) economic, meaning the search for economic opportunities; (2) political, meaning escape from the persecution of a particular group of people and from social institutions such as slavery; and (3) environmental, meaning escape from the effects of earthquakes, floods, and famines. In examining the factors affecting migration, you must remember that push and pull factors occur at the same time, that is, some factors pull people toward an area while others push them away. For instance, an urban setting generally offers a higher frequency and wider variety of jobs; therefore, it attracts people. However, the cost of living in an urban setting tends to be much higher than in a rural area and acts as a deterrent. Migration can also be viewed as either voluntary or involuntary. Voluntary migration occurs when the decision to move or not is up to the individual. For example, if you were offered a well-paying job in Calgary, the decision to move would be entirely yours. Migration is involuntary when the individual is forced to move or stay (see Critical Thinking Outside the Box 2.2), as during World War II when many were forced to flee Europe while others were prevented from doing so by the Nazi regime.

CRITICAL THINKING OUTSIDE THE BOX 2.2

Slavery and the Arrival of Black People in Nova Scotia

The first black people in Canada arrived here as slaves. The institution of slavery was formally acknowledged through numerous royal proclamations, beginning in Quebec in 1689, and continued well into the early 19th century. Black people were imported in large numbers into Nova Scotia primarily as a source of labour in the construction of the city of Halifax. The next major wave of black immigrants into Nova Scotia came after the American Revolution and the War of 1812.

Although many slaves fled from the United States to Canada via the Underground Railroad, between 1787 and 1800 they also fled from Canada into New England, where slavery had already been abolished. It was not until 1833 that slavery was abolished in Canada and the rest of the British Empire, and many now believe that this was more in the nature of an economic decision than a moral one, that is, related to the high monetary cost of maintaining slavery.

Black people, like many other ethnic groups who either voluntarily or involuntarily migrated to Canada, have made important contributions to our country. Why is their early presence in Canada downplayed at best or ignored at worst?

Source: T. Johnson, "The Canadian Black Population and Immigration," *Anthropos* 73(1978): 588–92; S.E. Williams, "Two Hundred Years in the Development of the Afro-Canadians in Nova Scotia, 1782–1982," in J.L. Elliott, ed., *Two Nations, Many Cultures: Ethnic Groups in Canada*, 2nd ed. (Scarborough: Prentice-Hall, 1983).

Several measurements of migration are commonly used. The in-migration or **immigration rate** consists of the number of people entering an area. The out-migration or **emigration rate** consists of the number of people leaving an area. The **gross migration rate** reflects the total number of people who both enter and leave an area. The **net migration rate** is the annual increase or decrease in the size of a population, based on the number of people entering an area minus the number who leave. Migration is often the single most important factor affecting the size—growth or decline—of a population, and it can play an important role in the spread of disease. For example, during the 19th century Canada suffered repeated epidemics of cholera, which were introduced by infected migrants.[4]

Migration can involve internal and external migrants. **Internal migrants** are those who move within a specific area. **External migrants** are those who move from outside a specific area. These areas can be defined at many different levels, such as a neighbourhood, province, or nation. For instance, in a sample from the 2006 Canadian census,[5] it was found that during the previous year 63.9 percent of migrants moved within the same province, 15.3 percent moved into a different province, and 20.8 percent immigrated from outside Canada (see Figure 2.8). These figures are different from those several decades ago. In 1976, 68.1 percent of migrants moved within the same province, 17.8 percent moved into a different province, and 14.0 percent immigrated from outside Canada.[6] It is important to note, however, that the rate of migration from outside Canada is under strict management with yearly quotas, whereas no such formal constraints exist on internal migration. Management of external migration can dictate the occupational, ethnic, age, gender, and political profiles of migrants. It can also severely limit their choices of an ultimate destination (see Critical Thinking Outside the Box 2.3). The majority of external migrants originate from Europe (37 percent), Asia (41 percent), Central and South America (6 percent), the Caribbean and Bermuda (5 percent), Africa (6 percent), and the United States (4 percent).[7]

Figure 2.8   Mobility in Canada, 2006

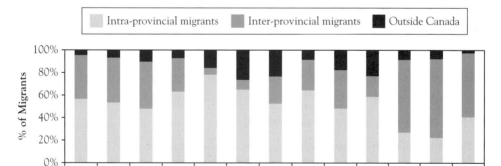

In most cases, the majority of migrants (individuals in this case who have migrated in the previous year) are moving within the same province. Migrants from outside Canada tend to congregate in provinces that have a more diverse economy, such as Quebec, Ontario, Manitoba, Alberta, and British Columbia.

Source: Adapted from Statistics Canada, Components of Migration, Mother Tongue, Age Groups, and Sex for Migrants Aged 5 years and Over of Canada, Provinces, Territories, Census Metropolitan Areas and Census Agglomerations, 2006 Census, Catalogue No. 97-556-XCB2006017.

CRITICAL THINKING OUTSIDE THE BOX 2.3

Chinese Immigration to Western Canada

Chinese immigration to Western Canada began with the British Columbia gold rush of 1858. Between 1881 and 1885 large numbers of Chinese men were recruited to help build the Canadian Pacific Railway. Immigration of Chinese was limited demographically because the Canadian government was primarily interested in attracting migrant labourers, not settlers. As such, restrictive immigration policies created an unusual demographic profile among Chinese communities: they were predominantly male. With the growth of organized labour in Western Canada, numerous policies were introduced that were designed at first to discourage new migrants (e.g., British Columbia levied a $50 tax on each new Chinese immigrant), then to end the arrival of Chinese migrants. (The Chinese Immigration Act of 1923 was only repealed in 1947; between those years, no Chinese migrants could legally enter Canada.) These policies were in response to a perceived threat to organized labour of cheap Chinese labour.

Can we trust government policymakers to have enough insight into the effects of their policies concerning immigration, or will they create irrevocable damage to individuals, cultures, and societies?

Source: J.L. Elliott, "Canadian Immigration: A Historical Assessment," in J.L. Elliott, ed., *Two Nations, Many Cultures: Ethnic Groups in Canada* (Scarborough: Prentice-Hall, 1983); P.S. Li, "Chinese Immigrants in the Canadian Prairie, 1910–47," *Canadian Review of Sociology and Anthropology* 19 (1982): 527–40.

Sources of Demographic Information

Numerous sources of information (data) are used in demography. All births, deaths, and marriages that occur in a population are usually recorded in vital registries. Two sources of registries are available: (1) **civil registries**, which are compiled by government, and (2) **ecclesiastical registries**, which are compiled by individual religious groups. The amount or detail of information recorded in these sources varies. For instance, a birth record usually includes the name of the child, the date of birth or baptism (depending on the source), the names of the parents, and the place of birth or baptism. Other information that may be included is the occupations of the parents, the place of birth, and religious affiliation. Death records typically record the name of the deceased, place of death, cause of death, and age at death. Other information sometimes available includes occupation and place of residence. Marriage records generally include the names of the couple, the date of their marriage, their marital status, the place where they were married, their occupation, age, and religious affiliation. On occasion, their place of birth and the names of their parents are also recorded.

Censuses, compiled by government, are also an important source of information. A **census** is a list of all people who reside in a particular geographical area during a specific period. The first Canadian census after Confederation was taken in 1871, although censuses were recorded before Confederation (the earliest of these dates to 1666). The **decennial census**, that is, a census taken every 10th year, was first established while Canada was still under British rule.[8] Information usually recorded in a census varies considerably, both over time and across space, but it usually includes household or dwelling, name, age, sex, relationship to the head of the household (e.g., wife, son, niece, boarder), religious affiliation, and occupation. From census records we can examine household composition and formation. A **household** is a group of individuals who live together; this need not be a family, and it can include hired servants and boarders. When combined with vital registries, census records can be used to reconstruct individual families, that is, to create **genealogies**.

Other sources that can complement those already mentioned are cemetery data, voters' lists, military records, wills, and personal journals, to name but a few. The type of sources used will often depend on the topic of research and the availability of records. For instance, if you want to study fertility, you would need access to birth registries, either civil or ecclesiastical; if possible the use of both sources is recommended, as this provides a check on the accuracy of the data. However, both the government and ecclesiastical institutions can restrict access to **nominative records**, which list names. Therefore, you might not be able to reconstruct the fertility experience of specific women; instead, you would generalize about fertility on the basis of the number of women aged 15 to 44 in a given population and the number of births registered within a specific period of time.

Problems with Sources of Demographic Information

Numerous problems exist with using the mentioned sources. First, these sources were collected for reasons other than demographic research, and so they may contain hidden biases. **Crosschecking** the data—that is, using as many sources as possible—can minimize biases. For example, linking individuals from death records to both birth and census records will allow you to check the accuracy of the initial information, such as age, spelling of name, and so on. When linking various sources, there are often problems, many of which are related to the fact that the spelling of people's names and place names changes over time. Second, the quality of the data often varies because of errors in copying the initial information, level of literacy, method of initial data collection, and falsification of data (e.g., age is often misreported in censuses). Third, problems can also be related to changes in geographical boundaries, both ecclesiastical and civil. Therefore, a change in fertility might only be an artifact; that is, it might have been caused by the loss or gain in the number of communities included in a given parish or district.

Because of the variety of limitations associated with sources of demographic information, several techniques have been developed to assess them. In small populations with, say, fewer than one hundred **vital events**—births, marriages, and deaths—each year, a comparison of baptisms to marriages can be used. If this ratio is seven or eight to one, then it is possible that marriages were underregistered, because this ratio should be between four and five to one. The sex ratio of baptisms can also be used. If this ratio exceeds 110 over several years, then female baptisms are underregistered, because the ratio of males to females should be around 105 at birth. When examining large populations, those with hundreds of vital events (or more) recorded each year, you can use one of three methods to evaluate the quality of the data. The **documentary method** involves using the expertise of other researchers who have worked with those same sources—in other words, others may be able to attest to the accuracy and completeness of the records. The **expectation method** involves calculating expected proportions of vital events based on such factors as economic conditions, marriages, and migration. The **comparative method** entails calculating trends of vital events based on data from nearby populations. Overall, the more intimately researchers come to know their populations, the better they will be able to identify and assess any discrepancies.

Analyzing Demographic Information

The population is the focus of demographic research. Each **population** can be defined based on four aspects: (1) biological, involving shared genes; (2) ecological, involving shared environment; (3) social, involving a common cultural heritage; and (4) demographic, meaning shared time and space.[9] For instance, ethnicity is often used as a social factor defining a population. In 2006 the bulk of the Canadian population (60.5 percent) consisted of those of British, French, or European origin. The remainder identified their ethnic origin as Asian (8.6 percent), Aboriginal (3.4 percent), Caribbean (1.2 percent), Arab (1.0 percent), African (0.8 percent), Latin, Central, and South American (0.7 percent), and Other (23.8 percent—this includes those who identified themselves as North American)[10] (see Figure 2.9). Once the population has been identified, the data are collected, which often involves thousands of entries (births, marriages, deaths, and census entries). Therefore, before analysis can proceed, the data must be reduced to make them more manageable. This usually involves **aggregating** the data, that is, summarizing observations either over specific geographical areas, time

Figure 2.9   Ethnic Origins of Canada's Population, 2006

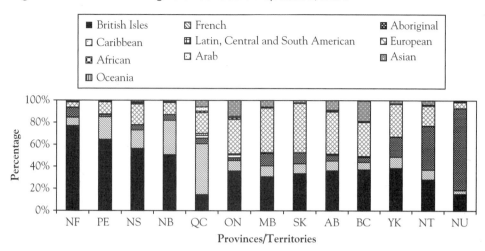

A great deal of variation exists across Canada regarding ethnic origin. A particular ethnic group dominates in Newfoundland, Prince Edward Island, Nova Scotia, New Brunswick, Quebec, Northwest Territories, and Nunavut. Those of British descent dominate in the east, ranging from 77 percent in Newfoundland to 51 percent in New Brunswick. In Quebec, individuals of French descent make up 46 percent of the population, while in Nunavut, 74 percent of the population is of Aboriginal descent. Due to the variation in its ethnic makeup, each province has a unique cultural mosaic. (Excluded are those who identified their ethnic origins as North American, which includes American, Canadian, Newfoundlander, Nova Scotian, Ontarian, Québécois, and other provincial or regional groups.)

Note: Other North American groups (American, Canadian, Newfoundlander, Nova Scotian, Ontarian, Québécois, other provincial or regional groups) have been excluded from this chart. "Asian" incorporates people of West, South, Southeast, and East Asian origin.

Source: Adapted from Statistics Canada, "Ethnic Origin (247), Generation Status (4), Single and Multiple Responses (3) and Sex (3) for Population 15 Years and Over of Canada, Provinces, Territories, Census Divisions and Census Subdivisions, 2006 Census—20% Sample Data," Catalogue No. 97-562-XCB2006015.

periods, or both. For instance, obtaining an average age at marriage for each decade over the study period reduces the data and makes comparisons easier.

In analyzing the data, two approaches are available: longitudinal and cross-sectional. **Longitudinal analysis** involves following a birth or marriage cohort through time. A *cohort* is a group of people who share the timing of a vital event—for example, all individuals in a population who were born in 1890. **Cross-sectional analysis** involves dividing data into nonoverlapping age categories to make demographic inferences about segments of the population who are at different stages of life (e.g., child versus adult). For instance, to examine fertility patterns using the longitudinal approach, you would take all of the population born in a specific period and follow them from birth to death; using the cross-sectional approach, you would group your population into different age groups, using these different groups to represent the patterns experienced over a lifetime. Of the two, the cross-sectional approach is the quickest and easiest, because it is not necessary to collect demographic information (e.g., births) over a long period; however, the longitudinal approach is potentially the most accurate, because you can examine the cumulative effects of social and environmental factors on the same group of people over time.

Biological Inferences

One of the goals of demographic research is to make inferences about the genetic structure of a population. This is achieved by either looking at marriages or looking at births and deaths.

Choosing a Marriage Partner

Marriage, which infers reproduction and, hence, the passing on of genes, can be either random or nonrandom. In most populations, humans included, the selection of a mate is nonrandom **(nonrandom mate selection)**—that is, a distinct preference in the choice of a mate is evident. This preference can be related to physical or socioeconomic characteristics, such as physical attractiveness, age, religious affiliation, socioeconomic status (social class), and ethnicity. Individuals tend to choose mates who share the same sociocultural background as they do. This preference may be related to a conscious decision not to marry outside of one's group (e.g., Jews and Catholics), or it may simply be the byproduct of geographical and social segregation of subgroups in a population. In other words, individuals belonging to a particular economic and ethnic group often live in the same general area and interact socially more within their group than outside it; therefore, the potential mates each is exposed to are in a sense "preselected" and have the same social background.

The task of the demographer is to identify these preferences in a population. Several methods are used to assess the frequency of nonrandom mating: genealogical analysis, isonomy, and kinship coefficients. **Genealogical analysis** requires years of effort, depending on the size of the population in question, because it involves reconstructing individual families. **Isonomy** is a faster method that involves looking at the frequency of marriages occurring between individuals who share a surname (e.g., John Martin marrying Susan Martin). Of course, this method involves several assumptions, not the least of which is that similar surnames have the same origin (e.g., all Martins ultimately descended from one family of Martins). **Kinship coefficients** are similar to isonomy in that surnames are also used; they differ in that they do not focus on marriages but simply look at the proportion of surnames in a population, calculating the probability that the individuals are related. Each method attempts to identify the existence of preferences in the exchange of mates between families; the demographer working with kinship coefficients is trying to determine whether individuals in certain families choose their marriage partners from specific families or whether they marry someone irrespective of that individual's family.

Evolution by Natural Selection

The disappearance of the dinosaurs and the appearance of anatomically modern humans are generally what come to mind when people think of evolutionary change. But **evolution** can also occur on a micro level that involves small changes in the gene frequency of a population. **Natural selection** refers to the preferential survival and reproduction of individuals in a population by virtue of possessing a genetic characteristic that gives them an advantage. For instance, if a certain blood type protected an individual from a deadly disease, those who shared that blood type would be more likely to survive than others and have a higher probability of successfully reproducing. The result would be that future generations would increasingly possess the advantageous blood type. The net result, when comparing generations, would be a change in gene frequency (e.g., an increase in individuals with blood type A and a decrease of those with blood type O—which has been tentatively associated with exposure to the bubonic plague).[11] Such a change can be referred to as "evolution." When this change results from the genetic adaptation to an environmental stress, we term it *natural selection.*

Natural selection is not easily detected in human populations.[12] The main reason for this is the length of the human generation, approximately twenty-five years. Therefore, we would need to study many generations in detail before we could detect natural selection. This is not possible, because researchers would not live long enough to complete their research, and it is unlikely that funding could be obtained for a project of such a long duration. The use of historical populations is also limited in this regard, because we are not able to obtain genetic samples (e.g., blood samples). However, a method has been developed that measures the potential for natural selection in human populations. This method is called **Crow's Index of Selection**. Crow's Index takes into account both deaths and births—mortality and fertility—and focuses on whether differences occur in subgroups of the population; subgroups can be defined using a variety of social factors, such as ethnicity, religious affiliation, and socioeconomic status. If differences do occur, the potential for natural selection exists, that is, a change in the frequency of a gene or genes that results because a segment of the population became genetically adapted to an environmental stress.[13]

HISTORICAL DEMOGRAPHIC ANALYSIS OF CANADIAN POPULATIONS

Common sources of demographic information include written documents, such as birth, death, and marriage registries. When focusing on historical sources in Canada, the time depth is limited to the arrival of people from Europe, Asia, and Africa. At the very best, some information is available as early as the 15th century. Early sources are geographically limited to what was referred to as New France and to several British colonies, such as New England and Rupert's Land; some of these areas were later known as Upper and Lower Canada. What follows is a survey of the types of demographic research on Canadian populations. Although it is excluded from this chapter because of space constraints, please note that a subfield of demography, **paleodemography**, focuses on nonwritten sources, such as skeletal remains, to study patterns of birth, death, and migration in prehistoric populations.

Regional Survey

Most demographic research in Canada has focused on Quebec and Ontario, with relatively less work done on other provinces and territories. This focus on central Canada is partly because of the availability of records; the majority of immigrants arrived and lived in central Canada, and thus this area has the longest time frame of demographic sources.

An exhaustive and complete survey of historical demographic studies of Canadian populations is not possible here. Instead, the intention is to introduce the topic of demography. It is hoped that interested readers will pursue specific areas in more depth (see the Selected Bibliography at the end of this book for names of journals that regularly feature a broad range of articles on Canadian historical demography). What follows is a brief examination of historical demographic studies of Canadian populations.

The study of migration in historical Canada is one of the most common types of research, which is easily explained by the fact that, except for North American Aboriginals (see Critical Thinking Outside the Box 2.4), Canada was settled by migrants. Such studies often focus on the contributions of particular ethnic groups, such as the Arabs,[14] Irish,[15] Ukrainians,[16] Italians,[17] and Armenians,[18] to name but a few. Others take a more general approach, focusing on trends over a wider area and including several ethnic groups.[19] Considerably less attention has been given to emigration from Canada.[20] Research on the growth of urbanism and urban centres in Canada is also of interest, and it often relates directly to patterns of immigration.[21]

Research on fertility and nuptiality examines such issues as birth control and abortion,[22] illegitimacy,[23] and changes in fertility patterns over time and across space.[24] In many cases, fertility is linked to a variety of economic factors. In some instances, marriage and fertility patterns are described for specific ethnic groups, which is useful in identifying sociocultural differences affecting these and other demographic variables.[25] A related focus of Canadian research is family and household composition, both of which are strongly influenced by local economic patterns.[26]

Studies of historical patterns of mortality often focus on epidemics, such as cholera,[27] smallpox,[28] typhoid,[29] and influenza.[30] This type of research not only examines the mortality associated with these diseases, but also looks at the sociocultural effects they caused.

CRITICAL THINKING OUTSIDE THE BOX 2.4

The First People in North America

The first people to arrive in North America were the ancestors of today's Aboriginal population, who crossed from the Old World via a land bridge that linked northeastern Siberia to Alaska. This land bridge, called **Beringia**, was last in existence between 27 000 and 11 000 years ago. The Aboriginals are thought to have arrived in North America sometime between 20 000 and 15 000 years ago; we have evidence from archaeology that humans had reached central Mexico about 11 000 years ago. It seems likely that people crossed the land bridge in pursuit of migrating herds of animals, such as mammoths, caribou, and bison.

The archaeological record indicates that the North American Aboriginals had diversified into a variety of cultural groups, some of which attained complex levels of sociopolitical organization, that is, tribes and chiefdoms. However, the arrival of Europeans disrupted Aboriginal cultures, in some instances irrevocably. Today, many descendants of these early migrants are in the process of resurrecting their rich cultural heritage.

Because we are all immigrants to this country, and if length of residence has any meaning, then why are the land claims of North American Aboriginals not given precedence over our own?

Source: B.M. Fagan, *People of the Earth*, 7th ed. (New York: Harper Collins, 1992).

Other methods examine the more general patterns of mortality.[31] Again the importance lies in the comparisons with other populations to identify the role of human behaviour in the spread of disease, for example, the role of food preparation techniques, method of water storage, or crowding.

These studies illustrate the diverse nature of the Canadian population. Each geographical region has experienced a unique demographic history, which, in turn, has affected local, social, and economic conditions; it is important to note that this interaction continues to this day. We are dealing with an inherently dynamic system, and we can expect that the legacy created by past demographic behaviour will continue to affect future populations. By understanding this phenomenon we will be better equipped to identify future trends and to plan for potential problems, such as the stress on local economies when 50 percent of our population consists of people over the age of 64.

CONCLUSION

Demographic research can be useful in demonstrating the importance of social and economic factors on human behaviour. By looking at fertility, nuptiality, mortality, and migration, the effects of numerous variables, such as resource exploitation, patterns of occupation, and social class, can be uncovered. This information can then be combined with other sources, not only to build a profile of life in the past, but also to help us understand the dynamic nature of human populations today. Understanding the interrelationship between the biological and social aspects of human groups can have important implications for a variety of policies directed at living populations, ranging from the effective delivery of community health care to the development and introduction of population control measures. Such information can also contribute to our understanding of the interrelationship between human populations and their physical environments. Knowledge of complex systems may enable us to more effectively deal with, and perhaps avoid, a variety of crises—most of which are created by humans—such as the emergence and spread of new and virulent diseases.

CHAPTER SUMMARY

This chapter introduces the major concepts used in demography. Sources of information on populations vary and include records compiled by government, such as birth registries, ecclesiastical institutions, such as church marriage registries, and individual people, such as wills, journals, or diaries. However, because no source of demographic information is perfect, care should be taken to identify biases in the information. The methods used by demographers are sometimes dictated by the nature of the data. For instance, if researchers do not have access to data over a long period, they are necessarily limited to performing cross-sectional analyses.

Some sources and methods used in demographic analysis are examined by focusing on four key areas: fertility, nuptiality, mortality, and migration. Fertility and mortality affect the natural growth or decline in a population's size; the ratio between the two determines whether a population increases, decreases, or remains stable. Nuptiality, or marriage, influences fertility in several ways. For instance, the timing of marriage can define the length of the female reproductive period, and variation in the proportion of the population who marry, or do not marry, can affect fertility by limiting or increasing the number of couples who are in a position to produce children—assuming that reproduction outside of marriage is low. Migration is one of the most important factors affecting the growth or decline of a population; if more individuals enter an area than leave it, the size of the population will increase. The reverse is also true; if more individuals leave an area than enter it, the size of the population will decline. Each of these four variables (fertility, nuptiality, mortality, and migration) varies within and among populations. Over time they define the unique demographic nature of a population, and they are ultimately responsible for generating the degree of diversity currently observed, regardless of how that diversity is defined (e.g., culturally, politically, or economically).

This chapter briefly surveys the types of demographic research on historical Canadian populations. These include studies of immigration and emigration, birth control, illegitimacy, households, and epidemics. In most cases the aim of such research is not only to describe events in the past, but also to link them to social, economic, and (when possible) biological factors. The ultimate aim of such research is to understand the factors that can affect a population's demographic profile. This information may then be applied to current issues and problems, such as overpopulation and the spread of deadly viruses.

KEY TERMS

age at first marriage, p. 42

age-specific marriage rate, p. 42

age-specific mortality rates, p. 44

aggregating, p. 52

Beringia, p. 57

celibacy, p. 42

census, p. 51

civil registries, p. 50

comparative method, p. 52

crosschecking, p. 51

cross-sectional analysis, p. 53

Crow's Index of Selection, p. 55

crude birth rate, p. 41

crude death rate, p. 44

crude marriage rate, p. 42

decennial census, p. 51

demography, p. 40

dependency ratio, p. 47

documentary method, p. 52

ecclesiastical registries, p. 50

emigration, p. 47

emigration rate, p. 48

evolution, p. 55

expectation method, p. 52

external migrants, p. 49

fecundity, p. 40

fertility, p. 40

fertility rate, p. 41

genealogical analysis, p. 54

genealogies, p. 51

gross migration rate, p. 48

household, p. 51

immigration, p. 46

immigration rate, p. 48

infant mortality rate, p. 44

internal migrants, p. 49

isonomy, p. 54

kinship coefficients, p. 54

life expectancy, p. 43

life span, p. 43

live births, p. 40

longitudinal analysis, p. 53

migration, p. 46

morbidity, p. 46

mortality, p. 43

natural selection, p. 55

net migration rate, p. 48

nominative records, p. 51

nonrandom mate selection, p. 54

nuptiality, p. 41

paleodemography, p. 56

population, p. 52

variable, p. 40

vital events, p. 52

DISCUSSION QUESTIONS

1. If you were going to reconstruct your own family history (genealogy), what types of information would you need? Which sources would provide you with this information? What potential problems might arise the further back in time you proceeded?

2. What factors might affect the timing of marriage today (age at marriage)? Would these factors be similar to or different from those affecting marriage in the past? What effect could these factors have on fertility?

3. To meet the needs of a changing economy (new technology), our population needs to become more educated. What effects might increased educational attainment, that is, spending more time in school, have on age at marriage and fertility?

4. Until the 20th century, the growth of the Canadian population was not the result of natural growth (births exceeding deaths) but primarily the result of immigration. Which factors do you think might have attracted these early migrants? Which factors might be attracting immigrants today?

5. Compare and contrast the mortality experience of the Canadian population over a 100-year period. Obtain the information you need from Statistics Canada. Look at the different categories of causes of death (e.g., infectious disease, degenerative disease). Are there any differences between the sexes regarding the mortality experience? Are there any differences in the mortality experience across the provinces? If so, what might account for these differences? Has the pattern of mortality changed over time? If so, explain how (and perhaps why) it has changed.

NOTES

1. K.H. Connell, *The Population of Ireland 1750–1845* (Oxford: Clarendon Press, 1950), p. 47.
2. Statistics Canada, *Deaths*, Catalogue No. 84F0211X, 2007, February 2010, Table 6, p.16.
3. Statistics Canada, *Age, Sex and Marital Status, Data Products: Nation Series: 1991 Census Population*, Catalogue No. 93-310, Table 1, 6 July 1992 (for the 1951 data), and from *Age & Sex Highlight Tables, 2006 Census*, Catalogue No. 97-551-XWE2006002, 17 July 2007.
4. G. Bilson, *A Darkened House: Cholera in Nineteenth-Century Canada* (Toronto: University of Toronto Press, 1980), p. 23.
5. Statistics Canada, "2006 Census of Canada," available <www12.statcan.ca/census-recensement/2006/dp-pd/index-eng.cfm>.

6. Statistics Canada, *Population: Demographic Characteristics—Mobility Status* (Ottawa: Supply and Services Canada, 1978), p. 1.

7. Adapted from Statistics Canada, "Immigrant Population by Place of Birth, by Province and Territory, 2006 Census," 11 December 2007.

8. Statistics Canada, "2006 Census Reference Materials: About the Census: History of the Census of Canada," <www12.statcan.gc.ca/census-recensement/2006/ref/about-apropos/hist-eng.cfm> (Ottawa: Minister of Industry, 2009).

9. G.A. Harrison and A.J. Boyce, "Introduction: The Framework of Population Studies," in G.A. Harrison and A.J. Boyce, eds., *The Structure of Human Populations* (Oxford: Clarendon Press, 1972), pp. 3–4.

10. Statistics Canada, "Ethnic Origin (247), Generation Status (4), Single and Multiple Responses (3) and Sex (3) for Population 15 Years and Over of Canada, Provinces, Territories, Census Divisions and Census Subdivisions, 2006 Census—20% Sample Data," Catalogue No. 97-562-XCB2006015. These figures are based on those who listed single and multiple responses.

11. A.K. Roychoudhury and M. Nei, *Human Polymorphic Genes: World Distribution* (Oxford: Oxford University Press, 1988).

12. T. Dobzhansky, "Natural Selection in Mankind," in G.A. Harrison and A.J. Boyce, eds., *The Structure of Human Populations* (Oxford: Clarendon Press, 1972), p. 232.

13. J.F. Crow, "Some Possibilities for Measuring Selection Intensities in Man," *Human Biology* 30 (1958): 1.

14. B. Abu-Laban, "Arab Immigration to Canada," in J.L. Elliott, ed., *Two Nations, Many Cultures: Ethnic Groups in Canada* (Scarborough: Prentice-Hall, 1979), p. 372.

15. A.G. Brunger, "Geographical Propinquity Among Pre-famine Catholic Irish Settlers in Upper Canada," *Journal of Historical Geography* 8 (1982): 265.

16. V.J. Kaye and C.W. Hobart, "Origins and Characteristics of the Ukrainian Migration to Canada," in C.W. Hobart W.E. Kalbach, J.T. Borhek, and A.P. Jacoby, eds., *Persistence and Change: A Study of Ukrainians in Alberta* (Toronto: Ukrainian Canadian Research Foundation, 1978), p. 25.

17. R.F. Harney, "Men Without Women: Italian Migrants in Canada 1885–1930," *Canadian Ethnic Studies* 11 (1979): 29.

18. I. Kaprielian, "Immigration and Settlement of Armenians in Southern Ontario: The First Wave," *Polyphony* 4 (1982): 14.

19. See for example J.L. Elliott, "Canadian Immigration: A Historical Assessment," in J.L. Elliott, ed., *Two Nations, Many Cultures: Ethnic Groups in Canada* (Scarborough: Prentice-Hall, 1979), p. 289; W. Parker, "The Canadas," in A. Lemon and N. Pollock, eds., *Studies in Overseas Settlement and Population* (New York: Longman, 1980), p. 267; J.C. Weaver, "Hamilton and the Immigration Tide," *Families* 20 (1981): 197; G. Wynn, "Ethnic Migrations and Atlantic Canada: Geographical Perspectives," *Canadian Ethnic Studies* 18 (1986): 1.

20. See for example A.A. Brookes, "The Golden Age and the Exodus: The Case of Canning, Kings County," *Acadiensis* 11 (1981): 57; R. Crawley, "Off to Sydney: Newfoundlanders Emigrate to Industrial Cape Breton 1890–1914," *Acadiensis* 17 (1988): 27; Y. Lavoie, *L'Émigration des Québécois aux États-Unis de 1840 à 1930* (Quebec: Editeur officiel du Québec, 1979).

21. See for example C.M. Gaffield, "Boom and Bust: The Demography and Economy of the Lower Ottawa Valley in the Nineteenth Century," *Canadian Historical Association. Historical Papers* (1982): 172; M.B. Katz, M.J. Doucet, and M.J. Stern, "Population Persistence and Early Industrialization in a Canadian City: Hamilton, Ontario, 1851–1971," *Social Science History* 2 (1978): 208; P. Matwijiw, "Ethnicity and Urban Residence: Winnipeg, 1941–1971," *Canadian Geographer* 23 (1979): 45; Weaver, "Hamilton and the Immigration Tide," p. 197.

22. P. Gossage, "Absorbing Junior: The Use of Patent Medicines as Abortifacients in Nineteenth-Century Montreal," *The Register* 3 (1978): 1; A. McLaren, "Birth Control and Abortion in Canada, 1870–1920," *Canadian Historical Review* 59 (1978): 319–40.

23. R.D. Sharna, "Premarital and Ex-nuptial Fertility (Illegitimacy) in Canada 1921–1972," *Canadian Studies in Population* 9 (1982): 1.

24. H. Charbonneau, "Jeunes femmes et vieux maris: la fécondité des mariages précoces," *Population* 35 (1980): 1101; E.M.T. Gee, "Early Canadian Fertility Transition: A Components Analysis of Census Data," *Canadian Studies in Population* 6 (1979): 23; E. Roth, "Historic Fertility Differentials in a Northern Athapaskan Community," *Culture* 2 (1982): 63; J.E. Veevers, "Age Discrepant Marriages: Cross-National Comparisons of Canadian–American Trends," *Social Biology* 31 (1984): 118.

25. See for example J. Keyes, "Marriage Patterns Among Early Quakers," *Nova Scotia Historical Quarterly* 8 (1978): 299.

26. A.G. Darroch and M.D. Ornstein, "Family and Household in Nineteenth-Century Canada: Regional Patterns and Regional Economies," *Journal of Family History* 9 (1984): 158; F.K. Donnelly, "Occupational and Household Structures of a New Brunswick Fishing Settlement: Campobello Island, 1851," in R. Chanteloup, ed., *Labour in Atlantic Canada* (Saint John: University of New Brunswick, 1981), p. 55; P.S. Li, "Immigration Laws and Family Patterns: Some Demographic Changes Among Chinese Families in Canada, 1885–1971," *Canadian Ethnic Studies* 13 (1980): 58; S. Medjuck, "The Social Consequences of Economic Cycles on Nineteenth-Century Households and Family Life," *Social Indicators Research* 18 (1986): 233; D.A. Norris, "Household and Transiency in a Loyalist Township: The People of Adolphustown, 1784–1822," *Social History* 13 (1980): 399.

27. Bilson, *A Darkened House*, p. 23.

28. J.R. Gibson, "Smallpox on the Northwest Coast, 1835–1838," *BC Studies* 56 (1982): 61.

29. S. Lloyd, "The Ottawa Typhoid Epidemics of 1911 and 1912: A Case Study of Disease as a Catalyst for Urban Reform," *Urban History Review* 8 (1979): 66.

30. J.D.P. McGinnis, "The Impact of Epidemic Influenza: Canada, 1918–1919," *The Canadian Historical Association, Historical Papers* (1977): 121.

31. R. Bourbeau and J. Légaré, *Évolution de la mortalité au Canada et au Québec, 1831–1931: Essai de mésure par génération* (Montreal: Les Presses de l'Université de Montréal, 1982); H. Charbonneau and A. LaRose, eds., *The Great Mortalities: Methodological Studies of Demographic Crises in the Past* (Liège: Ordina Éditions, 1979); Robert W. Fogel, Stanley L. Engerman, James Trussell, Roderick Floud, and Clayne L. Pope, "The Economics of Mortality in North America, 1650–1910: A Description of a Research Project," *Historical Methods* 11 (1979): 75; Y. Landry, "Mortalité, nuptialité et canadianisation des troupes française de la guerre de Sept Ans," *Social History* 12 (1979): 298; B. Osborne, "The Cemeteries of the Midland District of Upper Canada: A Note on Mortality in a Frontier Society," *Pioneer America* 6 (1974): 46.

PART TWO

THE MANY FACES OF DIVERSITY

Part II takes a micro approach to diversity in Canada. Chapters 3 to 9 each examine a particular kind of diversity. The topics range from "traditional" diversities such as race, ethnicity, social inequality, and gender, to less traditional ones, including sexual orientation, the family, and disabilities.

Continuing with our house analogy, if Part I is the foundation and the structure of the house, then Part II is the details of the interior. The text moves from the general, in Part I, to the specific, in Part II, as reflected in the title of Part II, "The Many Faces of Diversity." Just like the housing interiors are constantly renovated to reflect new trends and ideas, new data from the 2006 Canadian census and recent developments are included in each chapter.

Chapter 3 looks at social inequality in Canada. It introduces the reader to the inequalities of income and wealth and to the social structure in Canada. It reviews the major theories of inequality and stratification and examines their strengths and weaknesses.

Chapter 4 explores race and ethnicity in Canada. It outlines the major determinants of personal and group identity, the factors that influence societal interaction, and the problems of prejudice, discrimination, and racism. It also briefly outlines the history of immigration to Canada and the meaning of "race."

Chapter 5 looks at Aboriginal Peoples. It vividly illustrates the heterogeneous nature of Aboriginal Peoples, cultures, and languages. It also examines the deep historical presence of Aboriginal Peoples in Canada, allowing you to better understand contemporary native issues including the legal circumstances of Aboriginal Peoples today.

Chapter 6 deals with the religious experience in Canada. It is divided into two principal sections. The first discusses issues involved in forming a working definition of religion; the second deals with several aspects of the history of religion in Canada.

Chapter 7 deals with disability. After briefly looking at the history of disability in Canada, it explores the roles of several institutions in the lives of disabled people, including the government, religious organizations, schools, and the family. The chapter ends with a look at important social policy issues for disabled Canadians.

Chapter 8 examines the issue of gender. It defines the reality of gender identity and makes it clear that men and women occupy different spheres in society. Finally, it addresses the question of whether gender divisions are positive or negative, both for society and for the individual.

Chapter 9 is completely new. It examines the history and recent developments in the field of sexuality in Canada. Canadian issues and legislation are put in clear international perspective to enhance our understanding of who we are and our place in the world.

Chapter 10 analyzes diversity in Canadian families. It challenges the notion of the traditional family, redefining the word *family* to help explain the different types of families that exist in Canada today.

CHAPTER 3

Social Inequality and Stratification in Canada

Eddie Grattan

Men are by nature unequal. It is vain, therefore, to treat them as if they were equal.
—James Anthony Froude, "Party Politics"

We hold these truths to be self-evident, that all men are created equal.
—Thomas Jefferson

Objectives
. . . .

After reading this chapter, you should be able to

- describe the degree of social inequality in Canada

- present a summary of the major theories of social inequality

- detail the impact of social inequality on our daily lives

- list the variety of forms of social inequality

- describe the social class system of Canada

INTRODUCTION

All societies are characterized by **social inequality** and **stratification.** Social inequality is the varying degree to which different people have access to and control over valued resources, such as money, wealth, status, and power. In Canada, access and control are severely restricted by a person's social background, sex, and race or ethnicity. The differing degrees of access to and control over valued resources serve to divide Canadian society into recognizably distinct and unequal groups, or strata. Canada is a stratified society.

Let me provide an example from a personal experience. During the 2009 Canadian Football League season, I attended a playoff game in Hamilton. Ticket prices ranged from $22 to $162. Sitting in one of the so-called cheap seats (at around $75 each!), I had a limited experience of the game, often finding the play difficult to follow. Spectators in more expensive seats, however, appeared to experience the event more intensely and personally: they could hear the players shouting to one another, and see more clearly the players' expressions as well as the action on the field.

The difference between my experience and that of the people in the more expensive seats may appear to be an issue of little significance. Nevertheless, if I have a relatively low income, it is unlikely I will be able to afford a more desirable seat; if, however, my income is relatively high, it is likely I will be able to purchase a more expensive ticket and thus increase my enjoyment of the game. See Have You Heard? 3.1.

These differing (or unequal) experiences reflect wider patterns of inequality (in this case, income differences) in society.

HAVE YOU HEARD? 3.1

Who Can Afford Tickets for Sports Events?

. . . .

Over the past several years, ticket prices for major sporting events have increased dramatically. In 2009, regular season tickets for the Hamilton Tiger Cats ranged from $20 to $90, and tickets for the 2009 Grey Cup in Vancouver started at $195, increasing to a top price of $370. The availability of many of these tickets, however, is limited, as many of the seats in arenas and stadiums belong to season-ticket holders who renew their seats annually.

CRITICAL THINKING OUTSIDE THE BOX 3.1

How does the amount of income affect the types of sport a person will play?

The ability to pay is, of course, dependent largely on income level. The amount of income a family earns determines many aspects of its existence, including the types of food it consumes, where (or, indeed, if) to travel on vacation, where, and for how long, the children will attend an educational institution, as well as many of the family's values and beliefs.

In some instances, the ability (or inability) to pay literally can determine whether one lives or dies. This reality is illustrated by the sinking of the ocean liner *Titanic* in 1912, when around 1500 of the 2300 passengers lost their lives. Passengers in the more expensive, upper-deck cabins had a greater chance of survival than those in the cheaper, lower-deck cabins:

> Of those holding first-class tickets, more than 60 percent were saved, primarily because they were on the upper decks, where warnings were sounded first and lifeboats were accessible. Only 36 percent of the second-class passengers survived, and of the third-class passengers on the lower-decks, only 24 percent escaped drowning. On board the *Titanic* class turned out to mean much more than the quality of accommodations: it was truly a matter of life or death.[1]

In Canada, social inequality is strongly associated with a person's social background, race, ethnicity, and sex. Canadians born into families with low incomes will generally receive less education and, thus, find it difficult to obtain high-income occupations. Immigrants to Canada, particularly those with little education, generally face greater obstacles to finding employment. Women, although sharing similar levels of education as men, on average earn significantly less.

INEQUALITIES OF INCOME AND WEALTH IN CANADA

Inequality of Income

In everyday conversation the terms "income" and "wealth" are used interchangeably; however, although closely related, an important distinction exists between them. **Income** is the *flow* of money received over a specified period of time, usually a year. Ms. Smith, for example, when asked her income, will most likely reply X dollars per year. For most Canadians, the largest part of income is received in the form of wages and salary. A smaller part derives from government financial assistance, such as unemployment and welfare benefits—although for some people, these constitute a significant portion of total income.

Other, less identifiable, forms of income are also important. These include gifts, money received from cashing in an insurance policy, and capital gains (e.g., money received from selling shares of stock at a price higher than their initial cost). It is often difficult to calculate precisely how much these contribute to the average income of Canadians, as the necessary information is difficult to obtain.

Canada is a wealthy country. In terms of per capita income, it ranks among the top in the world. In 2007, the average total, after-tax, income of Canadian families was $71 900 (see Table 3.1).

Average income, however, disguises significant income differences among families. An informative way of looking at these differences is to split all Canadian families into five equal groups, each referred to as a *quintile*. The groups are assembled in the following way. Imagine that all families are placed in a line, a family's place being determined by its income level. The poorest family is placed at the front of the line, followed by the next poorest, and so on, until the last family, with the highest income, is placed at the end. Next, the line is split into five equal groups. The first group, or quintile, is composed of the first 20 percent of the line. Obviously, this group will consist of the poorest people. The next group

Table 3.1   Average Total After-Tax Income of Canadian Families,[i] by Income Quintile, 2003–2007 (2007 constant dollars)

	2003	2004	2005	2006	2007
Total	65 000	66 600	67 500	69 100	71 900
Lowest quintile	23 200	23 600	23 800	25 200	26 400
Second quintile	40 900	41 500	42 600	43 500	45 200
Middle quintile	56 700	57 500	58 600	59 800	62 000
Fourth quintile	75 900	77 200	78 900	80 300	83 200
Highest quintile	128 500	133 200	133 600	136 800	142 600

[i] Economic family of two persons or more, and therefore excludes unattached individuals.

Source: Adapted from Statistics Canada, *Income in Canada*, Table 8-5, "Average Income and Income Shares by After-tax Income Quintiles, Showing Different Income Concepts, Canada–Average After-tax Income," p. 79, 75-202-XIE 2007000 2007, Released June 3, 2009.

consists of the next 20 percent. A similar process occurs in selecting the third, fourth, and fifth groups. The fifth group, of course, comprises those families with the highest incomes.

Table 3.1 reveals a significant difference between the average after-tax income of the lowest and highest quintiles. In 2007, for example, the average after-tax income of the lowest quintile was $26 400, less than one-fifth that of the highest quintile. The fourth quintile averaged $83 200 in 2007, just over half that of the highest quintile. These differences changed little over the period from 2003–2007.

The income an individual or family receives can come from a variety of sources. Table 3.2 indicates that people in the first, or lowest quintile, on average, receive around half of their income from government transfer payments, such as welfare benefits, children's benefits, and employment insurance. Single-parent families, as well as recently arrived immigrants, make up a large proportion of these families.

As income levels increase, the proportion of income received from transfer payments decreases significantly. The highest family quintile, for example, consisting of those families with the highest incomes in Canada, in 2007 received only 2.6 percent of its income from transfer payments (compared to 45.7 percent for the lowest quintile).

A starker portrayal of income inequality is provided by Table 3.3. Of the total income received by Canadian households in 2007, the lowest quintile received only 4 percent. If Canada were an equal society, this quintile, composed of 20 percent of the population, would receive 20 percent of the total income. So, with only 4 percent of total income, it obtains only a small percentage of what it would receive in a perfectly equal society. The fourth and fifth quintiles, consisting collectively of the top 40 percent of income-earners in

Table 3.2 Government Transfers and Income Tax, 2006 and 2007, as Percentage of Income by Income Quintile for Families and Unattached Individuals (2003 constant dollars)

	Families		Unattached Individuals	
	2006	2007	2006	2007
Lowest quintile	47.2	45.7	49.0	53.3
Second quintile	22.8	20.7	54.3	55.7
Third quintile	13.2	12.9	31.0	27.6
Fourth quintile	7.2	6.9	10.6	11.3
Highest quintile	2.7	2.6	3.2	3.0

Source: Adapted from Statistics Canada, *Income in Canada*, Table 2-1, p. 35, "Government Transfers by After-tax Income Quintiles–Canada", 75-202-XIE 2007000 2007, Released June 3, 2009.

Table 3.3   Distribution of Total Income in Canada by Quintile for All Family Units
(in percentage)

Sources	Lowest Quintile	Second Quintile	Middle Quintile	Fourth Quintile	Highest Income Quintile
1998	4	10	16	24	46
2003	4	10	16	24	46
2007	4	10	16	24	46

Source: Adapted from Statistics Canada, *Income in Canada*, p. 77, Table 8-3, "Average Income and Income Shares by After-Tax Income Quintiles, Showing Different Income Concepts, Canada–Average Total Income", 75-202-XIE 2007000 2007, Released June 3, 2009.

Canada, received a combined 70 percent of total income. This contrasts with 14 percent for the bottom 40 percent of income-earners.

Over the past ten years or so, income disparities have remained virtually stationary (see Table 3.3 above). However, from the mid-1980s to the end of the century, the disparity in income levels increased. Using data from the 2006 Census, Tavia Grant[2] demonstrates that from around the mid-1980s to the present, the income of the top 20 percent of earners increased 16.4 percent, while the lowest 20 percent of income earners actually saw their earnings *drop* 20.6 percent. The middle 60 percent of income earners saw their earnings remain virtually stagnant. There are many reasons for these developments, including the impact of globalization, diminishing union power, and changes in the workforce. More specifically for the bottom 20 percent, a reduction in government transfers starting in the mid-1990s[3] has served to reduce their incomes. In Ontario, for example, the social assistance rate fell from 12.1 percent in 1993 to 5.5 percent in 2003.[4] Such reductions obviously affect more severely those at the lower end of the income scale. This contrasts with the period of the early 1980s to the mid-1990s, when income levels in Canada remained virtually stationary. Before this, from about 1920 to 1980, incomes in Canada quadrupled, with Canadians in 1980 being able to purchase four times as many goods and services as in 1920. The change since the early 1980s, specifically the increase in income inequality, has forced many Canadians, particularly those entering the labour market, to adjust their expectations with the awareness that their level of income may be substantially below that of their parents and grandparents.

During the past ten years or so, beginning with the terrorist attacks on the United States in September 2001, the North American economy has experienced major difficulties. A reduction in interest rates in response to the economic downturn following the attacks appeared to stimulate economic growth, spurred in part by more people opting to buy rather than rent homes in response to record-low mortgage rates; however, over the past two years, starting in 2008, there has occurred a severe economic downturn. In the United States, this has seen the bankruptcy of many lending institutions and a wave of mortgage foreclosures. In North America more generally, a rapid increase in unemployment and decline in manufacturing (significantly, automobiles) appear to indicate the economic downturn may actually be symptomatic of a more fundamental shift in the structural under-pinnings of the economy itself. In response to these developments, North American govern-ments (and others around the world) have injected billions of dollars into their economies in an effort to reduce unemployment and stimulate demand. Slowly, if unevenly, economies are starting to rebound. However, concerns remain. The increasing cost of oil and gas, high debt levels of consumers and governments,[5] the growing competitiveness of countries out-side North America, the shrinking of the middle class, high levels of unemployment, and growing income disparities—all are provoking debate about the nature and breadth of the role of government in economic development, and the extent to which the financial sector requires greater government control. The 2011 Census should provide an indication of specifically how people have been affected by these recent economic and financial develop-ments, and how they have impacted social and economic inequality in Canada.

Inequality of Wealth

Wealth is the accumulation of assets, such as a house, car, savings, cottage, land, jewel-lery, and art objects. As already mentioned, there is a close relationship between wealth and income: those people with a higher income are more able to accumulate wealth. This stems from excess **disposable income**—income above that required for necessities, such as food, clothing, and accommodation. However, for many others, especially those living near or below the poverty line, it is often difficult, if not impossible, to accumulate wealth because little disposable income remains after purchasing necessities.

Sociologist Alf Hunter provided a more detailed illustration of this in his classic work on social inequality in Canada.[6] Writing in 1981, Hunter noted that workers earning about $25 000 per year possess average wealth of half ($12 500) that amount; those earning more than $50 000 annually have wealth double ($100 000) that amount; and those earning more than $100 000 possess wealth more than ten times ($1 000 000) that amount. So, if a person's income increases by $75 000 ($25 000 to $100 000), his or her wealth might increase by almost $1 million! These large increases in wealth, resulting from relatively small increases in income, emerge from the increasing amounts of disposable income available as income increases. A relatively small increase in income can have extraordinary effects on wealth accumulation.

Table 3.4 reveals related information. In 2005, the lowest 20 percent of family units in Canada owned 0.1 percent of total net worth. Even if the next quintile is included, the per-centage of total net worth owned by the bottom 40 percent of all family units only increases to 2.4 percent. The highest quintile, on the other hand, owned 69 percent of total net worth.

Table 3.4   Distribution of Net Worth in Canada by Quintile, 2005
(in 2005 constant dollars)

Quintiles	% of Net Worth Owned by Quintile	Total Net Worth
	%	Millions $
All family units	100.0	4 862 000
Lowest 20%	0.1	–6 300
Second 20%	2.3	110 000
Third 20%	8.4	409 000
Fourth 20%	20.2	983 000
Highest 20%	69.2	3 367 000

Source: Adapted from Statistics Canada, Pension and Wealth Research Series: *The Wealth of Canadians: An Overview of the Results of the Survey of Financial Security*, 13F0026MIE 2006001 2005, no. 1, Released December 7, 2006. p. 9.

Table 3.5 reveals a related dimension of net worth. In the early part of the 21st century, median net worth increased overall by 23.2 percent. When broken into quintiles, however, significant differences emerge. The lowest quintile actually saw its median net worth *decrease* by 9.1 percent. The second quintile fared slightly better, increasing 7.2 percent. The fourth quintile, however, improved significantly, jumping 31.1 percent, with the fifth

Table 3.5   Change in Median Net Worth from 1999 to 2005, by Net Worth Quintile

	Median Net Worth (constant 2005 dollars)		Change from 1999 to 2005 (constant 2005 dollars)	
	1999 ($) Millions	2005 ($) Millions	($)	(%)
All family units	120 500	148 400	27 900	23.2
Lowest 20%	1 100	1 000	–1 000	–9.1
Second 20%	34 800	37 300	2 500	7.2
Third 20%	120 500	148 400	27 900	23.2
Fourth 20%	275 600	361 200	85 600	31.1
Fifth 20%	671 600	862 900	191 300	28.5

Source: Adapted from Statistics Canada, Pension and Wealth Research Series: *The Wealth of Canadians: An Overview of the Results of the Survey of Financial Security*, 13F0026MIE 2006001 2005, no. 1, Released December 7, 2006. p. 9.

quintile rising 28.5 percent. In the coming years it will be interesting to observe how the distribution of net worth will be impacted by the severe economic difficulties most countries are presently experiencing.

ASCRIPTION AND INEQUALITY

Inequalities of income and wealth reflect the stratified nature of Canadian society. Important in this respect are race and ethnicity, male and female relations, and a person's social background. Our ethnicity and race, sex, and social background have fundamental effects on our lives, often restricting (or increasing) our ability to achieve desired educational, occupational, and financial goals. We possess little or no control over our racial or ethnic identity, over whether we are male or female, or over our social background. For this reason, these factors are called **ascribed statuses.**

Increasingly, attention is being given to the role of age and physical or mental disability in affecting social inequality. Although traditionally viewed as having less of an impact on inequality than ethnicity and race, sex, and social background, recently they have been shown to contribute significantly in some instances to social inequality.

Ascribed statuses affect our chances of success in society. Because education is essential to occupational and financial success, those ascribed statuses that hinder educational success are important in understanding inequalities of income and wealth. A close link exists between number of years of schooling and a person's occupation and income. Of the many factors involved in determining a person's occupation (especially her or his first), the most important is education. However, the type and amount of education a person receives is itself strongly determined by ascribed statuses.

Ethnicity and Race

Canadians of Asian, black, British, and Jewish ancestry have the highest average years of schooling; Indians, Inuit, and Italians tend to have the lowest.[7] This would, on the surface at least, suggest that ethnicity corresponds positively with income level. That is, British, Asians, blacks, and Jews will earn the most, Indians, Inuit, and Italians the least. Evidence suggests this is partially correct.[8] In 1985 men of Jewish ancestry earned the highest average income ($47 000). Men of British ancestry made average incomes of between $30 000 and $36 000. Blacks earned approximately $25 000, and Asians slightly more than $20 000. Those with the least education—Inuit, Métis, and Natives—also ranked near the bottom, between $23 000 and $25 000.

More recent data suggests that the situation may be changing slightly. Although there continue to be marked differences in the income earned by non-visible and visible minorities, some non-visible ethnic groups, such as Italians, Portuguese, and Poles, received average incomes in 1991 about equal to that of the British.[9] According to Gee and Prus, there exists a "racial divide" in Canada between whites and non-whites, with coloured Canadians "less likely to be full-time workers and more likely to be unemployed or out of the paid labour force."[10]

Blacks and Asians, despite their high average levels of postsecondary education, do not earn incomes equivalent to their educational credentials. Of Asian and black immigrants arriving in Canada between 1981 and 1991, 22 to 28 percent held university degrees, almost double the rate of the Canadian population. However, compared with the Canadian population, a greater proportion of Asians and blacks have education levels less than Grade 9.

Even if the high number of Asians and blacks with less than a Grade 9 education is taken into account—as well as region of birth and ability to speak English or French—a recent study suggests the continuing low average earnings of the groups remain largely unexplained.[11] This may be the result of several related developments.[12] First, more than other ethnic groups, blacks and Asians are the targets of racist and discriminatory employment and hiring practices. Second, having only recently arrived in Canada, immigrants are employed, like most new workers, at the lower end of business organizations. It may take several years for many of them to reach the upper levels of business organizations.

Furthermore, although these ethnic and racial groups may eventually succeed in achieving a significant degree of occupational, and hence financial success, it is unlikely that even a few will ever secure a position within the economic elite in Canada. Since the 19th century, the Canadian economic elite—the owners and controllers of the major corporations and banks—has been overwhelmingly of British origin.

By establishing control early in Canadian development, this elite has been able to consolidate its dominant position and prevent other ethnic groups from gaining access to top positions. In 1972, 86.2 percent of the economic elite was of British origin, compared with a British-origin population in Canada of 44.7 percent. People of French origin, making up 28.6 percent of the population, in 1971 constituted only 8.4 percent of this elite. Canada's economy is in the hands of a relatively small group of men of British origin, who continue to pass on their privileges and positions of power to their children, in the process excluding others from elite positions. As the sociologist Wallace Clement observed,

Top decision making positions in the economy in Canada are dominated by a small upper class. This provides them with a life style much different than that experienced by the vast majority of Canadians and the privileges that accrue to them are passed on to their children. Canada has not fulfilled its promise as a society with equal opportunity. As long as corporate power is allowed to remain in its present concentrated state, there is no hope for equality of opportunity or equality of condition in Canada.[13]

A more recent study[14] argues that this has not changed significantly over the past four decades.

Clement also illustrates the changing class origins of the Canadian economic elite. In 1951, 50 percent of the economic elite had class origins in the upper class. By 1972, this figure had increased to 59.4 percent. In 1951, 32 percent of the economic elite had class origins in the middle class. This figure had increased to 34.8 percent by 1972 changing only slightly over the period. The most significant change is in the proportion of the economic elite with working-class origins decreasing from 18 percent to 5.8 percent from 1951 to 1972.

Social Background

Social background is an important determinant of education levels. Working-class men and women tend to have lower levels of postsecondary schooling than their counterparts in the middle class. This occurs for at least two reasons: (1) lower incomes mean working-class students have more difficulty financing the cost of postsecondary education; (2) education and studying are not a major part of working-class life and culture. Middle-class parents are more likely to have books around the house and encourage their children's schooling; working-class parents, on the other hand, are less involved in educational concerns, preferring to defer to the knowledge of the teacher and the school system.

Sex

Men and women in Canada have similar levels of education. Only at the highest levels of the education system (master and doctorate) do men outnumber women, although this is changing. Despite similar education levels, however, men have higher average incomes than women, even in cases where they perform the same jobs. Despite evidence of an increase in weekly wages of full-time female workers in the early 1990s and a levelling of the earnings of male workers,[15] in 2008 the median annual earnings of women in Canada was still at only about 77 percent that of employed males.[16] There are several reasons for this discrepancy.

CRITICAL THINKING OUTSIDE THE BOX 3.2

Should wealthy families in Canada be made to redistribute their wealth?

First, men occupy most management and ownership positions, and they make the decisions on the appropriate incomes for employees. Traditionally regarded as the second income-earner, out to supplement the main income of the husband, women have generally been paid substantially less. This discriminatory practice, although slowly changing, makes it difficult for many women, in particular single mothers, to provide a satisfactory standard of living for themselves and their families.

Second, and related, women are disproportionately employed in occupations viewed as an extension of their household duties, such as teaching, nursing, and social work. The cultural perceptions surrounding such occupations reflect those of the "homemaker," someone who is nurturing, caring, sensitive, efficient, and emotional. Although such stereotypes are also slowly being modified, many women remain in occupations traditionally regarded as "women's work." Elementary-school teachers and nurses, for example, are overwhelmingly women. Furthermore, women who strive to build a career are often treated and viewed differently from men with similar ambitions. Women who prefer not to marry or have children in the hope of pursuing a career are frequently depicted as selfish, greedy, and "unfeminine."

Third, many women find themselves in what is called a "double ghetto." This occurs when a woman both works for a wage and undertakes housework, including looking after the children and the needs of her husband.

Fourth, over the past 25 years the number of single-parent families in Canada headed by women has almost doubled. However, the proportion of single mothers in the workforce has fallen slightly, from 32 to 26 percent. As Susan Crompton, a sociologist, noted, this shift has occurred for several reasons.[17] First, the tremendous increase in the number of working wives has essentially displaced single mothers from certain occupations. Second, as the educational requirements of jobs have increased, single mothers have found it increasingly difficult to obtain these necessary qualifications. The difficulties and expense of raising a child, or children, frequently make it financially infeasible for many single mothers to seek employment (see Have You Heard? 3.2). Many mothers receive little or no child support from the fathers and so are forced to live almost wholly on government assistance. In 2005, 32.2 percent of lone-parent families (headed overwhelmingly by women) were considered low-income families, in contrast to 8.4 percent of two-parent families with children.[18] The situation is partly responsible for the **feminization of poverty** over the past three decades.

Age

Increasingly, attention is being paid to the importance of age in promoting inequality. Many observers have focused particularly on the financial plight of senior citizens. It has been pointed out that over the course of the 20th century, the number of people age

---

HAVE YOU HEARD? 3.2

Left Behind: Lone Mothers in the Labour Market

The stagnating employment situation of lone mothers is not for lack of willingness to work. Many lone mothers currently outside the labour force want to work; those who are working are more likely than wives to be employed full time, and a substantial proportion of those working part time would rather have full-time jobs. However, wives are older and better educated and have more work experience. Moreover, having another adult to help with childcare arrangements can only make it easier for married mothers to look for and retain a job. Faced with competition from a large pool of better-educated women, it is not surprising that many lone mothers have difficulty establishing themselves in the job market.

But a "hierarchy of success" can also be found in the population of lone mothers. Separated or divorced mothers are "ex-wives" who occupy a more advantageous position in the labour market than never-married women because they have more education and more work experience. Much of the labour market disadvantage of never-married lone mothers may be attributable to their lower educational attainment, which raises the question of whether pregnancy outside marriage increases the likelihood of interrupting formal education and delaying the acquisition of work experience. It is certainly clear that two distinct types of women, with considerably different demographic and socioeconomic characteristics, are merged under the rubric "lone mother." It seems a disservice to both groups to ignore the differences between them.

Source: Statistics Canada, *Perspectives on Labour and Income*, Catalogue No. 75-001, Summer 1994.

---

65 and over has steadily risen and will rise even more markedly this century. Improved medical technologies, healthier lifestyles, and the large number of births between the years 1945 and 1965 are responsible for this increase.

As individuals, living well past the traditional retirement age of 65 may appear to be a happy prospect; but as a society, it is becoming apparent that there are many difficulties associated with a greying population. First, partly because most elderly people do not do paid work, they are stereotyped as lazy, mentally slow, traditionally minded, and incapable of contributing to society. Second, as more and more people live well into

> ## CRITICAL THINKING OUTSIDE THE BOX 3.3
>
> Should lone, or single, mothers be given greater government financial assistance in light of the difficulties they face?

their retirement years, many quickly find themselves spending whatever savings they may have accumulated over their working lives. This forces many seniors to seek employment and/or live in poverty. Indeed, outside of children and youth, the elderly—most of whom are women—constitute the largest group in poverty in North America. For example, according to Statistics Canada,[19] in 2007 an estimated 14.3 percent of unattached elderly women and 13 percent of unattached elderly men were below the low income cut-off. In those instances when seniors are physically able to work, they generally find themselves in low-prestige, minimum-wage jobs.

With a growing senior population, the Canadian government faces increased pressure to improve the financial situation of those entering retirement. At the same time, however, government cutbacks and continued public demand to reduce spending on the unemployed, welfare recipients, and seniors (in the form of an income security system), suggest that the situation of the elderly in this century may deteriorate further.

Disability

Historically, people with physical or mental disabilities have generally been excluded from participating in mainstream society, particularly in the workforce. More recently, however, as a result of the lobbying efforts of organizations representing the disabled and a variety of employment equity programs, many people with disabilities now find themselves participating fully in work and social activities. Nevertheless, people with disabilities continue to confront stereotyping, prejudice, and discrimination. People with disabilities, as a group, suffer severe social inequality, experiencing high levels of unemployment and welfare.

VIEWS OF INEQUALITY

The existence of inequality does not tell us whether it is good or bad, positive or negative, moral or immoral. Does inequality of income and wealth, for example, contribute to a more peaceful and stable society? Does it provide greater financial rewards to those who work the hardest? Or does it serve to further the exploitation and oppression of one section of society by another? Responses to these types of questions have been numerous, but it is possible to classify them into two basic positions.

Structural–Functionalism: Inequality Is Good, Necessary, and Inevitable

The first position, **structural–functionalism**, argues that inequality is positive and necessary for the proper functioning of society. Writers adopting this position view society as operating in a manner similar to the human body. Just as the different parts of the body—skin, muscles, bones, organs, and so on—collectively function to maintain the operation and survival of the whole body, the different parts—the structure—of society together function to promote the overall peace and stability of society.

Everything that exists in society serves a function. Prostitution, for example, although illegal and commonly regarded as a major problem, is seen as serving the important function of allowing men, and women, to vent their sexual frustrations. Without prostitution, according to structural–functionalists, it is likely that rape and other sexual assaults would increase, along with the rate of divorce. Prostitution, then, according to this view, simultaneously functions to reduce violent sexual assaults and maintain intact the important role of the family unit.

Inequality is viewed in a similar manner. Structural–functionalists consider inequality both unavoidable and desirable. The existence of inequality in all societies, past and present, indicates that it must serve a positive function. But how does inequality contribute to the stability and functioning of society? Inequality, in the form of different income levels, in this view, provides an incentive for the most able people in society to work the hardest to attain those jobs considered by society to be the most functionally important. Doctors, lawyers, dentists, and so on, earn substantial incomes because of their great importance to the stability and continuing operation of society.

If a doctor and a bus driver, for example, received similar incomes, few people would want to endure the years of education and hard work required to qualify as a doctor. Not only would there arise a critical shortage of doctors, but it is also likely this shortage would lead to the acceptance into medical school of many unsuitable applicants. It is necessary, therefore, that a differential reward system exist, whereby those performing the most important jobs receive higher incomes and more prestige than those in occupations considered less important. Without differential rewards, the most talented would have no incentive to pursue the functionally most important jobs. Inequality, then, as an essential and inherent feature of the economic structure of society, is vital to the proper functioning of the whole society. For this reason, those making this argument are referred to as structural–functionalists.

Some Problems with Structural–Functionalism

Structural–functionalists emphasize the need for some form of incentive to ensure that the most talented attain those jobs requiring extensive knowledge and training. It is unlikely that in a society in which everyone receives the same level of income, regardless of occupation, the most talented would seek to undertake the most important occupations.

There are several problems, however, with the structural–functionalist position. First, the emphasis on individual talents and abilities suggests that those with the most talent and ability will succeed and that those less able and less intelligent will be less successful. To structural–functionalists, a person's degree of success should be determined solely by individual effort. Consequently, everyone should have an equal chance to succeed—there should be **equality of opportunity**. This involves equal access to education and the elimination of sexual and ethnic discrimination in employment and hiring practices. This type of argument fails to satisfactorily analyze the impact of ethnicity, class, and gender on the creation and continuation of inequalities in society. Many ethnic groups, the poor, and women face severe impediments to educational and occupational success. "The point to stress," as sociologist Edward Grabb noted,[20] "is that established structures tend to define the prospects and life chances of people in most instances." As a society, we may want everyone to be given an equal opportunity, but it is apparent that many people cannot overcome major obstacles that have been put in their way, thus preventing them from moving ahead.

Second, are occupations financially rewarded based on their functional importance to society? Not always, it seems. For example, what is the functional importance of professional athletes and entertainers? Sidney Crosby, LeBron James, and Lady Gaga may annually earn millions of dollars, but are they crucial to the functioning of society?

A less obvious example relates to the functional importance of doctors. Are they more important than, say, garbage collectors? According to structural–functionalists, garbage collectors receive lower incomes than doctors do because of their lesser importance to the overall functioning of society. But there is little evidence to back this up. Indeed, it could strongly be argued that as a society we could do without doctors more readily than without garbage collectors. On the one hand, the elimination of garbage collectors would result in mountains of rotting garbage and the epidemic outbreak of potentially fatal diseases. Without doctors, on the other hand, more people would undoubtedly die and at an earlier age, but it is unlikely that society would suffer serious damage.

Another example is provided by the recent arguments made by a variety of analysts regarding the value of housework. Although unpaid in financial terms, such work is obviously important, if not crucial, to the overall functioning of society.

Third, some people are motivated by factors other than money. Bryan S. Turner, in his book *Equality*, noted the nonmonetary motives that are traditionally associated with the nursing profession: "A number of social roles such as nursing may be regarded as socially important despite their low income and persons who occupy such roles are typically motivated by moral or religious arguments where a direct monetary reward is absent."[21]

Fourth, structural–functionalists emphasize the importance of individual hard work and perseverance in determining occupational and financial success. This assumes that movement from one class to another, both up and down, is largely a consequence of individual strengths or weaknesses and pays little attention to the role of inherited wealth in preserving economic inequalities and class differences over time. The majority of Canada's wealthiest families, as already noted, are of Anglo-Saxon origin and the beneficiaries of inherited wealth.

Conflict Theory: Inequality Is Bad, Avoidable, and Unnecessary

The second position, **conflict theory**, relates inequality to conflict in society. Conflict theorists view inequality as both a cause and an effect of exploitation, conflict, and oppression. There are many different types of conflict theorists, with disagreement centring on the precise form conflict takes and how it can be reduced or eliminated. Some conflict theorists view class inequality and conflict as central, whereas for others gender or race is more important.

Karl Marx

One of the most important conflict theorists was Karl Marx (1818–1883). Marx argued that all societies are divided between those who possess wealth and power and those who do not. In modern society, the major division, or inequality, is between the **capitalist class**, or bourgeoisie, and the **working class**, or proletariat. Capitalists are those who own the factories, land, machinery, and other materials used for the production of goods and services. Marx termed these materials the **means of production**—they are, simply, the means to produce goods and services. Workers, on the other hand, do not own property, and to survive they must sell their labour power to capitalists.

CRITICAL THINKING OUTSIDE THE BOX 3.4

Are some workers, such as nurses and teachers, less motivated by money and more by a desire to help people?

To Marx, the relationship between capitalists and workers is based on a fundamental conflict of interest. Capitalists are motivated by profit, and workers are interested in obtaining as much income as possible. But because higher wages mean less profit, workers and capitalists have different, and conflicting, interests and objectives. According to Marx, capitalists exploit workers by paying them less than the real value of their work. For example, suppose I work as a bartender for eight hours one day, at $6 an hour. At the end of the day, I receive $48 ($6 × $8). However, the amount of money I have in the cash register is considerably more, say $98. It is apparent, then, that I am paid $50 ($98 – $48) less than the amount I collected. Of this $50, my boss, the owner of the bar, will be required to pay business expenses, such as hydro, food, mortgage, and so on. Of the $50, then, my boss may make a profit of only $20. Nevertheless, this is money that I worked for, not my boss. To Marx, this $20, the difference between what I am paid and the value of my work, represents the degree to which I am exploited. Marx termed this difference—in this case, $20—surplus value, or profit.

The greater the amount of surplus value, the greater the level of **exploitation**. For example, if my boss's profits increase every year and my wages remain unchanged, the profit, and hence the level of exploitation, increases. During Marx's lifetime, this is indeed what occurred, as most workers were unable to survive without the aid of charity of some kind. Many starved to death as capitalists increased their share of income and wealth.

Marx referred to the process of increasing inequality and poverty as the "immiseration" of the working class. He hoped it would force workers into recognizing the exploitative nature of the system in which they lived and the need to overthrow the capitalist class and institute a new, more equal, society.

But Marx was unsure whether workers would recognize their real interests and revolt. He observed that the capitalist class, as a consequence of its ownership of all institutions in society, including the media, was informing workers that their poverty resulted not from exploitation, but from their own personal failings: they simply did not work hard enough. This made most workers feel responsible for their own poverty. Marx referred to this outlook on the part of the working class as *false consciousness*: workers essentially believed it was not the system of capitalist exploitation that was to blame, but themselves.

The increasing exploitation of the working class, Marx believed, would lead eventually to conflict between capitalists and workers (see Figure 3.1). Workers would rid themselves of their false consciousness and recognize their shared experience: exploitation. Marx referred to this shared experience as *class consciousness*. It would eventually result in an organizational effort to overthrow the capitalist class and to the establishment of a new communist society, based on equality and freedom.

In communism, exploitation would no longer exist, as all goods and services would be produced by and for the whole population. There would no longer be a division between owners and workers; all property would be owned by the whole population, not by one class or group of people. Goods and services would be distributed on the basis of, not a person's ability to pay, but instead a person's need: "From each according to his ability, to each according to his need" (Marx).[22]

Figure 3.1   From Class to Cash Consciousness

Source: Eddie Grattan and Mark Galante.

Some Problems with Marx's Theory

Marx presented an accurate depiction of 19th-century society; however, at the time of his death in 1883, major changes were occurring in the societies of Europe and North America. Consequently, today we consider his analysis of, and many of his predictions about, the development of Western society to be somewhat misplaced or greatly in need of revision.

First, Marx's assumption of property ownership as constituting the central source of conflict within society has not proven wholly correct. Many observers argue that other factors, such as gender, race, ethnicity, and national identity have generated greater conflict and tension.

Second, Marx predicted increasing income disparities and conflicts between capitalists and workers; however, two developments have occurred to prevent this. The first is the growth, starting about 1880, of a large middle class. The growth of government services over the past hundred years has created a large group of clerical (white-collar) workers who tend to view themselves as distinct, in prestige and status, from the working class. Relatedly, in the 20th century all workers experienced significant increases in their standard of living. Compared with the 19th century, poverty levels have declined sharply, and average incomes have risen dramatically. Consequently, many workers feel little animosity toward their employers.

Third, governments over the past century or so have assumed control of increasingly more areas of society. Although this has arguably lessened individual freedom—as will be discussed shortly—it has also enabled governments to maintain greater control of the economy in an effort to avoid major economic crises, such as the Great Depression of the 1930s, that provide the preconditions for worker unrest.

Although they have lessened over the course of the 20th century, income and wealth inequalities impact Canadians. Moreover, the present economic and financial difficulties facing the countries of Europe and North America have led many commentators to critically question capitalism as a viable economic system. This suggests that Marx's analysis of capitalist society as comprising the haves and have-nots, and as inherently contradictory, still provides insight into the workings of modern society.

CRITICAL THINKING OUTSIDE THE BOX 3.5

Most workers may be exploited, as Marx argued. Do you believe that most workers feel exploited?

Max Weber

Max Weber (pronounced VAY-ber) (1864–1921) accepted Marx's assertion of the importance of the ownership or nonownership of property as a major source of inequality and as a potentially important source of conflict. However, Weber highlighted the other sources of potential conflicts, as well as offering a more complex system of stratification.

Weber agreed with Marx that class, ownership or nonownership of property, is a central feature of modern society. Capitalists possess great amounts of wealth, power, and prestige. However, argued Weber, often the possession of business property is not accompanied by power and prestige. Social prestige, or status, as the degree of positive evaluation by members of society, often derives from a person's level of education, income, and occupation. Doctors, lawyers, dentists, university professors, and so on, enjoy high status in large part because of their income level and the education they possess. Wait staff, shop attendants, and bartenders experience low status or prestige because of their low incomes and the limited education requirements of their jobs.

Political power is the degree of political influence a group has. Some unions, for example, acting on behalf of workers, often exert extensive pressure on employers, including the government, in an effort to increase salaries and improve working conditions. But because not all unions have the same degree of influence, some workers are more politically influential than others. Furthermore, other groups in society, such as those sharing a common lifestyle, similar income levels, and so on, possess greater prestige and political power than many business property owners. To Weber then, differences in social prestige (status) and access to and control of the political system have important effects on the degree of income and wealth inequalities and on the nature of the stratification system.

Because Weber viewed inequality as stemming from a variety of sources and conceived of stratification as a complex phenomenon, he talked about social class and status groups rather than simply about class, the ownership or nonownership of property as defined by Marx. Furthermore, Weber contended that frequently there is no necessary relationship between economic (class), prestige (status), and political (power) rankings. For example, university professors, who have long rejected unionization, tend to have a low power ranking but a high status ranking. In addition, the economic ranking of professors tends to be significantly lower than suggested by their high status. Some manual workers, on the other hand, ranking low in terms of status, earn higher incomes (have higher economic ranking) and often have greater power than professors.

The aristocracy in Britain also serves to illustrate the often-wide discrepancies among economic, status, and political rankings. The British aristocracy, based on heredity, for centuries has enjoyed great prestige. Politically, however, its strength has been declining and no longer matches its high status ranking. The British aristocracy has also been declining economically, with many families forced to sell valuable assets in an effort to maintain their traditional lifestyle and status ranking.

Although recognizing the importance of the ownership or nonownership of property, Weber believed society to be more profoundly affected by the growth of bureaucratic institutions, such as government and large businesses. He believed these limited individual freedom. Workers may indeed be exploited, conceded Weber, but it is unlikely that this will provoke conflict with the capitalist class, and it will certainly not bring about a new, communist, society. Furthermore, even if workers were to overthrow the capitalist class and establish a new society, communism would require an even larger bureaucracy and so further restrict individual freedom. The new leaders would establish themselves as a bureaucratic ruling class, and the workers would simply be trading in one set of rulers for another.

Weber's emphasis on status as an important indicator of social class provides a more accurate representation of the class structure of modern society. The growth of the middle class, and its desire to purchase consumer products such as cars, houses, televisions, and designer clothes, symbolizes its concern with status and prestige. Also, it is apparent that growth in the number of government departments has reduced individual freedom: more and more areas of our life are controlled by rules and regulations, requiring little individual expression or decision making.

THE SOCIAL CLASS STRUCTURE OF CANADA

Depending on the theoretical perspective you adopt, you can define the nature and number of social classes in Canada in several ways. Nevertheless, this section presents a brief description of what are commonly viewed as the major social classes in Canada: the upper class, middle class, working class, and subworking class.

The Upper Class

The **upper class** in Canada comprises those who own substantial amounts of wealth, about 4 or 5 percent of the population. Within the upper class a distinction is often made between those possessing wealth passed down from generation to generation (inherited wealth) and those acquiring wealth through recent business successes ("new money"), such as Bill Gates and Jim Balsillie. The Eaton's department stores, for example, established in the late 19th century, until recently were still owned by the Eaton family of Toronto. Having inherited wealth over several generations, this type of family is often referred to as *bluebloods*, or the upper-upper class. It is estimated that at least half the wealthiest families have benefited to some degree from inheritance.[23]

Figure 3.2   Lifestyles of the Wealthy

Source: Eddie Grattan and Mark Galante.

Members of the upper-upper class characteristically attend expensive private schools and universities, at home and abroad. These institutions serve to teach the values, beliefs, manners, and ways of looking at the world that are exclusive to this class (see Figure 3.2).

The other members of the upper class earn income from well-paying occupations or investments. These "new money" capitalists make up the bulk, between 70 and 80 percent, of the upper class. They are often prohibited from socializing with "old money" families through the many private clubs and associations, as well as social events, established exclusively by and for those with inherited wealth. Bluebloods also prefer avoiding the publicity and media attention frequently craved by new money capitalists such as Jim Balsillie.

The Middle Class

Members of the **middle class** in Canada own some property—usually a house, one or two cars, and perhaps a cottage. They have relatively high-paying, secure occupations, providing a degree of satisfaction and feeling of accomplishment. Many of these occupations are in the public sector, and often offer generous benefit allowances, for example, sick, dental, and maternity benefits, privately established pensions, and, long-term job security.

The Working Class

The working class comprises those who own little or no wealth and are employed in low-paying and generally insecure occupations, such as most of those within the service sector. It is largely because of limited education—most working-class people have not progressed beyond high school or community college—that members of the working class face limited, and typically low-paying, employment opportunities.

The Subworking Class

The subworking class is made up of those, around 20 percent of the population, with the lowest or no incomes—the homeless, welfare recipients, the unemployed, single-parent families, the aged, and those in extremely low-paying occupations. Life for this class tends to be very unstable, both financially and emotionally. Families have limited, or no, savings as nearly all income is required for the purchase of necessities.

Members of the subworking class often live in a separate area of a town or city, and their cultural environment—values, beliefs, attitudes, behaviour, and social activities—tends to be distinctive.

SOCIAL MOBILITY IN CANADA

In North America, especially the United States, it is commonly suggested, particularly by structural–functionalists, that economic success is achieved through individual hard work and determination. This idea implies that movement up and down the social class structure occurs frequently and primarily because of personal effort and initiative. This view of social mobility is ritually portrayed and celebrated in television programs and Hollywood movies: obstacles to personal success reside solely within the individual.

How accurate is this portrayal? How many people actually move up the class ladder? How many fall down? What is the pattern of social mobility in Canada? What is the likelihood, for example, of the daughter or son of a cleaner eventually becoming a member of the middle class? While this section does not endeavour to answer all of these questions, it will elucidate some of the issues surrounding intergenerational social mobility.

The social class structure of Canada has remained relatively stable for several decades. The number of people within each class has remained constant, although many of those within each class have changed. A study conducted in 1986, looking back on the previous years, revealed that close to 40 percent of men and women experienced some form of upward mobility, and a similar figure moved downward.[24]

CRITICAL THINKING OUTSIDE THE BOX 3.6

Can you provide an example of a middle-class family experiencing upward social mobility?

A more recent study, comparing Canada to the rest of the OECD, concluded that Canadians experience a greater degree of social mobility than most other Western countries.[25] Nevertheless, as pointed out earlier, ascribed statuses continue to affect movement up and down the social and occupational hierarchy. In Canada, as Joanne Naiman concluded, "the very top and the very bottom of the status hierarchy remain relatively closed, and most occupational mobility is mainly small movement in the middle."[26]

An important element of upward mobility is level of education. As already mentioned, studies indicate a close relationship between a person's first job and his or her education level. However, it would appear that this may be changing as the educational requirements of jobs increase and the Canadian economy, like economies in the rest of the industrialized world, experiences major structural changes. Free trade, the growth of service industries, the shrinking of industrial and manufacturing production, the development of non-western economies—all suggest that the mobility and social class patterns of the past forty or fifty years may be undergoing a fundamental restructuring.

CHAPTER SUMMARY

This chapter has examined several aspects of social inequality in Canada. (1) There is inequality of income and wealth in our society. Although both income and wealth are unequally distributed, historically inequality of wealth has exhibited greater extremes. (2) Two major theories, structural–functionalism and conflict theory, provide insight into the nature of social inequality, although neither is without problems. (3) Social inequality pervades nearly all aspects of our lives. Social class, race and ethnicity, sex, age, and physical and mental ability all have an impact on social inequality. (4) Canada has four (three, if working and subworking classes are combined) major social classes. (5) In recent years structural changes in the global economy have increased social inequality in Canada and elsewhere, and in the future, this looks likely to continue.

KEY TERMS

ascribed status, p. 73

capitalist class, p. 81

conflict theory, p. 81

disposable income, p. 71

equality of opportunity, p. 80

exploitation, p. 82

feminization of poverty, p. 76

income, p. 67

means of production, p. 81

middle class, p. 87

political power, p. 85

social inequality, p. 66

stratification, p. 66

structural–functionalism, p. 79

upper class, p. 86

wealth, p. 71

working class, p. 81

DISCUSSION QUESTIONS

1. To explain social inequality, which of the ascribed statuses (social class, race and ethnicity, sex, age, disability) do you consider the most important? Provide evidence.
2. Which theory do you believe more adequately explains social inequality: conflict theory or structural–functionalism?
3. Why are single women more likely to be living below the poverty line?
4. Provide reasons why you believe the Canadian government should or should not attempt to reduce the degree of income and wealth inequality in Canada.
5. As a person grows older, which ascribed statuses do you think become more significant in his or her life?

NOTES

1. John J. Macionis, Juanne Nancarrow Clarke, and Linda M. Gerber, *Sociology* (New Jersey: Prentice-Hall, 1993), p. 243.
2. Tavia Grant, "The Rich, the Poor, and the Chasm Between," *The Globe and Mail*, 1 May 2008.
3. G. Picot and A. Heisz, "The Labour Market in the 1990s," in *Canadian Economic Observer*, February 2000, Statistics Canada, Catalogue No. 11-010-XPB (Ottawa: Statistics Canada, 2000), pp. 312, 315.
4. The number of social assistance recipients dropped from 3.1 million to under 2 million by 2000, with benefit payments decreasing from $14.3 billion in 1994 to $10.4 billion in 2001 (see F. Roy, "Social Assistance by Province, 1993–2003" in Statistics Canada, *Canadian Economic Observer*, November 2004, Catalogue No. 11-010), p. 3.1.
5. North American and European governments responded to the major economic downturn of 2008 by injecting large sums of money into their economies. In some cases, this spending led to a government debt crisis. In 2010, the European Union provided the government of Greece financial assistance amid fears of government insolvencies and currency devaluation across Europe. See "Euro Sinks to Four-year Low as Hungary Fears being the Next Greece," *The Guardian*, 4 June 2010.
6. Alfred A. Hunter, *Class Tells: On Social Inequality in Canada* (Toronto: Butterworths, 1981), p. 99.
7. "Likelihood of Saving Increase with Income," *Infomat, A Weekly Review*, 20 July 2001, Catalogue No. 11-002E, p. 132; Macionis et al., *Sociology*, p. 337.
8. Jane Badets and Tina W.L. Chui, *Focus on Canada: Canada's Changing Immigrant Population*, Statistics Canada, Catalogue No. 96-311E (Ottawa and Scarborough: Statistics Canada and Prentice-Hall, 1994), p. 79.
9. Anton L. Allahar and James E. Cote, *The Structure of Inequality in Canada* (Toronto: James Lorimer and Company Ltd., 1998), p. 63. Using data for 1990, Feng Hou and T.R. Balakrishnan reach the same conclusion in "The Economic Integration of Visible

Minorities in Contemporary Canadian Society," in James Curtis, Edward Grabb, and Neil Guppy, eds., *Social Inequality in Canada: Patterns, Problems, Policies,* 3rd ed. (Scarborough: Prentice Hall Allyn and Bacon Canada, 1999), p. 223.

10. Ellen M. Gee and Steven G. Prus, "Income Inequality in Canada: A 'Racial Divide'" in Madeline A. Kalbach and Warren E. Kalbach, eds., *Perspectives on Ethnicity in Canada: A Reader* (Toronto: Harcourt Brace, 2000).

11. Yuri Ostrovsky, "Earnings Inequality and Earnings Instability of Immigrants in Canada," Analytical Studies Branch Research Paper Series, April 2008 Statistics Canada, Catalogue No. 11F0019M—309.

12. Macionis et al., *Sociology,* p. 337.

13. Wallace Clement, *The Canadian Corporate Elite: An Analysis of Economic Power* (Ottawa: Carleton University Press, 1986), pp. 192, 364–65.

14. M. Reza Nakhaie, "Vertical Mosaic among the Elites: The New Imagery Revisited," *The Canadian Review of Sociology and Anthropology,* February 1997.

15. Picot and Heisz, "The Labour Market," p. 312.

16. See *The Institute for Women's Policy Research Fact Sheet* IWPR #C350 March 2010.

17. Susan Crompton, "Left Behind: Lone Mothers in the Labour Market," *Perspectives,* Summer 1994: 23.

18. Statistics Canada, *Income in Canada,* 2007, Catalogue No. 75-202-X.

19. Ibid.

20. Edward G. Grabb, *Theories of Social Inequality: Classical and Contemporary Perspectives* (Toronto: Holt, Rinehart, and Winston, 1990), p. 190.

21. Bryan S. Turner, *Equality* (London: Tavistock Publications, 1986), pp. 40–41.

22. This quotation appears in Karl Marx, *Critique of the Gotha Programme* (Moscow: Progress Publishers, 1970). See Chapter five, "A Family Affair: Intergenerational Social Mobility across OECD Countries" in *Economic Policy Reform: Going for Growth 2010* (Belgium: Organisation for Economic Co-operation and Development, 2010).

23. James B. Davies, "The Distribution of Wealth and Economic Inequality," in James Curtis, Edward Grabb, and Neil Guppy, eds., *Social Inequality in Canada: Patterns, Problems, Policies,* 3rd ed. (Scarborough: Prentice Hall Allyn and Bacon Canada, 1999), p. 72.

24. Gillian Creese, Neil Guppy, and Martin Meissner, *Ups and Downs on the Ladder of Success* (Ottawa: Statistics Canada, 1991).

25. See Chapter five, "A Family Affair: Intergenerational Social Mobility across OECD Countries" in *Economic Policy Reform: Going for Growth 2010* (Belgium: Organisation for Economic Co-operation and Development, 2010).

26. Joanne Naiman, *How Societies Work: Class, Power, and Change in a Canadian Context,* 2nd ed. (Toronto: Irwin Publishing, 2000), p. 224.

CHAPTER 4

Race and Ethnicity: The Obvious Diversity

Paul U. Angelini and Michelle Broderick

We kept the blacks out and we did it in a peculiarly Canadian fashion—by pretending publicly that our immigration laws did not discriminate against anyone by reason of race, creed or colour while at the same time preventing all Negroes from crossing the border into Canada.

—Pierre Berton, *Why We Act Like Canadians*

We are all immigrants.

—common Canadian saying

Objectives

After reading this chapter, you should be able to

- sketch the diverse history of Canadian immigration

- outline the major determinants of personal and group identity and clarify the meaning and implications of the term *multiculturalism*

- analyze the most important factors that influence societal interaction

- appreciate the nature and seriousness of the problems and issues in race and ethnic relations in Canada

- talk about who you are in a manner that develops a positive self-image and acceptance of racial and ethnic differences.

INTRODUCTION

Few issues can raise temperatures to such heights, with relative ease, as the issue of race and ethnic relations in Canadian society. Discussions inevitably lead to debates concerning what it means to be Canadian and how one becomes Canadian. From its very beginnings, Canada has been a multicultural and multiracial society. Sadly, this fact is frequently omitted from school curricula. As a result, Canadians tend to be largely ignorant of the history of immigration in Canada. It is assumed that British and French settlers "founded" Canada, irrespective of the Native Peoples who already occupied much of what we call North America. In fact, people from many parts of the world arrived on Canadian shores expecting to begin a prosperous life in a new land. People arrived from all over Europe, Asia, and the United States—people from all walks of life, including slaves and free people of colour. With so many different people arriving from so many different parts of the world, it is little wonder that Canada has experienced and is experiencing all the growing pains of so many different people living together. This does not mean we should accept some of the problems as "normal"; it simply means we should acknowledge them (past and present) and deal with them directly in hopes of not repeating what we have done in the past or are doing now. History does not repeat itself—human beings do!

The purpose of this chapter is to introduce students to the history of immigration to Canada, multiculturalism, identity, and the factors that affect interaction in Canadian society. The hope is to help students come to understand the challenges facing them in developing a society tolerant and accepting of cultural and racial differences.

A BRIEF HISTORY OF IMMIGRATION TO CANADA

Discussions concerning the merits of immigration to Canada are never far from debates on Canadian identity—what is a Canadian, who is a Canadian? One of the most widely held myths in Canada is the belief that Canada has always been a "white" British and French country; from its very beginnings, Canada has been multiethnic (see Have You Heard? 4.1). A historical analysis of Canadian immigration patterns is essential if we are to have a thorough understanding of race and ethnic diversity in Canada.

In 1970 the Royal Commission on Bilingualism and Biculturalism outlined four distinct stages to Canada's immigration history.[1] Let us look briefly at each of these. We will then discuss a fifth stage resulting from a later change in policy.

Stage 1: The Beginnings to 1901

Immigration to Canada before 1901 was slow. People came to Canada possessing many different skills and with quite different experiences: fishermen, farmers, merchants,

HAVE YOU HEARD? 4.1

An Insidious Myth

. . . .

The myth that Canada was and is a "white" country has no foundation in fact, yet it is part of our national consciousness. Writer Adrienne Shadd refers to this as an "insidious" myth. People tend to forget that Native Peoples were here first: black slaves were among the earliest to arrive in Canada during the 17th and 18th centuries; the Chinese presence in Canada dates back to the 19th century. A wide variety of races and nationalities helped to build Canada. This truth, however, is not properly reflected in school curricula.

Source: Carl E. James, *Seeing Ourselves: Exploring Race, Ethnicity and Culture*, 2nd ed. (Toronto: TEP, 1999), p. 160.

traders, soldiers, adventurers, slaves, and fugitives. French and British immigrants were dominant in terms of their numbers, cultural influences, and power, but they were not the only ones to arrive. Before 1800 or so, only 10 percent of Canada's population was not British, French, or Native. More than half of all immigrants who arrived in Canada during the 19th century, however, were of German origins. Germans settled in New France and Nova Scotia, where 1500 of them founded the Lunenburg settlement between 1750 and 1753. Germans also settled in other parts of the Maritimes and in what is today Quebec. German sectarians, including Mennonites, Moravians, and Tunkers, predominantly from the United States, came to Canada from about 1780 until well into the 1800s. In the middle of the 19th century, some of them settled in Ontario, especially in Waterloo County.

About 10 percent of the United Empire Loyalists who came to Canada after the American Revolution were black.[2] Some of these people were slaves that white owners brought with them. Contrary to popular myth, slavery did indeed exist in Canada (see Have You Heard? 4.2, 4.3, and 4.4). Moreover, between 1815 and 1860, 40 000 to 60 000 fugitive slaves and free people of colour arrived.[3] The Dutch and the Scandinavians were the only other large groups who came, accounting for less than 1 percent of the total immigration population at this time.

The extinction of the Native inhabitants of Newfoundland, the Beothuk, is almost universally forgotten. The tribe died out by the 1820s due to a combination of starvation (not having free access to their traditional fishing grounds), tuberculosis (which took a heavy toll), and being hunted for sport by the European settlers![4]

Slavery in Canada, Part I

· ·

TO BE SOLD,

A BLACK WOMAN, named PEGGY, aged about forty years ; and a Black boy her fon, named JUPITER, aged about fifteen years, both of them the property of the Subfcriber.

The Woman is a tolerable Cook and wafher woman and perfectly underftands making Soap and Candles.

The Boy is tall and ftrong of his age, and has been employed in Country bufinefs, but brought up prin-cipally as a Houfe Servant—They are each of them Servants for life. The Price for the Wowan is one hundred and fifty Dollars—for the Boy two hundred Dollars, payable in three years with Intereft from the day of Sale and to be properly fecured by Bond &c.—But one fourth lefs will be taken in ready Money.

PETER RUSSELL.

York, Feb. 10th 1806.

Source: Daniel G. Hill, *Human Rights in Canada: A Focus on Racism* (Ottawa: Canadian Labour Congress, 1977), p. 3.

Stage 2: 1880–1918

Stage 2 is characterized by Europeans leaving Europe. So many left for the New World that these years have been described as "the mightiest movement of people in modern history."

As European society continued its evolution from a rural one to an urban one and as its population continued to grow, millions and millions decided to leave, hoping to find better opportunities for themselves elsewhere. Many went to the United States, South

CRITICAL THINKING OUTSIDE THE BOX 4.1

Why is the past existence of slavery in Canada not a well-known fact? Why is it not a standard part of high-school curricula? Did you know slavery once existed in Canada? If so, where did you find out? If not, why?

HAVE YOU HEARD? 4.3

Slavery in Canada, Part II

Slavery did indeed exist in Canada. The first slave was brought to New France in 1628 from Madagascar. During and after the American Revolution, United Empire Loyalists brought slaves with them. At least six of sixteen members of the first Parliament of Upper Canada owned slaves.

Source: Daniel G. Hill, *Human Rights in Canada: A Focus on Racism* (Ottawa: Canadian Labour Congress, 1977), p. 7.

Slavery in Canada, Part III

In 1734, Marie-Joseph Angelique, a black female slave, burned down part of the city of Montreal after she was informed of her owner's intention to sell her.

Source: Carl E. James, *Seeing Ourselves: Exploring Race, Ethnicity and Culture*, 2nd ed. (Toronto: TEP, 1999), p. 161.

HAVE YOU HEARD? 4.4

Maroons

Maroons were slaves originally stolen from Africa who escaped slavery and their British masters in Jamaica. The Maroons established settlements in the central mountains and hills of Jamaica and subsequently fought two wars against the white colonists. At the conclusion of the second war in 1795, many Maroons were deported to Nova Scotia and Sierra Leone.

Source: Harry Harmer, *The Longman Companion to Slavery, Emancipation and Civil Rights* (Toronto: Pearson Education Ltd., 2001), pp. 158, 168, and 203.

America (especially Argentina and Brazil), and, beginning in the late 1890s, Canada. By this time the federal government had decided to settle the empty Canadian West and was encouraging migration there.

Other factors, too, brought immigrants here: the closing of the American frontier, the Yukon gold rush, huge construction projects like the transcontinental railway, and new developments in farming technology all made Canada more attractive.

In 1913 alone more than 400 000 immigrants arrived, the largest number in any single year. Between 1896 and 1914 more than 3 000 000 came to Canada. Of these, about 1 250 000 were from the United Kingdom and approximately 1 000 000 from the United States. The important feature of this period was the arrival of people from Central and Eastern Europe, including Ukrainians, Poles, Hungarians, Romanians, and Russians. By 1921, 15 percent of Canada's population was of neither French nor British origin.

The increased numbers for those groups already settled in Western Canada were nothing short of amazing. The population of German origin went from 46 800 in 1901 to 148 000 in 1911, and by 1931, 242 000 Germans were living in the Prairies. The Scandinavian population went from 17 300 in 1901 to 130 000 in 1921. The Ukrainian population increased almost twentyfold, from 5600 in 1901 to 96 000 in 1921, and the population of Polish origin experienced similar growth, from 2800 in 1901 to 32 000 in 1921.

CRITICAL THINKING OUTSIDE THE BOX 4.2

As of 2010, every immigrant to Canada must pay application fees for simply applying to immigrate to Canada. A Family Class Principal applicant must pay $475 plus $150 per child less than 22 years of age and $550 for every family member 22 years of age or older. Plus, there is an additional Family Class Sponsorship Application fee of $75 per application. For the Investor, Entrepreneur or Self Employed Persons Class the fees are $1050, $150, and $550, respectively. Finally, there is a charge of $490 for filling out the Right of Permanent Residence Application.

Are these fees really a head tax? Is it fair to ask immigrants to pay such fees? What are the benefits and weaknesses of asking immigrants to pay such a fee? List three benefits and three weaknesses.

Source: Government of Canada website <https://services3.cic.gc.ca/efee/efee.do>, accessed 3 May 2010.

In the rest of Canada other groups also saw their numbers rise dramatically. The Italian population went from 11 000 in 1901 to 67 000 in 1921, and the Jewish from 16 100 to 126 000 in 1921. Other arrivals included Greeks, Syrians, Lebanese, and Armenians. Like the Italians and Jews, these immigrants preferred to settle in the cities of central Canada rather than the farming communities of the West.

Stage 2 also saw the imposition of the head tax on Chinese immigrants. (The racist treatment of Asian immigrants was to be repeated during World War II; the only difference was the target—this time it was Japanese-Canadians.) The head tax was intended to slow the arrival of Chinese. In 1885 it was set at $50. In 1900 it was set at $100. This tax, however, did not slow the influx of Chinese, so the tax was increased to $500 per person, or head, in 1903.

The racist workings of the Canadian immigration policy did not stop there. In 1908 the government attempted to limit East Indian immigration by requiring that anyone arriving from India had to do so by coming to Canada directly without stopping. This became known as the "direct passage" stipulation. In 1914, 376 Sikhs arrived from India directly—they did not stop at any other site during their voyage. Their ship, the S. S. Komagata Maru, was made to wait in Vancouver harbour for three months—before it was shamelessly turned away.[5]

In 1907, more than 8000 Japanese immigrants arrived in Canada, particularly in British Columbia. This heightened anti-Asian sentiment in British Columbia, and led to tighter restrictions on immigration. These feelings culminated in racial riots in September of that year. By 1921, 16 000 Japanese were living in Canada, 15 000 of them in British Columbia.

Chinese immigrants are always credited with having made a huge contribution to the building of Canada's railways. This accolade, however, masks the exploitative and often brutal treatment they received during the building itself. Pierre Berton and others have remarked that there is one dead Chinese worker for every mile of rail laid. By 1921, there were 40 000 Chinese in Canada, 24 000 of them in British Columbia.

Stage 3: 1918–1945

Between World Wars I and II, immigration continued, but it never reached the explosive numbers of Stage 2. Between 1914 and 1939 the United States severely reduced the number of immigrants it would take, and this made Canada the favoured destination. But Canada, too, began to put restrictions on immigration. Whereas the United States chose to adopt a system based on quotas, Canada decided to make lists of countries that were "preferred" or "nonpreferred." These categories usually excluded Chinese immigrants, for example, and severely limited others from Asia.

Stage 3 saw the campaign against Japanese and Chinese immigrants known as the campaign against the "Yellow Peril." A Chinese exclusion law was passed banning poor Chinese immigrants: it was not repealed until 1947.[6] By 1931 there was an increase of

19 000 Asians in Canada, bringing the total to 85 600, but the census of 1941 showed the number had declined to 74 000.

During the 1920s blacks also suffered from the racist nature of Canada's immigration policy. In the middle of the decade the government decided that a "British subject" would be defined as a citizen of a Commonwealth country whose population was predominantly white.

In the meantime, other ethnic groups continued to arrive. Between 1923 and 1930, 20 000 Swedes, 19 500 Norwegians, and 17 000 Danes immigrated to Canada.

The Great Depression essentially stopped immigration to Canada. Between 1931 and 1941 only 140 000 immigrants arrived. Some groups saw their numbers decline. The populations of German, Russian, and Asian origin in Canada declined by 9000, 4000, and 10 500, respectively. Throughout the war, Canada was reluctant to accept the victims of terror from Nazi Germany.

Stage 4: 1945–1974

Large numbers of people came to Canada after World War II. Between 1945 and 1961, 2 100 000 arrived. This was the most prolonged period of immigration in Canadian history. It was also the most diverse in terms of social class, ethnicity, and occupation. Large numbers of Italians, Germans, Poles, Jews, and Dutch came. Immigrants from Britain, however, accounted for the largest number—one-third of the total.

Canada at this time began to experience all the benefits and problems associated with an advanced, industrialized, urban country. Not surprisingly, immigrants began to settle in cities and towns. Toronto became the favourite destination. By 1961, 42 percent of Toronto's population and one-third of Metro Toronto's were not born in Canada. In fact, 29 percent of those living in Toronto and one-third of those living in Metro Toronto arrived there between 1946 and 1961.

The largest wave of immigration in Stage 4 occurred between 1951 and 1960. In just nine years more than 250 000 Italians, for example, entered Canada. Like the Greeks and Portuguese, many of them left rural areas to settle in Canadian cities. These immigrants shared many other characteristics. They were largely unskilled, had no experience with city living, and had low levels of formal education. These three groups headed mostly for Toronto, where today they live in large recognizable communities.

The case of Italians living in Toronto is especially interesting. The Italian population of Metro Toronto now is estimated at more than 400 000, making it the largest Italian community outside of Italy.

This period is also remembered for its racist and brutal treatment of Japanese-Canadians. At the end of World War II, 4000 Japanese-Canadians were forced to leave

Canada under a "repatriation" program. More than half had been born here, and more than two-thirds were Canadian citizens! How would it feel to know that your birthplace and citizenship mean nothing if the government decides to deprive you of your basic human rights? The story of Japanese-Canadians sent to internment camps, most of them in British Columbia—with only what they could carry and the remainder of their belongings being confiscated and sold by the government—now form an integral part of discussions of Canada and the war years. When released after the war was over, most of the internees left British Columbia, and, by 1961, 8000 Japanese-Canadians were living in Metro Toronto.

Although the Bilingualism and Biculturalism Report on Immigration ended its analysis in 1974, immigration to Canada did not. We can add a fifth stage to Canadian immigration history, largely as a result of the 1974 change in Canadian immigration policy away from seeking those with specific skills to satisfying the demands of the Canadian economy. As the economy changes, so do the skills demanded of immigrants.

Stage 5: 1975 to the Present

The dominant feature of Stage 5 is emigration from countries in the developing world. Low levels of economic development characterize these countries and the overwhelming majority of their populations are not white. The arrival of these people, who form racial minorities in Canada, has had a profound effect. With new immigrants arrive new challenges; this is especially true for their preferred destination, Metro Toronto.

The most reported origins of immigrants between 1991 and 1996 were Chinese, East Indian, Filipino, Sri Lankan, Polish, and Vietnamese.[7] In fact, Statistics Canada reports that the visible minority population has consistently grown the past 25 years from 9.4 percent of the Canadian population (2.5 million) in 1991, to 11.2 percent (3.2 million) in 1996, to 13.4 percent (3.9 million) in 2001, to 16. 2 percent (5 million) of the population in 2006 with Metropolitan Toronto as the preferred destination (see Have You Heard? 4.5); the rate of growth for the visible minority population between 2001and 2006 was 27.2 percent, five times faster than the increase for the rest of the population.[8] The 2006 Census showed that the percentage of immigrants born in regions other than Europe has steadily increased from 68.5 percent in 1981, to 78.3 percent in 1991, to 83.5 percent between 2001 and 2006.[9] See Table 4.1. By 2017, Statistics Canada's population projections predict that the racially visible population of Canada will account for approximately 20 percent of the total Canadian population.[10] See Have You Heard? 4.5.

Table 4.1   Origins of Canadian (foreign born) Racial Minority Groups

South Asian	Chinese	Black
Total: 1 262 900	1 216 600	783 800
India	PRC	Jamaica
48.8 percent	52.9 percent	25.8 percent
Pakistan	Hong Kong (Special Admin Region)	Haiti
14.6 percent	24.2 percent	14.9 percent
Sri Lanka	Taiwan	Trinidad and Tobago
11.7 percent	7.2 percent	5.2 percent
Guyana	Viet Nam	Ethiopia
4.2 percent	5.7 percent	4.5 percent
Bangladesh		Somalia
3.6 percent		4.4 percent

More than half, 52.2 percent of Canada's visible minorities live in Ontario followed by British Columbia at 19.9 percent—six out of every ten visible minorities live in Toronto or Vancouver. Between 2001 and 2006, 40.4 percent of all new immigrants coming to Canada chose Metropolitan Toronto as their destination—81.9 percent of these belonged to visible minority groups. South Asians account for 13.5 percent of Toronto's total population, 31.5 percent of its visible minority population. The numbers for the Chinese are 9.6 and 22.4 percent, respectively.

Source: Adapted from Statistics Canada, *Canada's Ethnocultural Mosaic, 2006 Census Findings,* 97-562-XIE2006001 Census year 2006, Released April 2, 2008, p. 14.

HAVE YOU HEARD? 4.5

The Brain Gain

Generally, there are only four countries on earth that actively seek out immigrants to help their countries grow and stimulate/sustain economic activity: Australia, Canada, the United States, and the United Kingdom. If these four countries target the best educated and brightest of the developing world, who will be left to help the developing world change its "underdeveloped" status? This is a "Brain Drain" for the developing world and a "Brain Gain" for the developed one. In the wake of 11 September 2001, the new Immigration and Refugee Protection Act 2002 and provisions set out in Bill C-36 reaffirmed the kind of immigrant Canada wishes to attract: highly skilled, experienced, well educated, and fluent in French or English.

Source: Yasmin Abu-Laban and Christina Gabriel, "Security, Immigration, and Post-September 11 Canada," in Janine Brodie and Linda Trimble, eds., *Reinventing Canada: Politics of the 21st Century* (Toronto: Prentice Hall, 2003), p. 299.

ETHNICITY, RACE, AND SOCIOLOGICAL THEORY

We will now examine three dominant theoretical approaches to society and how they differ with respect to what constitutes society, its development, and the various issues and problems about society that need to be discussed and debated.

Symbolic Interaction Theory

Interactionists believe that relations in society can be viewed by examining the communication and manipulation of symbols. Understanding race and ethnic relations and dealing with conflicts in society must be done by examining how each individual defines the situation he or she is in and how this definition is influenced by culture, race, and ethnicity. Interactionists ask questions such as: How do members of different groups define the world around them? What role does language play in helping define the situation? Why do symbols play such an important part in race and ethnic relations?

Conflict Theory

Conflict theorists believe that power is the key to understanding interaction in society. Power, they argue, comes primarily from the ownership of those things necessary to produce goods in society, such as land, resources, buildings, machines, technology, and knowledge. Different groups in society, those who own things and those who do not, compete for power. Some groups attempt to change the status quo, whereas others work to preserve it. Conflict theorists ask questions such as why do some ethnic groups have more power than others? Do government policies such as multiculturalism and employment equity (affirmative action in the United States) really address the power imbalance in society, or, are they simply superficial modifications to prevent real changes to the distribution of power? Generally, conflict theorists believe a radical reorganization of the power structure in society is a prerequisite for stable race and ethnic relations.

Structural–Functionalist Theory

Structural–functionalists emphasize the importance of maintaining social order. In their analysis of race and ethnicity, they concentrate on the manner in which policies such as multiculturalism and affirmative action contribute to social order. Do stereotypes and prejudice have a negative effect on society? How do race and ethnic relations in Canada promote or destroy social order? These are common questions that a structural–functionalist might ask.

THE SOCIAL MEANING OF CULTURAL IDENTITY

Socially, a person's cultural identity comprises many different elements, including race, ethnicity, class, sex and gender, religion, region, occupation, language, country of origin, and sexual orientation. We will discuss two of the most crucial of these elements of identity: ethnicity and race.

Ethnicity

Your perception of your ethnicity is one of the most important elements of your identity. Many definitions of **ethnic groups** exist, and most of them have three common elements: (1) an ethnic group shares a common ancestry and history, (2) an ethnic group shares many norms, values, and traditions, and (3) an ethnic group is considered a group by those others who do not share the first two elements. We can define ethnic groups, therefore, as those who share several norms, values, and traditions; have a common ancestry and history; and are considered distinct by the rest of society because they share these elements.

Language is essential to the identity of any ethnic group, although not all ethnic groups require their members to share a language. Without question language is the most crucial aspect of identity. It is the symbolic mode of communication we use to transmit ideas, information, and history from one generation to the next and to socialize the young. As the well-known sociologists Peter and Brigitte Berger put it: "Language provides the lifelong context of our experience of others, of self, of the world . . . it provides the most powerful hold that society has over us."[11] It is not surprising that language is such an important component of ethnicity. See Have You Heard? 4.6.

Race

Race is the second major component of identity. Race is also one of the most misused and misunderstood words in the field of diversity. It has two separate meanings: (1) a biological meaning and (2) a sociological one.

From a biological perspective, we all belong to the same race—the human race. This simply means that all humans belong to one species. Therefore, all humans, regardless of which population they belong to, are genetically compatible. This in turn means that they can reproduce and produce viable (i.e., fertile) offspring. As an example, a person of Inuit descent can produce fertile offspring with an individual of Australian Aboriginal descent. If humans were not compatible genetically, we would belong to different species and, therefore, be unable to reproduce fertile offspring. A horse and a donkey belong to different species and their offspring, known as a mule, is sterile and cannot reproduce. Because we all belong to the same species, we can reproduce regardless of what other humans we decide to have children with.

The meaning of the term "race" has three problems. First, race refers to subspecies. Most traits used to define subspecies, or races, vary along a continuum. But when we attempt to divide people into different races, we do so in a completely subjective and arbitrary way. Suppose we divide people according to skin colour and type of earwax (wet versus dry), inevitably some people would share both these traits and some would not. So how would we be able to divide people into specific racial categories?

The second problem with the question of race concerns interbreeding between populations. Humans are and always have been, even before the development of mass transportation, a very mobile species. This means it is virtually impossible to accurately assess the amount of interbreeding that has taken place between human populations. As a consequence of this, there are no true "pure" human races, and there probably never have been.

Finally, the third problem with the question of race has to do with its origins— where did this term come from? The concept of race is associated with a history of exploitation. When Europeans started to travel to new lands, the economic benefit of exploiting others became the driving force of European colonization. It was easier to exploit and abuse a population if they were viewed as less than human. Systems of classifying people that were developed hundreds of years ago arranged populations into a hierarchy with the best ("closest to God") being white and the less human ("furthest from God") being darker skinned—the darker the skin the further away from God. Sadly, this kind of thinking persists, even in the field of education, where researchers assert that some populations are not as intelligent as others are by virtue of their genes (genetic makeup).

CRITICAL THINKING OUTSIDE THE BOX 4.3

Which sociological theory do you believe best explains race and ethnic relations in Canada? List at least three reasons for your choice and explain each in detail.

HAVE YOU HEARD? 4.6

Protection of the French Language: Bill 101 (1977) and Bill 178 (1988)

. . . .

With the intention of protecting Francophone identity, successive Quebec governments have gone to great lengths to ensure the use and survival of the French language in Quebec and, ultimately, in Canada.

In 1977 the Parti Québécois government introduced Bill 101. Bill 101 reaffirmed that French would be the language of business and labour and restricted English-language schooling to two groups of people: (1) those whose parents were educated in English and (2) those who were already attending English-language schools. The target of Bill 101 was the immigrants arriving in Quebec who were sending their children to English schools and not to French ones.

In 1988 the Liberal government of Quebec introduced its own language bill, Bill 178. Known as the "sign law," it restricted the use of English-language signs in two ways: first, by not allowing English on outside signs and second, by legislating that the letters on French signs inside stores be three times larger than English ones.

Sociologically, our differing physical features are symbols that are accompanied by emotionally charged meanings. In short, physical features influence the way people see themselves and the way people interact. As Carl E. James has written: "Race is significant as long as groups are determined by selected physical traits, and as long as people act upon these meanings. However, we must bear in mind that race is largely based on its social meaning."[12]

It is important to understand the emotionally charged nature of physical symbols. Sociologically, race is part of everyone's life. Whites in Canada tend to take their skin colour for granted while at the same time they identify others by the colour of their skin.[13] Indeed, white people in Canada are in large part socially ignorant of the benefits of being white in a white-dominated society. Whites in Canada (the dominant group) define what is good, acceptable, excellent, and successful. In short, they have the power to define the standards by which all members of society are judged. "Whiteness" is generally associated with good and "blackness," with few exceptions, is associated with negativity, gloominess, pessimism, hostility, and evil[14] (see Have You Heard? 4.7).

Over the years, many non-white students have identified incidents and situations where they have experienced different treatment when compared with white students of the same age. Students have sarcastically referred to these experiences as "special"

HAVE YOU HEARD? 4.7

Racism in Cultural Symbols

....

- black magic is evil (and white magic?)
- blackmail (why not whitemail?)
- a black cat is bad luck
- the black prince is the evil prince
- a black mark on your record is a negative thing
- a black heart has no love
- black humour (what about white humour?)
- black leather is worn by social and sexual deviants
- black lingerie is worn by sexually deviant women
- the black sheep of the family
- devil's food cake (chocolate)
- angel food cake (vanilla)

Can you think of any others? What about the names of professional sports teams?

---

treatment (see Have You Heard? 4.8). Some common experiences of non-white students include being watched more closely when shopping in malls, being accused of public loitering when conversing in groups, having change slapped down on the counter rather than being handed the change, being accused of being drug dealers when carrying pagers, and being served last in restaurants and bars.

To conclude, when we speak of identity, the social meaning of race takes precedence over the biological meaning. Biologically speaking, race is an outmoded and archaic concept.

ATTITUDES AND BEHAVIOURS THAT AFFECT SOCIAL INTERACTION

Many factors play a negative role in social interaction, including prejudice, discrimination, racism, and ethnocentrism.

Prejudice

Prejudice is the attitude of prejudging people on the basis of statements and beliefs that do not hold up to rational or critical scrutiny. Prejudice occurs when, in spite of evidence

---

HAVE YOU HEARD? 4.8

Other Examples of "Special" Treatment

. . . .

- Schools teach the history of British and French people in Canada but ignore the history and contributions of other people.
- The few minority members who are successful in the field of television news are concentrated in sports, weather, and traffic reporting. Few minorities are primetime anchors for national news programs.
- Politicians in Canada are usually white.
- White people tend to believe that there is a "black" culture but no such thing as a "white" culture.
- Many people believe that all blacks in Canada are from Jamaica.
- White people generally believe that people from the subcontinent (India, Pakistan, and Bangladesh) are poor.

For a similar but more focused discussion see Peggy McIntosh, "White Privilege: Unpacking the Invisible Knapsack," in *Peace and Freedom*, July/August 1989, pp. 10–12.

CRITICAL THINKING OUTSIDE THE BOX 4.4

How many events of "white privilege" have you witnessed or experienced recently? Why are whites largely ignorant of such "privileges"? Give at least three reasons.

---

to the contrary, a person still holds negative feelings and opinions toward other people and groups. Prejudgments are seldom based on experience. Carl E. James has written, "The tendency to make prejudgments may be seen as necessary, as the human mind needs to organize the stimuli with which it is bombarded."[15] In many respects prejudging is accepted and expected in a world where the amount of knowledge understood by the human race is said to double every five years. Prejudging seems to make a complicated world easier to deal with. It is not surprising, therefore, that prejudice is a universal phenomenon and a common problem in social interaction.

The human tendency to put things into groups or categories is clearly visible when we speak of **stereotypes**. A stereotype can be defined as a collection of generalizations about a group of people that are negative, exaggerated, and cannot be maintained when subjected to critical analysis. Some common stereotypes include the following:

- All Italians belong to the Mafia.
- All blacks are criminals.
- All Aboriginals are drunks.
- All Sikhs drive taxis.
- All Pakistanis own corner stores.
- All Jews are cheap.

The key feature that explains the attractiveness of stereotypes is that they are overly simplistic. Minority groups have continually complained of their stereotypical treatment by the mass media.

Discrimination

Prejudice is the attitude, and **discrimination** is the action. Discrimination can be defined as the unequal or unfavourable treatment of people because of their perceived or actual membership in a particular ethnic group that restricts their full participation in Canadian society. When discrimination is carried out on the basis of race (people who share physical characteristics) and when common behaviour is assumed (that people who share certain physical characteristics behave in a certain way), we call this **racism** (see Have You Heard? 4.9). Many regard the denial of Aboriginal land claims and self-government as a form of racism. Land claims and self-government are crucial to Aboriginal identity and survival—to regain control over their traditional land, including access to all resources, especially hunting and fishing rights. Others point to the 1999 Nisga'a agreement as a model for future agreements with Aboriginal people. This agreement met Nisga'a demands in the areas of fishing and hunting rights, land ownership, law, and financial compensation. The treatment of the Nisga'a contrasts sharply with Ottawa's treatment of the Mi'kmaq.

There are two types of discrimination, individual and institutional. **Individual discrimination** is perhaps the most common type, but, as we will see, it may not be the most damaging. Examples of such individual actions include refusing to sit next to or associate with members of minority groups while in public places; giving or receiving poor or slow service in restaurants and stores; refusing to date people from outside your ethnic or racial group; and, finally, discouraging your children from developing friendships with people from outside your ethnic or racial group. Sometimes individual discrimination takes the form of what Daniel Hill called "nice guy" discrimination.[16] This means people will act in a discriminatory manner and justify it according to the potential for negative reactions

HAVE YOU HEARD? 4.9

Racism in the Canadian Justice System

. . . .

The existence of racism in the Canadian justice system was acknowledged by the minister of state for multiculturalism and citizenship in 1990, the Law Reform Commission of Canada in 1992, and the Law Reform Commission on Systemic Racism in the Ontario Criminal Justice System in 1995. The report of the latter concluded that blacks constitute just less than 3 percent of the population of Ontario but 15 percent of the prison population. The *Toronto Star* reported in 2001 that analysis of police data from 1996 to 2001 showed people with black skin are twice as likely to be stopped by police as people with white skin. In fact, between 1997 and 2008 blacks were: disproportionately ticketed for "out-of-sight" offences (these offences surface only after a traffic stop) when compared to the white population; 3.6 times more likely (between 2003 and 2008) to be faced with criminal charges, including charges for serious violent offences and are held for bail more often (between 2003 and 2008) than white citizens when they are facing a single drug possession charge. A similar study released in Kingston in May 2005 found that black-skinned people were 3.7 times more likely to be stopped in that city than white-skinned people.

The same is true for Aboriginal Peoples. By March 2006 they represented 16.7 percent of federally sentenced inmates compared to 2.7 percent of the adult Canadian population while Aboriginal females composed 18.3 percent of the female population. In fact, Aboriginal males make up 18.7 percent of the total incarcerated population while Aboriginal females account for a staggering 31.4 percent.

Sources: Frances Henry and Carol Tator, *The Colour of Democracy: Racism in Canadian Society*, 2nd ed. (Toronto: Harcourt Brace, 2000), p. 147; John Sewell, "Same Old Diversionary Game," *Eye Weekly*, 7 November 2002, available <www.eye.net/eye/issue/issue_11.07.02/news/citystate.html>, accessed 30 March 2006; "Should Our Police Go on the Record?" *Toronto Star*, 15 February 2010, p. GT1; "Police Stop More Blacks, Ont. Study Finds," *CBC News*, 27 May 2005, available <www.cbc.ca/news/viewpoint/yourspace/racial_profiling.html>, accessed 2 May 2010; Correctional Services Canada, "Section 7: CSC Issues and Challenges," *Speakers Binder*, July 2007, available < www.csc-scc.gc.ca/text/pblct/sb-go/pdf/7-eng.pdf>, accessed 2 May 2010; Mark Lachmann, "Human Immunodeficiency Virus: Emerging Epidemic in Aboriginal People," *Canadian Family Physician*, October 2002, available <www.cfpc.ca/cfp/2002/Oct/vol48-oct-editorials-1.asp>, accessed 2 May 2010.

CRITICAL THINKING OUTSIDE THE BOX 4.5

What about Minority Experiences?

"When discussions of Canadian diversity begin and end with the ongoing struggles between English and French Canada, the accomplishments, experiences, desires, and troubles of minority groups are pushed to the margins of Canada's cultural discourse. As a result, consciously or unconsciously, politicians, professors, teachers, and community leaders erect another barrier to minority inclusion in society." Is this viewpoint true? If so, why? If not, why?

---

from others. So, for example, you don't hire members of minority groups for fear that other workers may "rebel" and not accept them.

The second type, **institutional discrimination**, occurs daily and limits the full participation of minority groups in the political, economic, and educational institutions in Canada. Some debate exists about the racist nature of this form of discrimination. The consensus seems to be that the intent is not racist but the outcomes certainly are. This is especially true of the people who work in these institutions—they are usually unaware of the outcomes of their institutional policies and practices.

An example of this form of discrimination is hiring practices. In 1989, racial minorities composed only 4 percent of the Metro Toronto Police Force.[17] These officers were highly concentrated in the ranks of cadets, constables, or in training; only three held the rank of inspector.[18] By 1998, gains by racial minorities were insignificant: only three held the rank of staff inspector, only three were senior police officers, and only 7.4 percent of all uniformed employees were racial minorities.[19] Yet, in 2001 only 15 percent (51 of 332) new recruits represented racial minorities; this number dropped to 11 percent

---

CRITICAL THINKING OUTSIDE THE BOX 4.6

Are jokes based on racial and ethnic stereotypes "just jokes," or do they reinforce negative attitudes and beliefs and in the process destroy self and group esteem? Why are these jokes so popular? Give at least three reasons and explain them.

---

in 2004.[20] This does not auger well for one of the most multicultural cities in the world where the racial minority population in 2017 is expected to surpass 50 percent.[21] The city of Montreal faces similar challenges. Between May 1999 and April 2000, only 42 of 278 new recruits of the Montreal police force were racial minorities.[22]

Another example of institutional discrimination includes textbook selection in schools, marketing, advertising, minimum levels of education for hiring, and cultural biases in aptitude or qualification tests. During the 1970s, the reading texts for the primary grades in Ontario schools were the *Mr. Mugs* series. The series centred entirely on a white, middle-class family. Small wonder that in 1971 a report on the study of 400 textbooks in Ontario, entitled *Teaching Prejudice*,[23] painted an unflattering picture of textbooks used in Ontario schools (see Have You Heard? 4.10).

Ethnocentrism

Ethnocentrism is the attitude whereby an individual views the world from the point of view of his or her own culture. There are two variations of ethnocentrism: (1) the assumption that what is true of your culture is true of other cultures and (2) the belief in the superiority of your culture in comparison with other cultures. The most common form of ethnocentrism is the first. It is embodied in statements that question why certain cultures do not behave or do things in the same manner as your own culture does. Statements of this nature would include variations of: "Why don't they do it like this [meaning, like we do]?" "That's a strange way of doing things." "They're weird." Ethnocentric attitudes definitely

---

HAVE YOU HEARD? 4.10

Teaching Prejudice in 1971

. . . .

Non-white groups were frequently referred to as bloodthirsty, primitive, cruel, and savage, in contrast with saintly and refined Europeans. With only a few passing exceptions, Aboriginals, blacks, and Asians who contributed to Canadian development in significant and positive ways were omitted from reference. In addition, major events in the sad history of Canada's mistreatment of minorities—the extinction of the Beothuk, the treatment of Japanese-Canadians during World War II, the abuse of Métis and other Aboriginal people throughout Canada—were barely touched upon, if at all.

Source: *Teaching Prejudice*, quoted by Daniel G. Hill, *Human Rights in Canada: A Focus on Racism* (Ottawa: Canadian Labour Congress, 1977), p. 15.

---

influence social interaction, and, furthermore, many ethnocentric attitudes and beliefs are held unconsciously. An example that vividly demonstrates how racism, prejudice, discrimination, and ethnocentrism affect social behaviour is the issue of racial profiling.

September 11 and the Rise of Racial Profiling

The Ontario Human Rights Commission defines **racial profiling** as any action undertaken for reasons of safety, security, or public protection, that relies on stereotypes about race, colour, ethnicity, ancestry, religion, or place of origin, or a combination of these, rather than on reasonable suspicion, to single out an individual for greater scrutiny or different treatment.[24] Racial profiling equates physical characteristics with particular negative behaviour. This makes the thinking that surrounds it prejudiced and the behaviour that it leads to discriminatory and racist.

According to the Ontario Human Rights Commission, racial profiling is considered widespread in the United States, United Kingdom, and Canada. Police and immigration officials have been singled out as the most consistent practitioners. The Ontario Court of Appeal found racial profiling exists in the province of Ontario when it upheld a lower court decision in the *Dee Brown* case.[25] The former Toronto Raptor had his drunk driving conviction overturned when the appeal court ruled the lower court failed to appreciate the fact that racial profiling can be a "subconscious factor" when exercising "discretionary power."[26] In recent years community policing has focused on combating and eliminating the use of racial profiling. In October 2002, on the basis of police arrest records, the *Toronto Star* published a series of articles dealing with racial profiling in the city; a similar article published in February 2010 dealing with statistics for 2003–2008 comes to similar conclusions.[27] (See Have You Heard? 4.11.) Some 10 000 cases between 1996 and early 2002 dealing with "simple" drug possession were analyzed, and they showed 63.8 percent of those arrested were designated as white while 23.6 percent were designated as black. Blacks were more likely than whites to experience being denied bail, held in jail overnight, and charged with driving offences (failing to update a driver's licence or driving without insurance). The use of racial profiling as an instrument of policing is not conducive to establishing good relations with different cultural groups. This is especially true in Toronto, Vancouver, and Montreal, Canada's largest and most diverse cities.

Since the terrorist attacks of 11 September 2001, racial minorities leaving Canada or returning to Canada have been subjected to racial profiling on a regular basis. During the same period, the United States pressured Canada to spend more on border/airport security and screening. American talk of "harmonizing" national regulations in these areas created a sense of uneasiness in many Canadians. These fears were legitimized and racial profiling received national attention when the case of Canadian citizen, Maher Arar, was made public. A 34-year-old, Syrian-born Canadian (in Canada since the age of 17) Arar was

---

HAVE YOU HEARD? 4.11

Racial/Ethnic Groups Are Not Monolithic Entities

No racial/ethnic group in Canadian society is a monolithic entity. There is huge variation within each group in every defining characteristic, especially income. Not all members of the dominant group earn the same or similar yearly income. Statistics Canada shows that earnings of Greeks, Portuguese, and other members of the "white" dominant group are far below British and French earnings. The same is true of racial minorities: the earnings of some groups rival and surpass those of the politically dominant group. Canadians of Japanese origin have average earnings that exceed those of most members of "white" ethnic groups—they are overrepresented in business, the arts, and universities considering their percentage of the Canadian population.

Sources: Statistics Canada, "Ethnocultural Portrait of Canada," Tables 15 and 18; Walter Johnson, *The Challenge of Diversity* (Montreal: Black Rose Books, 2006), p. 43.

---

vacationing in Tunisia in 2002 with his wife and children. While changing planes at New York's John F. Kennedy Airport, he was detained and questioned by American officials about supposed links to the terrorist group, al-Qaeda. Against his consent, he was flown to Jordan, then to Syria where he was jailed, beaten, tortured, and forced to sign a false confession. American officials knew details of Arar's life that could have only been provided by Canadian authorities. His case got so much attention in Canada that the federal government established a Commission of Inquiry on 28 January 2004 whose purpose was to investigate the role played by Canadian authorities in the affair, including the use of racial profiling. In January 2007, the Prime Minister and Head of the RCMP publically apologized to Maher Arar and his family, admitted he was tortured, publicly cleared him of any link to terrorism or terrorist organizations, and awarded him a financial settlement of just over $10 million.

THE MEANING AND IMPLICATIONS OF MULTICULTURALISM

Multiculturalism is one of the most used and most misunderstood words in the field of ethnicity. It has many definitions and explanations; some focus on the concept of culture, some on the ideology on which it is based, and still others refer to it in terms of government policy.

114

Multiculturalism is commonly associated with the idea of the "Canadian mosaic"—the view that different cultural groups come to Canada, retain their language and culture, and still become Canadian. It is not uncommon to consider yourself a hyphenated Canadian: French-Canadian, Greek-Canadian, Ukrainian-Canadian, Jamaican-Canadian, and the like. The concept of hyphenated citizenship is at odds with what has prevailed in the United States, where people are expected to abandon their heritage culture and assimilate into the dominant one. Thus, U.S. society is termed a "melting pot."

Perhaps one of the best attempts to define this complicated word is provided by Fleras and Elliott. They combine the cultural and ideological components with the reality of government policy for an all-inclusive definition. According to Fleras and Elliott, multiculturalism is "a doctrine that provides a political framework for the official promotion of cultural differences and social inequality as an integral component of social order."[28]

Multiculturalism is based on the ideology of **pluralism**, which is the belief that ethnic diversity and conflict remain central features of modern industrial societies and that ethnicity continues to be an essential aspect of individual identity and of group behaviour. The implications of the acceptance of pluralism are threefold. First, pluralism recognizes that cultural and racial conflict is inevitable and unavoidable; at best we can only hope to manage and mitigate this conflict as opposed to pursuing some fantasy of eliminating it. Second, pluralism recognizes that people hold on to their cultural heritage with much passion and commitment; therefore, to better manage cultural conflict, we must openly acknowledge and accept cultural differences. Third, pluralism is the belief that pursuing a multicultural policy is beneficial to Canadian unity, for it strengthens Canada and enriches the Canadian experience, especially in the fields of literature and the arts. In addition, pluralism lets Canadians know that they are part of a larger global community where we all must communicate and cooperate with each other if we are to survive.

Pluralism is the opposite of **assimilation**. Assimilation is the process by which immigrants adopt the language, values, norms, and worldview of the host culture. All immigrants experience some degree of assimilation. Immigrant cultures cannot totally insulate or isolate themselves from the influences of the host society—this is especially

CRITICAL THINKING OUTSIDE THE BOX 4.7

How do, or did, your high-school and postsecondary school texts compare with the standards of Teaching Prejudice? What about the newspaper you read, the news programs you watch, or the movies you see at the theatre and rent at the video store?

CRITICAL THINKING OUTSIDE THE BOX 4.8

In 2005, the Ontario government officially rejected formal calls from the Islamic community that Muslims be given the right to use the body of Shariah law for divorce proceedings for those Muslims who ask for it. In other words, some Muslims were asking for the right to forgo the application of Canadian divorce laws in favour of Muslim ones. Should the Islamic community be accommodated? If yes, why? If not, why? Give three reasons for each.

true of immigrant children, because children must attend school. The education system is perhaps the single most persuasive assimilationist force that immigrants are exposed to. While in school, immigrant children are socialized to the complete worldview of the host culture: its history, accomplishments, values, norms, customs, biases, and prejudices. Some assimilation on the part of immigrants is an inevitable fact of immigration and, thus, never completely avoidable.

The Purpose of Multiculturalism

The response of the federal government to the history of immigrant experiences with prejudice, racism, discrimination, stereotyping, and the like has been to officially recognize the racial and ethnic diversity in Canada and to support and encourage Canadians to learn more about the people of Canada and the country itself. For decades the federal government has encouraged the acceptance of different cultures through various policies and initiatives broadly labelled as "multicultural." In 1988, Parliament officially enacted the *Multiculturalism Act*, which pledges federal government assistance "in bringing about equal access and participation for all Canadians in the economic, social, cultural and political life of the nation."[29]

To achieve these goals the Act outlines ten specific objectives. The objectives have much consistency; we can narrow the list to three general goals:

1. The promotion of both official languages. The federal government declares that multiculturalism will be pursued within a bilingual, English and French, framework.

2. A commitment to help all members of cultural groups to overcome barriers that limit their full participation in Canadian society.

3. The promotion of understanding among different groups and the acceptance of cultural differences.

Multiculturalism is not the only government initiative designed to promote equality and equity. Other initiatives of the federal and provincial governments include the introduction of a *Charter of Rights and Freedoms* with the repatriated Constitution of 1982, human rights commissions, and employment equity programs (see Have You Heard? 4.12).

With these ideas in mind, Canadians need to come to a consensus concerning the purpose of multiculturalism. Too many people believe, with encouragement from the media, that multiculturalism is supposed to cure all problems in society that are a result of numerous different cultures living in close proximity to each other. Nothing could be further from the truth. The reality of multiculturalism, as government policy, is about the *management* of racial and ethnic conflict. It is not about the *elimination* of such conflict, which is unrealistic. Cultural conflict can be better managed if all groups have the same degree of cultural freedom. The more all groups feel they are free to live in and promote their culture; the more they will respect the culture of other members of society. This is one of the many ideas behind the September 2009 reintroduction of Afrocentric schooling in Toronto.

Black youth in Toronto have historically dropped out of school at rates higher than the Canadian average. The dropout rate for black youth is roughly 40 percent.[30] Black-

---

HAVE YOU HEARD? 4.12

Employment Equity and Toronto Firefighters

In the 1990s, more than 90 percent of the employees of the Toronto Fire Department were white males. To help the department better reflect the community they serve, the personnel committee of the Toronto City Council recommended that the department give preference to 13 qualified women and racial-minority candidates, ahead of white men who scored slightly higher during the qualification process. The chief of the department protested vigorously even though the 13 candidates were drawn from a total pool of 140 fully qualified candidates selected from 4000 applicants; all candidates had passed the physical, health, and aptitude tests. The motion to hire these candidates was defeated by city council. The Ontario Human Rights Commission filed a complaint, claiming that the Toronto firefighters' union was blocking the proposal and creating a "poisoned work environment."

Source: Frances Henry and Carol Tator, *The Colour of Democracy: Racism in Canadian Society,* 2nd ed. (Toronto: Harcourt Brace, 2000), p. 364.

CRITICAL THINKING OUTSIDE THE BOX 4.9

Salvation or Segregation?

The Africentric Alternative School successfully opened in September 2009. Classroom spaces filled immediately and a waiting list had to be put in place. This was not the first attempt at establishing Africentric schooling. The first such public school, D. B. Hood, opened in 1986 in the former city of York and was recognized as the first Afrocentric school in Canada. Continuous opposition to the school and the founding principles responsible for its creation eventually resulted in the closing of the school before its third anniversary. Most of the criticism revolved around the notion of racial segregation—the separation of people based on physical features, especially skin colour.

Source: Andrew Wallace, "A Special Report," *This Magazine*, January/February 2009. Visit the school website for more details <www.tdsb.on.ca/SchoolWeb/_site/AboutSchool.asp?sitei d=10423&menuid=23028&schno=3949>.

focused schooling, with the appropriate monetary and physical resources, administered and taught by qualified educators, where curriculum and narratives reflect the long, deep, and rich history of the black experience in Canada, is believed to be the key to reverse this alarming fact.[31] In May 2008, the Toronto District School Board approved a recommendation to establish an Afrocentric Alternative School for Junior Kindergarten to Grade 5 with the plan to expand to Grade 8 in future years. The Africentric Alternative School (JK–5) opened in September 2009 at Sheppard Public School (see Critical Thinking Outside the Box 4.9) The Toronto District School Board also asked for a feasibility study for a similar school at the secondary level.

THE TYRANNY OF MULTICULTURALISM OR MULTICULTURAL TYRANNY?

The Tyranny of Multiculturalism: The Experience of Minority Groups

If language is the key to the survival of culture, why does Canada only guarantee the use of two official languages? Language is the most important element of culture. Without it, there is no culture. It provides the symbols, tools, perceptions, and definitions for each and every culture. In fact, language provides worldviews that make cultures distinct. In all these ways, language provides the foundation for identity. Without guaranteeing language, multiculturalism is reduced to a "feel-good" policy designed to give people a false sense of cultural security in a country that officially and loudly professes a commitment to cultural acceptance but really prohibits and limits important cultural behaviours on a daily basis.

Official multiculturalism within a "bilingual framework" is problematic in many ways. As Carl James and others[32] point out, immigrant and minority full participation in society is limited without knowledge of the English and/or French languages. Minority ethnic groups are promised government help to "overcome barriers that limit their full participation in Canadian society" (the second purpose of multicultural policy—see goal 2 on page 116). Again, as James points out, at the same time, the government openly declares that "there is no official culture, nor does any ethnic group take precedence over any other," while publicly acknowledging "the undisputable role played by Canadians of French and British origins in 1867, and long before Confederation."[33] The dominance of the two dominant groups is strengthened by institutionalizing their worldviews. The English and French languages dominate the operation of government, the bureaucracy, and the most influential assimilating institution of all, public schools. With political, economic, and social dominance, the pressures on minority groups to conform are inescapable. Structural problems with the unequal distribution of power cannot be corrected with multicultural solutions.[34] In fact, official multiculturalism marginalizes minorities by blocking their access to power and resources.[35] The official policy of multiculturalism is really "monoculturalism in disguise."[36] As such, minority groups can realistically regard official multiculturalism as a tyrannical entity intent on destroying their various cultures.

Multicultural Tyranny: Majority Group Experiences

Does official multiculturalism help or hinder the acceptance of cultural diversity? There is a huge difference between cultural diversity and multiculturalism. As an idea, diversity means "difference" and refers to the different languages, religions, food, dress, sport, social customs, and leisure activities that make Canadians different from each other. Accepting the idea of diversity means accepting the fact that people are different. Generally, this is not regarded as a problem. Multiculturalism as official policy, however, means accepting all cultures as equal. This is simply not true in Canada at the beginning of the 21st century. The policy gives minority groups the illusion of being a part of Canadian society yet many of their norms, customs, and folkways are treated with contempt. Countless attitudes and behaviours that various minority groups have brought and continue to bring to Canada are deemed unacceptable to the vast majority of Canadians and in some cases, illegal (see Critical Thinking Outside the Box 4.10). In fact, when real cultural differences challenge

CRITICAL THINKING OUTSIDE THE BOX 4.10

Official Multiculturalism or Official Hypocrisy?

East African immigrants principally from Somalia and Sudan practise female circumcision. This procedure involves the removal of some, or in extreme cases all, of the female genitalia. Some negatively refer to this process as "female genital mutilation." The Canadian government has officially prohibited this practice, but it continues to allow male circumcision. Why is it permissible to eat cows, pigs, and chickens, but not dogs? How can we justify one set of practices and criminalize others? Can you think of other double standards?

In February 2010 the National Assembly in Quebec introduced Bill 94. It demands that women wearing the Niqab or Burkha must lift their veils and reveal their faces to receive provincial government services including education. The ban also applies to public employees, education and health workers. Is this 'reasonable accommodation'?

established Canadian traditions and Canadian law itself, the line between right and wrong becomes blurred. Most Canadians do not believe multiculturalism means the acceptance of cultural differences that challenge established norms, mores, and laws. Yet many immigrants believe that it does. Canadians are simply not prepared to accept polygamy, female circumcision, eating dogs, and using an assortment of hallucinogenic drugs. In some cultures, these behaviours are equally as acceptable as monogamy, male circumcision, eating cows, and drinking alcohol are in Canadian culture. Yet the former set of behaviours is illegal and the latter is not. Once some cultural behaviours are criminalized, the visible and "safe" differences of dress, music, faith, leisure activities, and cultural festivals are the ones that remain. In the end, individual tolerance of visibly mundane cultural behaviours is equated with societal acceptance of "multiculturalism."

There is a difference between multiculturalism as official government policy and multiculturalism as reality. Accepting our "hyphenated" labels (e.g., Jamaican-Canadian, Polish-Canadian, Philippino-Canadian) tends to take focus away from our shared "Canadian-ness" and highlight our minority status.[37] As Neil Bissoondath has pointed out, official multiculturalism stymies what the designers of the policy were looking to encourage, the acceptance of different people into Canadian society and the Canadian way of life. In fact, it has aggressively encouraged immigrants to demand that Canada adopt their laws, customs, mores, folkways, and worldviews and not the other way around.[38] The recent attempts by Muslims in Ontario to have Shariah law (dealing with divorce) implemented alongside established secular law and the continued debate over female circumcision are two such examples. The ongoing debates dealing with use of religious dress/symbols (e.g., Turban, Hijab, Niqab, and Kirpan) in everyday life continue to be contentious. Many Canadians believe official multiculturalism is at the root of continued minority demands for cultural and religious accommodation in the areas of law, language, dress, and attitudes. They view these neverending demands as a form of multicultural tyranny (see Have You Heard? 4.13). In fact, it is not uncommon to hear emphatic variations of the phrase, "If that's what they want, they can go back to where they came from—this is Canada!"

Quebec and Multiculturalism

Most provinces have accepted the principles of multiculturalism. In 1974, Saskatchewan was the first province to accept the principles of multiculturalism as a basis for defining majority–minority relations. Since 1974, most of the remaining provinces have done the same. Officially Quebec is designated as a multicultural province. For a variety of reasons, however, federal multiculturalism is officially rejected. The centre of this rejection deals with the belief that the federal policy challenges Québécois authority to determine the direction of majority–minority relations in their own province. In short, federal multiculturalism does the following: it contravenes Quebec's special status as one of the founder or charter members of Canada; it undermines Quebec's right to manage its own diversity

---

HAVE YOU HEARD? 4.13

Multicultural Tyranny

. . . .

In 1993, a Globe and Mail article suggested hockey examples used in school textbooks be removed since new immigrants are unaccustomed to the game. A doctoral student at the Ontario Institute for Studies in Education (OISE), Pushpa Seevaratnam, cited the case of a 10-year-old Sri Lankan student who couldn't conclude how long it would take a Bobby Hull slapshot travelling at 52.9 metres per second to travel 25 metres. Seevaratnam referred to the example as "ethnocentric." Does this situation meet the criteria for being "ethnocentric"?

Source: Daniel Stoffman, *Who Gets In? What's Wrong with Canada's Immigration Program and How to Fix It* (Toronto: Macfarlane Walter and Ross, 2002), p. 147.

---

as it sees fit; and finally, it violates the notion that Canadian federalism was constructed on a bicultural foundation.[39]

Employment Equity in a Multicultural Society

In 1986 the federal government introduced the *Employment Equity Act*. It affects all employees of the federal government and federally regulated industries. The purpose of the *Act* is to promote the equality of opportunity for four groups of workers: racial minorities, Native Peoples, women, and people with disabilities. The *Act* is based on the reality that these groups have historically been discriminated against in the labour market. Section 15.2 of the *Charter of Rights and Freedoms* protects employment equity.

Employment equity programs are considered by many to be the most effective way of reversing at least a century of discriminatory hiring practices that favoured white males. The dominant group has vigorously opposed such programs. Some of the more popular reasons cited for resisting such programs include that equity programs are reverse discrimination, that they ignore the merit principle, and that they ignore the belief that fairness is best achieved by treating everyone the same[40] (see Have You Heard? 4.12). Yet, as Henry and Tator point out, each of these reasons cannot stand up to critical scrutiny.[41] First, are such programs really reverse discrimination or urgently necessary to correct at least a century of preferential treatment of the dominant group, especially white males? Are white males the *only* qualified applicants? Second, do they really ignore the merit principle or simply choose to disregard personal characteristics that do not affect job performance, such as cultural background, skin colour, gender, and family/friendship networks? Third, does treating everyone fairly translate into equal treatment? Or does ignoring and refusing to accommodate ultimately lead to discrimination?[42]

Although employment equity programs are important, it is highly unlikely that they can achieve their goals without the implementation of other measures, such as institutions making individuals accountable for discriminatory and racist behaviour; sanctioning those who behave in unacceptable ways; and being committed to devoting significant resources to combating discrimination and racism even in difficult economic times.[43]

CONCLUSION

Race and ethnicity are powerful determinants of identity in Canadian society, and it is important to understand the nature and depths of the problems associated with developing stable relations in a society characterized by racial and ethnic difference. The nature and composition of Canada is changing. New immigrants are arriving from the developing world, especially from Asia and the Indian subcontinent. Like those who came between 1991 and 2001, they settle primarily in the urban areas of Ontario, Quebec, Alberta, and British Columbia. There is no evidence to suggest this trend will change anytime soon.

Canada is not the same country today that it was fifty years ago—nor will it be the same fifty years from now. The challenge is to ensure that the social institutions that serve our society reflect the people they serve. This must be done in a manner that accepts the cultural, linguistic, and racial diversity of all Canadians—it will be difficult. Prejudice, racism, and discrimination seem to be part of every society, and it may be naive to think that we can eliminate them. We must, however, work to manage them in a productive manner so that all Canadians can develop a positive self-image and a more complete understanding of our country.

CHAPTER SUMMARY

It is almost impossible to overstate the importance of race and ethnic relations in Canada. An analysis of Canadian immigration history is crucial for a complete understanding of Canadian society and to destroy prevalent myths. Canada has never been just a purely British and French, white society—Aboriginal Peoples were here, and other people arrived and continue to come from all over the world. In the early 19th century this included black slaves and in later decades Chinese and Japanese people as well. Immigrants from the developing, non-white world continue to arrive in Canada in large numbers—the Canadian mosaic is becoming ever more colourful.

Race and ethnicity are important components of individual and group identity. Meanwhile, prejudice, racism, stereotyping, ethnocentrism, and discrimination continue to have a strong negative impact on social interaction. Therefore, a policy of official multiculturalism has been enacted to help manage social interaction in Canada.

KEY TERMS

assimilation, p. 115

discrimination, p. 109

ethnic groups, p. 104

ethnocentrism, p. 112

individual discrimination, p. 109

institutional discrimination, p. 111

multiculturalism, p. 114

Multiculturalism Act, p. 116

pluralism, p. 115

prejudice, p. 107

race, p. 104

racial profiling, p. 113

racism, p. 109

stereotypes, p. 108

DISCUSSION QUESTIONS

1. What stage of immigration is known as "the mightiest movement of people" in modern history? What accounted for this mass movement of people?
2. What is the significance of the fifth stage (1975 to the present) of Canadian immigration history?
3. Define prejudice and discrimination. What is the difference between them?
4. What do we mean by race and ethnicity? Why are these ideas so important to Canadians? Provide some examples.
5. How does conflict theory account for the existence of racism and discrimination?
6. How would structural–functionalism interpret Canada's policy of multiculturalism?
7. Provide three criticisms of official multiculturalism. Give an example for each.
8. Describe what is meant by the term *racial profiling*? Why is racial profiling always detrimental to community cohesiveness?

NOTES

1. "Report of the Royal Commission on Bilingualism and Biculturalism, Book IV, The Contributions of Other Ethnic Groups," in Howard Palmer, ed., *Immigration and the Rise of Multiculturalism* (Toronto: Copp Clark, 1975), pp. 1–16. Unless otherwise noted, all statistics and examples of historical events are drawn from these pages.
2. Adrienne Shadd, "Institutionalized Racism and Canadian History: Notes of a Black Canadian," in Carl E. James, ed., *Seeing Ourselves: Exploring Race, Ethnicity and Culture*, 3rd ed. (Toronto: TEP, 2003), pp. 165–68.
3. Ibid.
4. Ninette Kelly and Michael Trebilcock, *The Making of the Mosaic: A History of Canadian Immigration Policy* (Toronto: UTP, 1998), p. 36.
5. Daniel G. Hill, *Human Rights in Canada: A Focus on Racism* (Ottawa: Canadian Labour Congress, 1977), p. 10.
6. Harry Hiller, *Canadian Society: A Macro Analysis* (Toronto: Prentice Hall, 2000), p. 174.
7. Statistics Canada, "1996 Census: Immigration and Citizenship," *The Daily*, 4 November 1997, available <www.statscan.ca/Daily/English/971104/d971104.htm>, accessed 5 May 2010.
8. Statistics Canada, "Canada's Ethnocultural Mosaic, 2006 Census," *Census Year 2006*, Catalogue No. 97-562-X, p. 12.
9. Statistics Canada, "Canada's Ethnocultural Mosaic, 2006 Census," *Census Year 2006*, Catalogue No. 97-562-X, p. 12.
10. Statistics Canada, 2005, *Population Projections of Visible Minority Groups, Canada, Provinces, and Regions, 2001–2017*, Catalogue No. 91-541-XIE, in Ibid., p. 12.
11. Peter Berger and Brigitte Berger, *Sociology: A Biographical Approach* (New York: Basic Books, 1971), p. 75.
12. Carl E. James, *Seeing Ourselves: Exploring Race, Ethnicity and Culture*, 3rd ed. (Toronto: TEP, 2003), pp. 41–42.

13. Ibid., p. 42.
14. P. Essed, *Everyday Racism: Reports from Women of Two Cultures* (Claremont, CA: Hunter House, 1990).
15. James, op. cit., pp. 134–135.
16. Hill, op. cit., p. 13.
17. Frances Henry and Carol Tator, *The Colour of Democracy: Racism in Canadian Society*, 2nd ed. (Toronto: Harcourt Brace, 2000), p. 105.
18. Ibid.
19. Ibid.
20. Walter Johnson, *The Challenge of Diversity* (Montreal: Black Rose Books, 2006), p. 43.
21. Heisz, op. cit., p. 14.
22. Johnson, op. cit., p. 90.
23. Hill, op. cit., p. 13.
24. Ontario Human Rights Commission, *Paying the Price: The Human Cost of Racial Profiling*, Inquiry Report 2004, p. 6. See also Charles C. Smith, "Crisis, Conflict and Accountability: The Impact and Implications of Police Racial Profiling" (Toronto: African Canadian Community Coalition on Racial Profiling, March 2004), and Tom Wise, "Racial Profiling and Its Apologists," *Z Magazine*, March 2002.
25. Johnson, op. cit., p. 91.
26. Ibid., p. 87.
27. James, op. cit., p. 150; "Should Our Police Go on the Record?" *Toronto Star*, 15 February 2010, p. GT1.
28. Augie Fleras and Jean Leonard Elliott, *Multiculturalism in Canada: The Challenge of Diversity* (Scarborough: Nelson, 1992), p. 272.
29. *The Multiculturalism Act*, 21 July 1988.
30. Andrew Wallace, "A Special Report," *This Magazine*, January/February 2009.
31. Ibid.
32. James, op. cit., p. 210.
33. Ibid.
34. Augie Fleras and Jean Leonard Elliot, *Engaging Diversity: Multiculturalism in Canada* (Scarborough: Nelson, 2002), p. 100.
35. Ibid.
36. Ibid., p. 48.
37. Ibid., p. 100.
38. Neil Bissoondath, *Selling Illusions: The Cult of Multiculturalism in Canada* (Markham, ON: Penguin Books, 2003), and Daniel Stoffman, *Who Gets In? What's Wrong with Canada's Immigration Program and How to Fix It* (Toronto: Macfarlane Walter and Ross, 2002).
39. Fleras and Elliot (2002), op. cit., p. 76.
40. Henry and Tator, op. cit., pp. 364–65.
41. Ibid., pp. 364–66.
42. R. Abella, *Report of the Commission on Equality in Employment* (Ottawa: Supply and Services Canada, 1984), p. 3.
43. Henry and Tator, op. cit., pp. 366–75. An excellent discussion.

CHAPTER 5

Aboriginal Peoples

John Steckley

Several years ago in a sociology class on social problems, I recall wondering if anyone else was poor, because the professor repeatedly referred to Native people as statistical examples of poverty. . . . Not for one moment would I make light of the ugly effects of poverty. But if classroom groups must talk about Indians and poverty, then they must also point out the ways in which Native people are operating on this cancer. To be sure, the operations are always struggles and sometimes failures, but each new operation is faced with more experience, more skill, more confidence and more success.

—Métis writer Emma LaRoque, "Three Conventional
Approaches to Native People"

Objectives

. . . .

After reading this chapter, you should be able to

- understand better the diversity of Canadian Native culture

- understand the historical background and development of Native issues and contemporary circumstances

- understand the extent to which Natives are in different legal circumstances than are other Canadians

- understand the negative impact on Natives of official policies in the areas of education, religion, and the justice system

- understand some of the strengths and challenges of a Native-run justice system

INTRODUCTION

Knowing about Aboriginal Canadian people takes years. There is much to learn, so little of which can be presented in a short chapter. First, you need to appreciate the incredible length of time that Aboriginal people have been in Canada. Second, you need to know that not all Aboriginal people are the same, be that in terms of traditions and such cultural features as language, housing, and food preferences, or in other ways. There are rich Aboriginal people and poor ones. There are Aboriginal alcoholics, but also those who have never had a drink or who just have a couple of beers "with the guys," like most other Canadians. Some Aboriginal people adhere to traditional religious ways, and others make Christianity a "traditional" Aboriginal belief system. There are Aboriginal hunters and trappers, and computer programmers, too.

Much, however, is held in common. Aboriginal people share a genetic heritage, an identity, and a complex set of legal regulations that both serve and restrict them. Neither abolishing those laws—basically one law, the **Indian Act**—nor keeping them as they are will create solutions. Redefining the *Act* is the only answer, but it is difficult. The question is not one of giving Aboriginal people a separate status, but of taking the separate status that now exists and changing it for the good of Aboriginal people—and for all Canadians.

BEGINNINGS: IT ALL STARTED LONG AGO

No one knows precisely how long Aboriginal people have been in Canada. Aboriginal traditions tell us that the Creator placed them here and that they lived nowhere else before. Anthropologists say that the people came from Asia. Current speculations, based on archaeology, biological anthropology (especially the study of DNA, dental patterns, and skull shapes), and linguistics speak of four waves of people. The first (and most controversial) wave may have come from Southeast Asia, taking boats up the Asian coast and down the west coast of the Americas. The next and main wave involved "just about everybody." They walked across what is now the Bering Strait (width 90 kilometres) on a 1600-kilometre north-to-south land bridge formed during the last Ice Age (12 to 15 thousand years ago), when the water level went down with the increase in ice. The third wave may have been of speakers of Athabaskan languages. The fourth is the Inuit.

Aboriginal traditions often tell a different story, one that speaks about the people being here from the beginning to human history. However, Natives and anthropologists can agree that Aboriginal people are the First Nations of Canada.

What date can we use? The North American archaeological site with the best evidence for early occupation is the Meadowcroft Rockshelter in Pennsylvania.[1] Two levels at this site have very early claims to human occupation: 20 000 and 15 000 years ago.

If we take the second date as valid, we can say that Aboriginal people came to Canada by at least 15 000 years ago. The Vikings came for a short stay in Newfoundland about 1000 years ago. This means roughly 93.3 percent of Canadian history is Aboriginal history before Europeans came. In terms of the analogy of a day of history, Aboriginal people came here at 12:00 midnight, and Europeans didn't even visit here until slightly after 10:30 the next night.

The great length of time that Aboriginal people have been here means that they have very deep roots in this country. From these roots have grown their sense of the sacredness of the land, their feeling of being its primary caretakers.

THEORY

What is the place of Aboriginal people in Canadian history since contact? This question can be answered from several different theoretical positions. The structural–functionalist position looks just at how Aboriginal people helped this country develop. During the first two centuries of postcontact history (the 17th and 18th centuries), the fur trade was Canada's biggest industry. Aboriginal people played a key role as both suppliers and intermediaries. Furthermore, the newcomers needed to learn how to survive here. Aboriginal people enabled them to travel by providing canoes, dog sleds, kayaks, snowshoes, toboggans, and information for maps. Aboriginal people taught the newcomers how to feed themselves, instructing them in how to make maple syrup and pemmican and how to grow Native crops that were new to Europeans—corn, beans, squash, and sunflowers—and by showing which berries and other wild foods were edible. In the wars of the 17th and 18th centuries, Aboriginal allies helped to ensure that whoever governed Canada, first the French and then the British, could stave off the forces from what is now the United States. In the War of 1812, the role of Aboriginal nations such as the Mohawk, Ojibwa, and Wyandot was critical to the survival of the colony that was to become Canada. In the 20th century, in both world wars, Aboriginal people were proportionately among the highest groups represented in our armed forces, despite the fact that they were not conscripted.

To stop here would be to paint too rosy a picture of Native/newcomer interaction. A conflict theory approach would emphasize that although the role of Natives in the fur trade often started between equals, exploitation of the Natives eventually developed, particularly with the introduction of alcohol in the trade. At the Hudson's Bay Company (HBC) trading post of York Factory, on the west side of Hudson Bay, the amount of rum traded per year hit a peak of 3928 litres by 1753. Between 1720 and 1774, the HBC traded 98 346 litres of rum from that post alone. Conflict theorists would denounce the clear manipulation of the treaties and other "legal" but morally questionable means by which Natives were removed from their lands, the cultural prejudice that led to the banning of traditional ceremonies from late in the 19th century until 1951, and the destructive effects of the residential schools (see "Native Education").

DIVERSITY: THE MANY TONGUES OF NATIVE CULTURES

At the time of first contact with Europeans, Aboriginal cultures in Canada were very diverse. Language illustrates this diversity well. There is no single 'Indian language.' Today roughly fifty Native languages still have speakers, although this number is decreasing. Native languages in Canada have a greater diversity than do languages long spoken in Europe: Canadian Native languages form eleven separate groups; eight are **language families** or groupings of related languages, and three are **language isolates**, with no known relatives. Europe has only two language families (Indo-European and Finno-Ugric) and one language isolate (Basque).

The largest language family is Algonquian, with languages in every province. Ojibwa has thousands of speakers from Quebec to British Columbia. Cree, from which Saskatchewan ("fast-flowing water") and Manitoba ("spirit strait") take their names, likewise has thousands of speakers, living from Quebec to Alberta. The other languages are more regionally restricted, with Mi'kmaq spoken in the Atlantic provinces and Quebec ("It narrows" in Mi'kmaq), Maliseet in New Brunswick, Innu (Montagnais and Naskapi) in Labrador and Quebec, Abenaki in Quebec, Delaware in Ontario, and Blackfoot (Blackfoot, Blood, and Peigan) in Alberta.

Athabaskan languages are found in the four western provinces, the Northwest Territories and Yukon Territory; they include Beaver, Carrier, Chilcotin, Chipewyan, Dogrib, Han, Hare, Kaska, Gwich'in, Sarcee, Sekani, Slavey, Tagish (now extinct), Tahltan, and Tutchone.

The Eskimo-Aleut family, which includes the various distinctive dialects of Inuktitut in Canada, is found in all three territories, and in Labrador and Quebec.

The Iroquoian family, whose languages gave Canada its name (meaning "village" in the extinct language of St. Lawrence Iroquoian), as well as the names for Ontario ("It is a large lake" in Huron) and Toronto ("poles in water" in Mohawk) comprises the languages of the six nations of the Iroquois Confederacy (Mohawk, Oneida, Onondaga, Cayuga, Seneca, and Tuscarora), which are spoken in Ontario and Quebec.

The Siouan family includes two languages spoken in the Prairies, Nakota or Assiniboine and Dakota.

British Columbia has the greatest Native language diversity in Canada. Found in that province, but no other, are the Salishan languages (Bella Coola, Comox, Halkomelem, Lillooet, Okanagan, Pentlatch, Sechelt, Semiahmo, Shuswap, Squamish, Straits, and

Thompson), the Wakashan languages (Haisla, Heiltsuk, Kwakwala, Nitinat, and Nootka), the two Tsimshian languages, and language isolates Haida, Kutenai, and Tlingit (which is spoken also in Yukon).

DEMOGRAPHICS

Historical Picture

The number of Native people in Canada at the time of first contact is estimated to have been between 500 000 and 2 000 000. The areas of greatest population were where Canada's three largest cities of Vancouver, Toronto, and Montreal are now. The Pacific coast, with its rich forests and marine resources of fish, seals, sea otters, shellfish, and whales, had the largest groups, perhaps totalling some 200 000 people in British Columbia. Groups in southern Ontario and the area along the St. Lawrence River in Quebec, where Native people grew crops, fished, and hunted deer, were next-largest, numbering probably more than 60 000.

Why, then, did so many 18th- and 19th-century European writers refer to the great open "empty" lands of Canada? Much of the country had been emptied by disease. Europeans who came to Canada carried with them, unknowingly, diseases they had endured for centuries. Natives had not experienced these afflictions before. Their bodies had not built up immunities with which to combat them. Native people became easy victims of smallpox, influenza, scarlet fever, whooping cough, typhus, measles, and tuberculosis. With deadly efficient regularity, most of a Native nation would die within a few years of first contact with Europeans.

The greatest killer was smallpox. It swept west gradually, but relentlessly, killing in high numbers. In the 1630s it hit the Montagnais, Algonquin, and Huron. The Huron lost perhaps two-thirds of their population in just four years. During the 1770s, Prairie peoples were mowed down like so much wheat. In 1776–77 the victims included the Cree and the Assiniboine. Explorer Simon Hearne claimed in 1781 that 90 percent of the Chipewyan had fallen prey. In 1862–64 smallpox found British Columbia. Coastal groups such as the Tsimshian, and interior peoples such as the Chilcotin, suffered high casualties. In 1870 smallpox returned to the Prairies and killed as many as 3500 Natives.

The Contemporary Picture

How many Native people are in Canada today? This is difficult to determine. There are registered Indians, Inuit, and Métis. Who is "Indian" and who is not is a complicated legal matter. The *Indian Act* of 1876 enshrined a sexist definition by stating that an "Indian" was any man of "Indian blood" reputed to belong to a particular band, any child of such a man, or any woman who is or was married to such a man. Under this *Act*, a man would keep his status, no matter whom he married; a woman, however, would lose her status if she married someone not legally an Indian. Her children would share that fate. Adding insult to injury, a white woman who married an Indian man would gain Indian status. This discriminatory law was in force until 1985.

In 1881 there were 108 547 "status Indians." By 1984, before the change in the *Indian Act*, this number had risen to roughly 349 000. **Bill C-31** was passed in 1985, enabling people who had lost their Indian status through marriage or through the marriage of their mother to apply to be reinstated. In the 2006 Census, 1 172 790 identified themselves as Aboriginal (which includes First Nations, Inuit, and Métis). See Have You Heard? 5.1.

CRITICAL THINKING OUTSIDE THE BOX 5.1

There has been a "sudden rise" in the number of registered Indians over the past twenty-five years. Why is this?

HAVE YOU HEARD? 5.1

Bill C-31 Double Standard

In Bonita Lawrence's recent study of people of mixed heritage living in Toronto, she noted a double standard held by the people she studied concerning Bill C-31 Indians. They generally believed that individual intent for asking for band membership was more important than collective entitlement:

It is clear that the forced estrangement of so many children from their mothers' home communities has been individualized in the minds of most Native community members. . . . While most of the participants expressed in an abstract manner that it was an injustice not to reinstate people to their bands, most of them implied that Bill C-31 Indians must demonstrate the *right* reasons for wanting reinstatement (selfless devotion to community) rather than the *wrong* reason (looking for education funding or other financial benefits from the band). . . . A selfless desire to put the wishes of the community before one's own educational or other needs is, in fact, demanded of nobody but individuals seeking reinstatement after Bill C-31.[2]

"**Registered Indian**" (the term that replaced "status") cards are one reason that people have applied to regain Indian status. Perhaps you have worked at a store when someone presented you with an "Indian card," which meant that the person did not have to pay provincial or federal taxes on what you were selling. This is because the land most Aboriginal people live on is technically "outside the province," federal land. Some non-Natives resent this, believing that Aboriginal people are receiving special privileges. The peoples' response to this is that they have prepaid these taxes many times over with the treaties that cost them their lands.

Inuit

The Inuit did not call themselves "Eskimo." That is an Algonquian term, referring to eating food (probably fat and meat) raw. Their being called "Eskimo" is rather like French people being called "frogs," or Germans "sausage-eaters." It lacks respect. "Inuit" is a plural noun in the Inuktitut language, and literally means "men." The singular is Inuk. There is no such word as "Inuits." Inuit differ from "Indians" in being in Canada for a shorter time, less than 10 000 years. Culturally, the Inuit developed items, such as the kayak and the igloo, unlike anything found among other Native people in Canada.

Not until 1939, when Canada asserted territorial claims in the Arctic, did the federal government take official responsibility for the Inuit. Each Inuk was given a metal disk with a number that was used as a token of their status. Today, about 60 percent of Inuit have disk numbers.

Since "joining Canada," much has happened that has been harmful to the Inuit. Southerners involved with various projects in the Arctic in the 1940s and early 1950s killed off sufficient caribou to make the Inuit who lived off that animal disappear as a people. In 1953 the federal government forced the people of Inukjuak (Port Harrison) in northern Quebec to move some 3200 kilometres north to uninhabited Ellesmere Island. Ottawa claimed that this was for the betterment of the people, as local natural resources were being depleted and Ellesmere Island was untouched. A darker interpretation is that this forced move was made primarily to guarantee Canadian rights to that contested territory, and that the government officials did not know or care that the kinds of resources in the two areas were very different. In the 1950s the Inuit had the highest rate of tuberculosis in the world.

Inuit status has taken on a new nature for some since the territory of Nunavut ("our land") came into being on 1 April 1999 in the eastern two-thirds of the Northwest Territories. More than 80 percent of Nunavut's population of almost 30 000 is Inuit. They own 18 percent of the land (almost all the rest being Crown land), have subsurface rights to oil, gas, and other minerals for about 2 percent of Nunavut, and will receive royalties from the extraction of those minerals from the rest of the territory. They do not require a licence to hunt or fish to meet their basic needs.

Métis

The term **Métis** is used in two ways. When written with a lowercase m, it typically refers to anyone of mixed genetic heritage: part Native and part white. When written with an uppercase M, it usually refers to the descendants of French fur traders and Cree women. Beginning in the late 18th century, these latter, the Métis, developed a culture that effectively combined European and Native features. They also developed the Michif language, which has nouns that are usually French and verbs that are usually Cree. They lived for part of the year in river-lot farms in the Winnipeg area, but their main annual activity was the buffalo hunt. From the hunt came pemmican, a key Métis contribution to the fur trade. It supplied much-needed, well-preserved food for the men who paddled the canoes and carried the huge loads transported in the fur trade.

The Métis came to think of themselves as a nation. They had earned this sense through battle, and in legal struggle with the Hudson's Bay Company (HBC). "The Bay" owned most of the Prairies and about half of present-day Canada, through a 1670 charter given by English King Charles II, who little knew what he was signing away. Charles II also granted the HBC a trading monopoly. In 1811, a senior HBC official placed settlers in the middle of Métis territory, not concerned that people already lived there. In 1814 the governor of these settlers declared that the Métis could not trade in pemmican, as the HBC had a monopoly. This led in 1816 to a struggle at Seven Oaks. The resulting Métis victory became a symbol of their nationhood, celebrated in song.

In 1849 the Métis apparently beat the HBC again. Pierre-Guillaume Sayer, charged with illicitly trafficking in furs, was released, even though he had been convicted. It is thought that the judge had been influenced by the armed presence of two to three hundred Métis outside the courtroom.

In 1867 the HBC started negotiating with Canada to sell its land, and the federal government moved to set up a colony in Manitoba. Métis rights to the land were not considered. The Métis took action. Led by 25-year-old, college-educated Louis Riel, the Métis achieved a military takeover in 1869 and set up an independent government to negotiate with Ottawa. Initially, things went well for them.

The *Manitoba Act* of 1870 established the province of that name with a legal recognition of Métis rights. This took the form of "scrip," a certificate declaring that the bearer could receive payment in land, cash, or goods. But government officials and land speculators ensured that the Métis were "legally" cheated—the laws changed eleven times in twelve years—of their land. Only a few remained. Most Métis moved west. But in 1885, with their rights ignored again, and again led by Louis Riel, the Métis set up an independent government in Saskatchewan. They were defeated by federal Canadian forces. Riel was hanged for "treason."

During the 1930s, Alberta Métis pushed for the creation of communal settlements similar to reserves. In the words of Métis leader Adrian Hope: "We've had enough of negotiable scrip . . . to buy booze. . . . What we are asking for is land we cannot sell, cannot mortgage, but land to which we can belong."[3] In 1938 eleven Métis "colonies" were formed (eight still exist). Unfortunately, the Alberta government controlled them. The Métis could only advise or recommend. From 1969 to the present, the colony Métis have been engaged in a legal fight for two basic rights:

1. They want the colony to have the political power of a municipality. For the most part, that was granted during the 1980s.

2. They want more say concerning economic development. In this they have not been so successful.

The colony Métis have tried to obtain royalty payments for gas and oil extracted from their land, but this has been a bitter and unrewarding fight. Any economic plans that they make are still subject to provincial veto. Beyond the colonies, there are the Métis National Council and provincial organizations in Ontario and in the Prairie provinces; these suffer from difficulties of legal definition and lack of recognition. See Have You Heard? 5.2.

HAVE YOU HEARD? 5.2

The Powley Case: Métis Hunting Rights

In 1993, Steve Powley and his son killed a bull moose in the area of Sault Ste. Marie, in northwest Ontario, without a provincial licence. They were charged under the Ontario Game and Fish Act with unlawfully hunting and possessing a moose. Their defence was that Powley was Métis, and that hunting for food was his Aboriginal right. On 23 September 2003 a unanimous decision of the Supreme Court of Canada upheld his right to hunt for food. It established what has been called the **Powley test** for Métis hunting rights. The test has ten main components:

1. Characterization of the Right
The right involved is the right to hunt for food (not sale) in designated territories, not confined by provincially set hunting season or licence.

2. Identification of the Historic Rights-Bearing Community
A Métis community has existed from the 18th century in the Sault Ste. Marie area.

(cont'd)

---

3. Identification of the Contemporary Rights-Bearing Community

The historic Métis community (which has a population of roughly 900 people) had persisted into contemporary times.

4. Verification of the Claimant's Membership in the Relevant Contemporary Community

This involves three elements: (a) long-term self-identification as Métis; (b) evidence of an ancestral connection to a historic Métis community; and (c) acceptance by the contemporary community that the individual is a member.

5. Identification of the Relevant Time Frame

This entailed shifting the time frame for Aboriginal rights from the precontact "time immemorial" of status or registered "Indians" to one that was relevant to the creation of Métis communities after contact.

6. Determination of Whether the Practice Is Integral to the Claimant's Distinctive Culture

Hunting for food was a key element of the traditional culture of the community.

7. Establishment of Continuity Between the Historic Practice and the Contemporary Right Asserted

Hunting for food has continued from the historic period to contemporary time.

8. Determination of Whether the Right Was Extinguished

When an Aboriginal right is extinguished it means that there has been specific legislation that has taken the right away. No such legislation had been passed.

9. If There Is a Right, Determination of Whether There Is an Infringement of That Right

It was determined in this case that arresting the Powleys for hunting for food was an infringement of their Aboriginal right.

10. Determination of Whether the Infringement Is Justified

It was *not* determined that the infringement of the Powleys' Aboriginal right was justified.

This has had implications for Métis elsewhere in Canada. By the end of 2005 the Powley case had been used as justification for Métis hunting rights in parts of British Columbia, in Alberta, and in Saskatchewan. It was still being contested in Manitoba.

In the 2006 Census, 389 785 people identified themselves as Métis, representing a 91 percent increase from 1996. Their recorded percentage of the Aboriginal population during that time also increased, from 26 percent to 34 percent. This is probably due mainly to a heightened tendency for people to self-identify as Métis, a tendency owing to increased Métis political and cultural activities.

TREATIES

What is a **treaty**? It is difficult to determine the original meaning of any treaty for those on either side of the negotiating table. The government felt that Natives would eventually disappear. Precise wording might not have been important to them. Native people had no precedent for giving away land forever. Today's Aboriginal people tend to feel that these treaties are international agreements between "nations." They consider treaties to be statements of recognition of their sovereign or independent status, made necessary by the *Royal Proclamation of 1763*. This key document contained two statements of significance to Native issues in Canada.

First, land not part of New France and not owned by the Hudson's Bay Company was declared to be "Indian land." Second, Indian land could only be taken from them through "public purchase," that is, treaties. Most of Canada is covered by such treaties, but significant exceptions exist. British Columbia has a few treaties, but the province removed Natives from most of their land without public purchase. Quebec received its northern half on the understanding that Native land rights would be dealt with, but nothing was done until the James Bay Agreement. Newfoundland and Labrador, separate from Canada until 1949, has no such treaties.

Generally, in treaties, the Natives involved would agree to give up their rights to a certain area of land that they traditionally used. In return they would have a smaller area or areas reserved for their use, hence the name **reserves** for these blocks of land. The calculation was typically a certain amount of land per family of five, say 65 hectares. The Natives would also receive a certain amount of money. In that sense, treaties were like land sales. They were different, however, in that Natives could not get their hands on the money. It was held for them "in trust" by the federal government. From 1818 on, Natives would also receive *annuities*, or annual payments, usually involving a small sum per person, such as three dollars a year.

Treaties generally moved westward with non-Native settlement. The oldest treaties (the "Peace and Friendship Treaties") were with the Aboriginal Peoples of the Atlantic provinces. These treaties have generated a great deal of controversy concerning their promises of hunting and fishing rights. In 1713, the Treaty of Portsmouth, New Hampshire included the Maliseet and the Mi'kmaq in Canada. It involved not only "peace and friendship," but also "free liberty for Hunting, Fishing, Fowling, and all other of their Lawful Liberties and Privileges."[4] Similar statements of hunting and fishing rights for the Mi'kmaq occurred in two treaties of 1725. In 1752 another treaty was signed, which reaffirmed the rights promised earlier. In the case of *Regina v. James Matthew Simon* (1985), the Chief Justice recognized that the 1752 treaty had supremacy over provincial game laws, saying, "It is an enforceable obligation between the Indians and the white man."[5] Conflict arose in 1988 and 1989 between the Nova Scotia Ministry of Lands and Forests and Mi'kmaq hunters concerning their rights to hunt moose to provide their families with food. The Mi'kmaq were granted special one-week extensions one week before and after the two-week hunting season for non-Natives.

Greater conflict occurred in 1999 and 2000 concerning a treaty of 1760. After a Mi'kmaq man was convicted in 1996 for catching eels out of season, the court's decision was overturned on 17 September 1999 by the Supreme Court of Canada. The Supreme Court's ruling was that the Mi'kmaq could hunt or fish not for "economic gain" but to obtain a "moderate livelihood" for a family's sustenance and survival. As this decision was handed down around the beginning of lobster season, the Mi'kmaq began to set up lobster traps without obtaining licences. Non-Natives possessing those licences were angry. Some responded with violence to Mi'kmaq lobster traps, the boats they used, and processing plants thought to be handling Mi'kmaq-caught lobster. The state of tension was increased by the clumsy response of the federal government. A thirty-day Mi'kmaq lobster fishing moratorium was declared, which was accepted by all but two affected Mi'kmaq communities. One in particular, Burnt Church, in New Brunswick, became the scene of several confrontations. Eventually the Mi'kmaq were awarded the right to use about 13 000 traps, in an Atlantic fishery that generally involved about 2 000 000 traps.

During the last part of the 18th century and the early part of the 19th, a series of treaties covered most of southern Ontario. Following these were the Robinson Treaties of 1850, involving the land immediately north of Lakes Superior and Huron. Then came the "numbered treaties," 1 to 11, which covered most of northern Ontario, across the Prairie provinces to the eastern part of British Columbia, and parts of Yukon Territory and the Northwest Territories. Almost all of these treaties can be connected with the federal government wanting something, particularly mineral resources. The Robinson Treaties were signed after the discovery of metals in northern Ontario. Treaty Number 8 was occasioned by the Klondike Gold Rush near the end of the 19th century. Oil found in 1920 led to Treaty Number 11.

Why do Aboriginal people make such a big deal about the treaties? First, they hold the view that in the treaties they were recognized as sovereign nations. Second, there are few treaties in which the Native groups involved have not had some grievance concerning either verbal promises that were not written or written promises that were not

CRITICAL THINKING OUTSIDE THE BOX 5.2

Why is it difficult to determine how many Native people there are in Canada?

fulfilled. For example, in 1818 in partial payment for giving up the "Mississauga Tract," land including in part what is now the city of Mississauga, the King's representative promised "to pay to the said Nation of Indians inhabiting as above mentioned, yearly and every year for ever the said sum of five hundred and twenty two pounds ten shillings currency in goods at the Montreal price."[6] Forever was brief. These annuities were paid for only a few years.

Two years later, the Mississauga reluctantly agreed to give up their exclusive fishing rights to a few local creeks and rivers, as well as all their remaining land, "[s]aving and reserving, nevertheless, always to . . . the people of the Mississagua [sic] Nation of Indians and their posterity for ever a certain parcel or tract of land containning [sic] two hundred acres."[7]

The Mississauga never signed away those 200 acres (about 80 hectares), but they soon came to understand that without a land deed of the type that the settlers had, they had no hope of keeping that land, despite the written treaty promise. They left the area in the 1840s. Fortunately, the Iroquois gave them land on which to live.

LAND CLAIMS

Typically, land claims are put forward by Aboriginal groups not covered by any treaties. They are based on the principle that people who have not signed away their rights to their land have Aboriginal rights that have not been extinguished. Sometimes, land claims involve dispute over whether a people is included in a treaty. The Temagami Anishnabe (Ojibwa) of northeastern Ontario asserted that they never signed the Robinson–Huron Treaty. For more than a century, they pushed to sign an agreement so that they could obtain a reserve where they worked and lived. The position of the provincial governments over the same period remained that someone had signed for them. Governments were reluctant to allow them a reserve in that pine-and-tourism-rich area. During the 1980s, the courts ruled against the people. The provincial government then made an offer that divided the band (only part of the community accepted the offer), creating a rift that still exists.

More often, a land claim is made where no treaty applies. One famous case involves the Cree of east James Bay. When the federal government handed over northern Quebec to the province of Quebec in 1898 and 1912, it was stipulated that the Cree, Inuit, and Innu would have their rights dealt with through treaty. No Quebec government did anything until 1971, when Premier Robert Bourassa announced his plans for the James Bay Project, a grand scheme of constructing power dams on four large rivers. These dams would have flooded the homes and the hunting and trapping territories of the Cree. Bourassa had not talked with the Cree, nor thought of negotiating with them concerning their rights to the land. After nearly three years of legal and public relations battles, the James Bay and Northern Quebec Agreement of 1975 was signed, with extensions north and east added in 1978 and 1984.

This agreement has been a mixed blessing. The Cree received a lot of money, although not as much as was promised. The Cree School Board has achieved a great deal more than their critics thought possible for a Native-run, Native-language, and culture-based system. Financially, some individuals have prospered, and some businesses have done well. Politically, the Cree have become a force to be reckoned with. They were able to stop the second phase of the Project.

On the negative side, mercury, raised by the flooding, exists in dangerously high amounts in fish, a major item in the local Cree diet. Communities that in the early 1970s were made up mainly of financially independent hunters and trappers have seen a good number of people forced onto welfare. Social problems such as substance abuse and suicide, unheard of before the James Bay Project, have emerged.

The Nisga'a Treaty

The Nisga'a treaty of 2000 has prompted much discussion, particularly in British Columbia, where a great deal of land "suddenly" became "Indian land." This is not a new land claim. The Nisga'a, a Tsimshian-speaking people, worked for more than a century to have their land claims resolved. They sent delegations to Victoria in 1881 and 1887. The premier told them that "when the whites first came among you, you were little better than the wild beasts of the field."[8] The Nisga'a spoke to prime ministers in 1885 and in 1910. In the latter year, Prime Minister Wilfrid Laurier promised to resolve the land issue. His government was defeated in 1911. In 1909 and 1913, the Nisga'a sent representatives to Britain, with no success.

In 1927, the federal government made it difficult for the Nisga'a to get their land claims settled. Ottawa took away from Natives the democratic right to organize to discuss land claims. The Nisga'a did not give up. They and other British Columbia Native groups formed the Native Brotherhood of British Columbia in 1931, which discussed in secret how they could get land claims settled.

In 1967, Nisga'a leader Frank Calder took the land question to court, seeking a declaration that his people had held Aboriginal title to the land before colonization and that their title had never been extinguished. The Nisga'a lost the decision in the B.C. court but appealed the decision, taking it to the Supreme Court of Canada. In 1973, the appeal was lost in a split decision: the judges agreed that Aboriginal title had existed but disagreed as to whether that title continued to exist.

In 1976, the federal government and the Nisga'a began negotiations to settle their land claims under the new "comprehensive land claims policy." British Columbia did not enter into the discussion until 1990, eight years after the Canadian Constitution recognized and affirmed Aboriginal title.

On 22 March 1996, the Minister of Indian Affairs, the B.C. Aboriginal Affairs minister, and Nisga'a Tribal Council President Joseph Gosnell Sr. signed an Agreement-in-Principle for the first modern treaty in British Columbia. In 1999 Parliament, and on 13 April 2000, the Senate, passed the bill.

The 5500 Nisga'a received title to 1930 square kilometres in their homeland and $487.1 million in benefits and cash. They obtained the right to make laws concerning land use, employment, and cultural preservation (resembling municipal, provincial, and federal governments in that lawmaking capacity). They own the forest and mineral resources on their land (as a private owner would) and have to manage them according to British Columbia's laws and standards.

It was not all gains. The Nisga'a lessened their original claim by 25 percent, and they gave up future claims on more than 80 percent of their traditional territory. They gave up their tax exemptions.

Although the non-Native media, particularly in British Columbia presented this treaty as a step toward separation, it is more accurate to say that it puts the Nisga'a in a legal position similar to that of other Canadians.

BANDS

Typically, an Indian **band** is made up of people of one cultural tradition with some historical connection with each other. They own land and funds in common and are governed in part by a band council headed by a chief. There are some 592 bands across Canada. The largest is Six Nations, an Iroquois band in southern Ontario whose website declares that they have more than 20 000 members.[9] Bands can be created or done away with by the federal **Department of Indian Affairs (DIA).**

Bands now face a problem that divides some communities. Membership is sharply rising, with no compensating increase in land or funds. The band council handles housing and postsecondary education money. With the influx of "Bill C-31 Indians" the competition for such programs is tight. Many reserves are already crowded, and the problem is getting worse. There is tension in many communities.

A great frustration for chiefs and band councillors has long been their lack of power. They have less power than a municipality, which can raise funds through taxation (a band cannot), and which possesses an independence that a band would envy. The DIA has the power to veto any decision that a band council may make. Much of what bands do has to be sent to DIA for approval.

Native self-government is something that non-Natives tend to fear, thinking that the country will be divided into little separate nations. Native groups differ as to what they think Native self-government is. Some just want the power that a comparably sized town or village has. Others desire the right to set up the structure of their choice, one that instead of having an elected chief and band council, has more-traditional-style leaders and spokespersons for clans. For most Canadian Native groups, "the chief" was more a foreign creation than a traditional form of leadership. All bands want to be less controlled by the DIA. Native government is already distinct. Natives just want that distinction to be less of a powerless one.

RESERVES

Students often ask me, "What is it like on a reserve?" It is as if they expected me to tell them stories of bizarre mystical rites and shape-shifting shamans. They are often disappointed when I say that many reserves look just like other, comparable communities. They wonder, too, why Native people seem to cling to reserves even when some are overcrowded and violent. One answer is that for many Native people the reserve is their "home and Native land." There they are not a minority, subject to stares and discrimination.

The uncertainty that sometimes surrounds reserve status creates problems. One major reason that the 1990 confrontation at Oka (in Quebec) took place was because the people there did not have a reserve that could protect their burial grounds from a local golf course. They still don't. The tragedy behind the story at Davis Inlet in 1993, with Innu children suffering from serious substance abuse and attempting suicide, has a lot to do with the federal and Newfoundland governments forcing the people to move the reserve from the Labrador mainland to an island. This was done against the wisdom and the will of the local Innu, who knew they would have less access to the natural resources they valued, such as caribou. The move took a lot of the heart out of the people.

Reserves have a unique legal status. Technically, a reserve can be called federal rather than provincial land. The band owns the land, but the federal government, through the DIA, has ultimate authority. Although people have their own houses and property lines, the band holds the land in common. They do not pay municipal taxes, and housing is usually cheap. On the negative side, a family's part of the reserve cannot be used as collateral to get a loan from a bank.

Most Natives live on reserves. A little less than 60 percent of registered Indians live on reserves. Reserve patterns differ across Canada. In central and eastern Canada each band has only one reserve. Out west, a band is more likely to have more. In British Columbia, for example, there are fewer than 200 bands but more than 1600 reserves. Typically, reserves are remote. In 1989 more than 60 percent were farther than 50 kilometres from a city or major town. A remarkable 18.6 percent were not connected to a city or major town by a year-round road.

A growing number of Native people work and live in towns and cities, however, estimate that in 1991, eleven Canadian cities had an Aboriginal population of at least 10 000.[10] Edmonton, Montreal, Toronto, and Vancouver top the list, with an estimated 40 000 to 50 000 each.[11] These figures are probably a lot lower than the actual numbers. Estimates for Toronto's Aboriginal population are often given as more than 70 000; it is sometimes called "the largest Indian reserve in Canada." This move to the city has been a trend of the past thirty-five years. In 1971 none of these cities had a reported Native population of more than 5000.

Unfortunately the greatest urban visibility of Aboriginal people is as the stereotypical "Indian drunk." In Toronto they are otherwise pretty much an "invisible minority." An Ojibwa student of mine told me that for years, when she worked in a bank in that city, customers would guess at her identity, asking her if she were Filipina, Chinese, or Korean. No one ever guessed correctly.

As more Natives move to the city, there is a growing need for Native-run organizations to help them cope with urban life. These are appearing, usually starting with a Native Friendship Centre.

Urban Reserves

A new type of reserve is being created in Saskatchewan: **urban reserves**. These are lands located in a municipality or Northern Administrative District. Their main function is to provide central urban locations for Aboriginal businesses. To enable the creation of these reserves, the Saskatchewan Treaty Land Entitlement Framework Agreement was signed in 1992. A fund of approximately $446 million was established so that the land could be purchased. Twenty-eight of the seventy Saskatchewan First Nations signed on, initiating the development of twenty-eight urban reserves. Nine of them are located in cities. More than 1350 people work in the businesses developed there.

Why did urban reserves come about? First of all, there were a good number of outstanding treaty land entitlements in Saskatchewan. Land promised in the treaties of over 100 years ago had yet to be delivered to the people. Secondly, an increasingly high percentage of the Aboriginal population is moving (at least temporarily) from the rural reserves and into cities. There they have been as a group markedly less successful than non-Aboriginal people. Thirdly, the economic potential of rural reserves, on average, could not be as great as reserves located in cities. Fourth, for shared and different reasons, the federal government and First Nations wanted the latter to be more economically self-sufficient, not so dependent on economic transfer payments from the federal government.

The first community to develop an urban reserve was the Muskeg Lake Cree Nation. It has about 1200 members, most of them living away from the main reserve (located 93 kilometres outside of Saskatoon). The leaders of this community first approached the federal government in 1984, and were granted 33 acres of land in Saskatoon. In 1993, they signed a services agreement with the city. This involved the band giving an annual payment for municipal services such as snow and garbage removal, with electricity and water being billed directly to individual customers on the reserve. Businesses operating there are almost all Aboriginal-owned, with some 300 employees.

NATIVES AND THE JUSTICE SYSTEM

Natives do not fare well in the Canadian justice system. They are less likely than non-Natives to be put on probation and to be released on their own recognizance. Natives are more likely to be ordered to pay fines, and much more likely to be put in jail because they cannot pay the fines. They are more likely to serve their full sentence rather than having their sentence shortened by parole. Drinking in the same bar with non-Natives, and consuming roughly the same amount of alcohol, they are more likely to be picked up for being drunk around closing time. Natives are overrepresented in our prisons. Shock-value statistics abound, often doing more harm than good (see the opening quote). Stories of what is happening and how solutions are being applied are less often presented and are more likely to improve the situation. The following are a few such stories and potential solutions.

Different Sides to Policing Natives

Starlight Tours in Saskatoon

Saskatoon has a population of about 200 000. Its Native population has been estimated at about 15 percent of that number, but the percentage of the poor in Saskatoon is almost double that at 30 percent.

In 1997, a veteran police officer wrote a column in the *Saskatoon Sun* that told about a night on the beat for two fictional officers. In the story, they pick up a loud, verbally abusive drunk and take him on what is sometimes known as a "starlight tour," driving him outside town and leaving him there to walk back.

On the night of 27 January 2000, 33-year-old Darrell Night, an unemployed brick-layer and a big, sturdy man, got drunk. In the early morning hours he was arrested outside a friend's apartment by two officers, handcuffed, and put into a police cruiser. He was then taken outside town and dropped off by Queen Elizabeth II Power Station south of the city, without a coat. The temperature had dropped to about –28°C. Darrell went to the station and got a night watchman to call him a cab. That may have saved his life.

He did not tell his story to anyone in legal authority at first. He was Cree. The officers were white. Who would be more likely to be believed? It would take the report of two tragedies to make him tell his own story.

What made him tell his story was the discovery the next night of the body of a 25-year-old Cree man, Rodney Naistus, and, a few nights later, of a 30-year-old Cree student, Lawrence Kim Wegner. Both had been drinking. On 20 September 2001, the two officers who took Darrell Night on his starlight tour were convicted of unlawful con-finement and were fired by the Saskatoon Police Service. An inquest into the deaths of Rodney Naistus and Lawrence Kim Wegner found no wrongdoing.

The Positive Side of the Saskatoon Police Service

It would be wrong to simply label the Saskatoon Police Service (SPS) as racist. Since 1994, the SPS has developed several programs and events dedicated to creating a bridge between the police service and the Saskatoon Native community. In 1995, the SPS won the National Ivan Ahenakew Award for efforts in employing Aboriginal officers and in the development of cultural programs.

Perhaps the most successful elements of the SPS's efforts to connect with the Native community have come through the peacekeeper programs, which put officers together with Aboriginal at-risk youth, often under the guidance of Elders and other Native leaders. The programs include innovative cultural activities such as Project Firewood/Rocks. This involves Aboriginal youth and SPS officers travelling to northern Saskatchewan to load a semi-trailer with firewood and rocks to be taken to Saskatoon for the Elders. The Elders will use these materials in **sweat lodge** ceremonies (see below), some involving both the youth and officers as participants.

Native Policing Services

Following the Manitoba Aboriginal Justice Inquiry of 1988–89 and the 1990 Oka con-frontation, the federal solicitor general initiated in 1991 the First Nations Policing Policy. It operates on a principle of partnership involving First Nations, the federal government, and the provincial or territorial governments. These three enter into tripartite agreements for police services that fit the needs of the particular Aboriginal communities involved. Fifty-two percent of the funding for the agreements comes from the federal government,

CRITICAL THINKING OUTSIDE THE BOX 5.3

What problems do band leaders face that leaders of towns and cities do not?

with the remaining 48 percent coming from the provincial or territorial government. By the end of 1999, there were fifty-two such agreements across the country. The following is the story of one such agreement.

The Stl'atl'imx Tribal Police Case Study

On 20 December 1999, British Columbia received its first Aboriginal police service with full jurisdictional authority. The Stl'atl'imx Tribal Police (STP) force is responsible for ten First Nations communities, serving roughly 3150 people in southern British Columbia. Nine of the participating communities are Lillooet, the 10th is Shuswap, a closely related people.

Although the force dates back to 1988, it wasn't until April 1992 that a tripartite agreement was signed. The STP is guided by the Stl'atl'imx Tribal Police Board (STPB), which has ten members, one from each of the participating communities. The STPB has more responsibility for managing and leading the STP than is found in most municipal police departments. The tripartite agreement included some dependence on the RCMP, with the latter providing assistance in the investigation of relatively serious cases.

The notion of a Native police service is new to non-Natives, easily interpreted by them as threatening—particularly, as in this case, when the Native police service is asked to give assistance to provincial police off-reserve. By May 1992, three petitions with 493 signatures were sent from the non-Native town of Lillooet to the B.C. Attorney General with complaints of non-Natives being "harassed" by Native police.

The British Columbia Police Commission reviewed the STP in 1996. At that time the STP had nine policing positions: a chief constable, a supervisor, three constables based in the community of Mount Currie, three in Lillooet (the Native community), and one in Seton Lake. The problems revealed in this review were typical of the fledgling Native police services across Canada: insufficient and often late year-to-year funding, difficulties in hiring experienced staff (particularly when contracts are a year long, rather than long-term), inadequate training, the difficulties of policing a broad area of separated communities with few officers (making full-service, full-time shift work almost impossible), low morale, discontent with the authoritarian management style of the non-Native chief constable, and what might be called a clash of policing cultures.

The Police Board members were unanimous in wanting to have a police service based on the traditional Lillooet "watchman" system. The "watchman" was respected for his decision making. Traditionally, members of the community felt comfortable in approaching him to hear their cases whenever they felt that someone had committed a transgression. The majority of STPB members believed that the chief constable and the STP officers were not applying this philosophy, but were following a more mainstream-culture policing approach. The officers themselves, most of whom were Native, were divided as to which philosophy or cultural style they preferred.

The culture of policing clash is one of the major challenges faced by all Aboriginal police services. It raises several important questions. How free are Aboriginal police services to innovate following traditional values? How might that freedom be restricted by the mainstream training their officers receive and the mainstream policing experiences of those who early on assume positions of leadership in these services? To what extent can Native police services reflect their traditional culture in trying to work with and get the respect of other, more established policing services and of provincial and federal funding administrators?

Despite some of the negative aspects of the review, the B.C. Police Commission noted that the Board and the STP were conscientious and dedicated to improving the quality of the service. This must have served to good effect, for three years after the review, the STP moved ahead to assume full jurisdictional authority. As Chief Constable Harry McLaughlin noted in the B.C. Attorney General's news release, "This occasion instills a new level of pride in our officers and a renewed sense of commitment to the Stl'atl'imx communities."[12]

Sentencing Circles

Sentencing circles provide alternatives to incarceration, through applying traditional notions of restorative justice. The circles typically involve community members such as Elders and Native social workers, lawyers, health care workers, and those affected by the crime, including the offenders, the victims, and their families. The circles are more informal than traditional courts. People sit in a circle. No judge is involved. Consensus is stressed in deciding what the sentence will be. The following is an example.[13]

In 1994, the United Chiefs and Councils of Manitoulin Justice Project began diverting cases from the courts to sentencing or justice circles. From 1 January 1998 to the end of June 1999, seventy-seven justice circles were created, involving 110 members of the community. The kind of cases were typically property offences (i.e., vandalism, break and enter, and theft) and relatively minor instances of assault, but they did not include more serious crimes such as murder, manslaughter, sexual or spousal abuse, or impaired driving.

Sentences are referred to as "plans of action." These are traditionally based, but also creative and new. Public apologies are made by the "clients," not only to the victims involved, but also to the police and others affected by the harmful acts. Some of the apologies have aired on a local cable TV station.

Personal healing is a significant part of the plans of action. This healing has included referrals to drug and alcohol addiction treatment centres or mental health facilities, but it has also entailed traditional activities. The intent of these activities is to heal clients by raising their self-esteem and sense of identity through learning about their culture. Examples of the traditional activities recommended are helping to gather traditional medicines in the bush, participating in an arduous canoe trip around Manitoulin Island, and researching a family tree. Some clients have done more than was required of them, as they felt rewarded by the activity.

Since healing the community is a priority, the plans of action often require some form of community service. This has involved doing such things as cleaning up the results of vandalism, painting a new detox centre, and participating in a walk held annually to raise awareness of violence against women.

Making amends is also important. In one case, a woman had assaulted another woman, a long-time neighbour. Had she decided to fight the charge, which was her initial intention, she probably would have been put on probation and told to stay away from the victim. Instead, with the apology, the two women have managed to remain on good terms, something that would have been less likely to happen in the confrontation format of the courtroom.

An easy criticism of the Justice Project would be that people get off lightly. However, the clients speak of it being more difficult to face people you know than the anonymous strangers who are judge and jury.

There are difficulties. The workload is heavy. A lot of time is taken in putting together reports and proposals for the funding necessary to continue and to grow. Still, during the period studied (January 1998 to June 1999) no one had to return to the circle for noncompliance with their plans of action.

ABORIGINAL RELIGION

What religion do Aboriginal people have? There is no simple answer. A number of First Nations have adopted and adapted forms of Catholicism that can now be considered "traditional" to their people (Angela Robinson gives a Mi'kmaq example[14]). Christian texts and hymns written in Moose Cree, and the important roles played by Aboriginal ministers in their home communities have made Anglicanism a part of Native religious traditions.

Older than these traditions are indigenous forms. From thousands of years before contact to the 21st century, these forms have flourished and adapted to changes in times.

Today Aboriginal religion centres primarily around a series of practices, some unique to particular peoples, some shared across Aboriginal Canada. Some of the latter will be discussed here.

The Four Medicines

The four medicines are sweetgrass, tobacco, sage, and cedar. Each is associated with a direction. When burned, each has medicinal functions that go beyond its mere physical properties. Sweetgrass, not a drug as the name might imply, is a sweet-smelling member of the grass family. When burned, it purifies the person and the immediate setting with its sacred smoke, much as incense does for Catholics, Hindus, Jews, and Buddhists. Its directional association, the north, is associated with purification and healing. People who fan the smoke over themselves are said to be **smudging**, and it is a daily morning ritual for some.

Tobacco is often put in a fire, and the smoke is said to communicate with the spirits. Tobacco is associated with the east, from which comes enlightenment and vision. In Ojibwa culture, when people want to obtain a name in their own language, an increasing phenomenon for adults and children, they go to someone who is known to provide names, and give the person tobacco. The namer places the tobacco into a fire, and asks the Creator for help in finding the name in a vision. Generally in Aboriginal culture people approach elders with tobacco if they want the elder to share knowledge or wisdom with them.

Sage and cedar, associated with the south and west respectively, are believed to cleanse in both a physical and a spiritual sense. You can smudge with sage. Cedar is often used in the sweat lodge, a key element of both traditional and contemporary Aboriginal spirituality (see below).

The Sweat Lodge

The following is a general description of the sweat lodge as the Ojibwa (Anishnabe) use it in the context of the modern vision quest.[15] Sweat lodges differ both within the traditions of the Ojibwa people, and between them and other Aboriginal Peoples.

The lodge is typically constructed of sixteen overlapping willow poles. It is shaped to resemble the sky world above that covers the earth like a dome. The entrance must face the east, where the sun rises.

A pit is dug in the centre, where the "grandfathers" are received and where they meet Mother Earth. The grandfathers are stones that because of their great age hold the mysteries of the past. Before the grandfathers are brought into the lodge, they are placed at the bottom of a sacred fire in front of the lodge, joined to it by a pathway of cedar. Here they are heated until white-hot. How long the vision quest seeker plans to sweat will determine how many stones will be called on to guide the individual in the sweat lodge.

The Elder and the participants throw tobacco into the fire and pray, giving thanks to the Creator. The Elder then tells how the sweat lodge came to be, a story that describes how a little boy was sent to the seven grandfather spirits in the star world during a time of great sickness and was given the gift of the sweat lodge to bring back to his people for healing. A water drum, called the "Little Boy Drum" in remembrance of the little boy who brought back the medicine teachings, is placed inside close to the entrance. The participants greet the drum as they enter. It has seven stones that surround the top, representing the seven grandfathers who first gave the little boy the teaching. When the sweat lodge is occupied, the Elder sings traditional ceremonial songs. The grandfathers are then brought in to the lodge and placed in the pit. The Elder throws water onto the grandfathers, and the steam makes the lodge quite hot.

Medicine Dances

Medicine dances are important elements in contemporary Aboriginal spirituality. One such dance is the *jingle dress dance*, which is recognized as Ojibwa in origin. Sometime between 1918 and 1920 in the reserve community of Whitefish Bay, on the shores of Lake of the Woods, near the Ontario/Manitoba border, a seven- or eight-year-old Ojibwa girl, Maggie White, became ill. There were no signs that she was getting any better, so her father sought a vision to help cure her. In his vision, he saw both the jingle dress and the healing dance that girls and women should perform while wearing it. The "jingle" of the dress comes from the metal cones that cover it. Typically these cones number 365, one for each day of the year. Traditionally, they were made out of snuff can lids bent into the shape of cones. When the jingle dress wearer dances, the sound is an amazingly soothing, lightly chiming sound.

The original jingle dance society was initially confined to four young girls (Maggie White and three others), each of whom wore a colour signifying one of the four directions. The primary purpose was healing. People would offer tobacco to a dancer who would dance as a prayer of healing for a person who was sick.

The jingle dance continued as an Ojibwa medicine dance until the late 1960s and early 1970s, when it was picked up by other peoples and included both as a medicine dance and as a woman's dance as part of intertribal powwows, even in competitions. For many, however, it is still a medicine dance, a way for a community to contribute to the healing of their people.

Religious Oppression

Aboriginal religion has had to face a long history of oppression in Canada. This peaked in the late 19th century with the banning of the potlatch and the Sun Dance. The potlatch is the most important traditional ceremony for British Columbia Native groups such as the Bella Coola, Haida, Kwakiutl, and Nootka. It is a celebration in some ways not unlike a birthday party, bar mitzvah, christening, mass, confirmation, or marriage. People dance, sing, drum, and wear masks and costumes to tell stories expressing who they are as a people. Traditionally, the celebration also involved a great giving of gifts, saved up for a year or more by the family holding the ceremony and its clan. The next year they might attend a potlatch in which they are the guests and therefore the receivers of equal gifts. In the 19th century, potlatch ceremonies might take days.

Missionaries saw the potlatch as a "pagan ritual"; governmental officials saw it as a "backward practice" that would prevent the Indians from becoming "civilized." So, in 1884, a ban on the potlatch was added to the *Indian Act*. Anyone who held or attended a potlatch would be "guilty of a misdemeanour, and liable to imprisonment for a term of not more than six nor less than two months in any gaol or other place of confinement, and any Indian or other person who encourages, either directly or indirectly, an Indian or Indians to get up such a festival or dance, or to celebrate the same, or who shall assist in the celebration of the same is guilty of like offense, and shall be liable to the same punishment."

The people resisted in several ways. Some took it underground, holding the ceremonies where no missionary or official could know what was going on. Other petitioned the government with no effect. The following petition was signed by Elders who showed more wisdom and knowledge of the spirit of justice in Canadian law than those who had banned their ceremony. It appeared in *The Daily Colonist*, a Victoria newspaper:

> If we wish to perform an act moral in its nature with no injury or damage, and pay for it, no law in equity can divest us of such right.
>
> We see the Salvation Army parade through the streets of your town with music and drum, enchanting the town. . . . We are puzzled to know whether in the estimation of civilization we are human or fish ... that the felicities of our ancestors should be denied us.[16]

In 1895, this ban spread to the equally significant Sun Dance of Prairie peoples such as the Blackfoot, Blood, Piegan, Sarcee, Assiniboine, and Plains Cree. In 1906, the ban was extended to all Aboriginal dancing. Aboriginal people could dance in a traditional way only with government permission. Not until 1951 was this part of the *Indian Act* repealed—17 years after the American government had repealed similar legislation.

NATIVE EDUCATION

Residential schools were formally initiated in 1910. Unfortunately, the negative effects of this education are its prominent features. One tragically mistaken idea in these schools was the notion that to educate Native children, it was necessary to separate them from the "corrupting influence" of their language, their culture, and ultimately, their parents. About half the schools were Roman Catholic, the rest primarily Anglican and United Church. The religious groups received a grant of land and money and were left more or less to run the schools on their own. Although intentions were good, the results were horrifying. Schools were frequently hundreds of kilometres away from the homes of the students, who were forced to board in prison-like buildings, often for ten months of the year. Students were sometimes dragged from their homes by police. See Have You Heard? 5.3.

Residential schools were not just bad educationally, with a simplified curriculum, under-trained teachers, hand-me-down educational materials, and "learning a trade"

HAVE YOU HEARD? 5.3

Richard Wagamese is Anishinabe or Ojibwa and a successful Canadian writer. In his *One Native Life*, he tells stories of how he survived abusive parents, foster homes, and living on the street from age 16 to his early twenties. In the following he describes the effects on his parents and family of residential schools:

> [My parents] had the Indian stripped out of them by the residential schools, and they felt ignorant and powerless. They'd been reduced to spiritual beggary, kneeling at the feet of the nuns and priests to beseech direction and fulfillment. Direction came in the form of rigorous discipline, harsh punishment and instilled religious fear.
>
> They were told their way of life was dead; the new world had not room for Indians, only for obedient servants of the white God. They were told that their beliefs were wrong, and that nothing in their worldview held any more. They were told that to live as savages was an abomination they needed to be cleansed of. . .
>
> In the bush where we lived, my family wrestled with demons. They drank to exorcise those demons, to mute the ache of whips and beatings and abuse. [17]

---

often an excuse for exploiting students as unpaid farm and domestic labourers; these schools also harmed the Native family. Generally, strict teachers and principals were the only parental figures that the Native children experienced for most of the year. Abuse—physical, emotional, and sexual—occurred far too frequently. When the students became parents, they would often come to repeat the practices of their white role models. Brothers and sisters were kept apart in sexually segregated classes and residences, sometimes not getting an opportunity to talk with each other for months on end. One female Native student in a residential school stated: "I never did get to know my brothers. We were kept away from each other for too long. To this day I don't know much about my brothers. I just know that they are my brothers."[18]

When children left for residential school, often they knew only the language of their home, community, and ancestors. But those who "spoke Indian" would be punished, usually with a severe beating.

The residential school system lasted until the 1960s, some individual schools a decade or two longer. Their effects are still felt. Many Native people are skeptical about education even with schools run by their own people. Still, increasingly Natives are taking over their own schools. In 1975–76, there were only 2842 pupils attending just 53 band-operated schools in reserves across Canada. That number shot up to more than 53 312 students in 372 band-operated schools by 1993–94.

Native students are staying in school much longer than before. The proportion of Native students living on reserve who remained in school until Grade 12 was only 15 percent in 1970–71. This reached 47 percent by 1990–91. Similar figures appear for postsecondary schooling. In 1973 fewer than 1000 college and university students were registered Indians. By 1987 that number had reached 14 000.

Taking charge of their own education is not an easy task for Native people. Provinces carefully guard their curriculum as the standard of education, sometimes making it difficult for Native students to gain accreditation for grades and courses taken in band-run schools when it comes to applying for transfer to any level of schooling outside the Native system. And the Department of Indian Affairs still controls the purse strings.

THE FUTURE

What is the future of Native people in Canada? Politically, it does not seem very bright. The federal government, concerned about debts not promises, is looking to divest itself of its responsibilities, either passing them down to the provinces or wiping the slate clean. Both strategies are looked upon with suspicion by Natives. See Have You Heard? 5.4.

Aboriginal Statistics and the 2006 Census

. . . .

It is difficult to obtain accurate statistics, as some First Nation communities are rightly suspicious of the ends to which government and other outsiders are using the statistics. They will not give their numbers to Statistics Canada. This is lessening somewhat. In 1996 there were seventy-seven non-enumerated reserves. In 2001, that number lowered to thirty, and was down to only twenty-two in 2006.

Census statistics deal with how people report their identity. The number of people who are legally or officially "registered Indians" is lower. This difference is particularly significant with respect to the on-reserve and off-reserve population of each First Nation. The Statistics Canada data for 2006 asserted that roughly 60 percent of First Nations (as opposed to Métis and Inuit) people lived on reserve, with 40 percent living off reserve. This makes it appear as if the First Nations population is leaving the reserves, which may affect federal policies and monies directed towards reserves. It also serves well the conservative political agenda to 'get Indians off reserves so that they can be like everyone else.' The Indian Register records the number of "registered Indians." At the end of 2006, there were 763 555 members, with 404 117 living on reserves (about 53 percent), 24 320 on Crown land, and only 335 109 off-reserve (about 43 percent).

Precise urban statistics are difficult to obtain, owing to suspicion of enumeration, as well as the transient nature of many urban Natives (i.e., they may have both reserve and non-reserve addresses, and may not be in the city year round). Sociologist James Frideres, in *Aboriginal Peoples in Canada* used estimates obtained from city officials. Notice how his 1996 estimates are typically higher in large urban centres in the East and in British Columbia, but are more like the Statistics Canada figures obtained from later years in Thunder Bay and the Prairie urban centres, when we can safely say there were more Aboriginal people in those cities than before. See Tables 5.1 and 5.2 below.

(cont'd)

Table 5.1   Aboriginal People in the Cities

	2001	2006	1996 Estimate[19]
Atlantic Provinces			
St. John's	1 195	2 015	1 000–2 000
Halifax	3 525	5 320	7 795
Saint John	945	1 255	2 000–3 000
Quebec			
Montreal	11 085	17 865	43 675
Quebec	4 130	4 000	6 000–10 000
Ontario			
Toronto	20 300	26 575	39 380
Ottawa-Gatineau	13 485	20 590	29 415
Thunder Bay	8 200	10 055	8 600
Prairie Provinces			
Winnipeg	55 760	68 385	52 525
Regina	15 685	17 105	14 570
Saskatoon	20 280	21 535	18 160
Calgary	21 915	26 575	23 850
Edmonton	40 930	52 100	44 130
British Columbia			
Vancouver	36 855	40 310	46 805
Victoria	8 695	10 905	10 000–15 000

Source: Adapted from Statistics Canada, *2006 Aboriginal Population Profile for Selected Cities and Communities, Ontario*: 89-638-XWE 2009001, no. 1, Released April 7, 2009, Corrected February 1, 2010; *Quebec and the Atlantic Provinces*: 89-638-XWE 2009002, no. 2, Released December 18, 2009; *Prairie Provinces*: 89-638-XWE 2010003, no. 3, Released February 25, 2010; *British Columbia*: 89-638-XWE 2010004, no. 4, Released March 24, 2010.

Table 5.2   Aboriginal Statistics: Provinces and Territories

	2001	2006	Increase	
			Number	Percentage
Canada	976 305	1 172 790	196 485	20%
Newfoundland & Labrador	18 775	23 450	4 675	23.8%
Prince Edward Island	1 345	1 730	385	28.6%
Nova Scotia	17 010	24 175	7 165	42.1%
New Brunswick	16 990	17 655	665	3.9%
Quebec	79 400	108 430	29 030	37.7%
Ontario	188 315	242 495	54 180	28.7%
Manitoba	150 045	175 395	25 350	16.8%
				(cont'd)

	2001	2006	Increase	
			Number	Percentage
Saskatchewan	130 185	141 890	11 705	9.0%
Alberta	156 225	188 365	32 140	20.6%
British Columbia	170 025	196 075	26 050	15.3%
Yukon	6 540	7 580	1040	15.9%
NWT	18 730	20 635	1905	10.2
Nunavut	22 720	24 920	2200	9.7%

Source: Adapted from Statistics Canada, *Aboriginal Population Profile, 2006 Census*, 92-594-XWE 2006001 Census year 2006, Released January 15, 2008.

CRITICAL THINKING OUTSIDE THE BOX 5.4

Why do you think the federal government banned the potlatch, the Sun Dance, and, eventually, all forms of Native dancing?

Still, some recent legal changes have a positive potential. The creation of urban reserves, although it does involve some devolution of federal responsibility, may be a way for bands to generate income and jobs and still keep their communities intact. The recognition of Métis hunting rights promises to lessen the deprivations some communities have had to endure.

There is a brighter side. Native people are saying that the answer to their difficulties will not come from making governments face their responsibilities, but from Natives healing themselves and getting their own cultures in line. Strength, health, and purpose come from within, not without. In fact, Native philosophy, rooted in the traditional but tested in the self-help, self-healing needs of Native life today, presents an alternative viewpoint for the rest of Canada to meet its challenges. This is already being seen in attitudes toward the environment. It might well guide us in justice and in other areas of life.

CHAPTER SUMMARY

In this chapter we have looked at a broad range of topics concerning Natives in Canada, especially with regard to four main points. (1) Diversity exists as well as sameness. Not all Natives are alike. We see this especially in language and other aspects of traditional culture, but it exists as well in adaptations to contemporary society. (2) Understanding any aspect of Native culture requires some knowledge of its historical roots, which often involve a very damaging prejudice and discrimination. In particular this is true concerning treaties, education, religion, and the justice system. (3) Native people are legally as well as culturally different from other Canadians. Native status brings with it different rights and limitations. And Natives are divided themselves into different legal classes: registered Indian, treaty Indian, Bill C-31 Indian, Métis, métis, and Inuit. (4) Native culture is vibrant and adaptive, not some dust-covered museum showpiece. As many Native people put it, "We're still here, and we will continue to be here."

KEY TERMS

band, p. 141

Bill C-31, p. 132

Department of Indian Affairs (DIA), p. 141

Indian Act, p. 128

language families, p. 130

language isolates, p. 130

Métis, p. 134

Powley test, p. 135

registered Indian, p. 133

reserves, p. 137

residential schools, p. 151

sentencing circles, p. 147

smudging, p. 149

sweat lodge, p. 145

treaty, p. 137

urban reserves, p. 143

DISCUSSION QUESTIONS

1. In percentage and in terms of "the year" of Canadian history, compare the length of time Natives and other Canadians have been living in this land.

2. Compare the diversity of Native languages in Canada to that of languages spoken in Europe.

3. How are the Inuit different from "Indians"?

4. Why are treaties of so long ago such an important political issue to Natives today?

5. Will urban reserves go a long way toward raising the standard of living of Aboriginal people in Canada?

6. What concerns might municipal officials and the owners of businesses in the area of urban reserves have? Are these justified?

7. How is the Native notion of medicine different from the usual mainstream Canadian idea of medicine?

8. What challenges are faced by Native police services?

NOTES

1. J.M. Adovasio and Jake Page, *The First Americans: In Pursuit of Archaeology's Greatest Mystery* (New York: Random House, 2002).
2. Bonita Lawrence, *"Real Indians" and Others: Mixed-Blood Urban Native Peoples and Indigenous Nationhood* (Vancouver: UBC Press, 2004).
3. Donald Purich, *The Métis* (Toronto: Lorimer, 1988), p. 140.
4. Olive P. Dickason, *Canada's First Nations: A History of Founding Peoples from Earliest Times* (Toronto: McClelland and Stewart, 1997).
5. Peter Kulchyski, *Unjust Relations* (Toronto: Oxford University Press, 1994).
6. *Indian Treaties and Surrenders*, Vol. 1 (Toronto: Coles Publishing, 1971), p. 48.
7. *Indian Treaties and Surrenders*, p. 52.
8. Premier William Smithe, 1887, quoted in Alex Rose, *Spirit Dance at Meziadin: Chief Joseph Gosnell and the Nisga'a Treaty* (Medeira Park, BC: Harbour Publishing, 2000), p. 13.
9. Six Nations Council, "Six Nations of the Grand River," available <www.sixnations.ca/index.htm>, accessed 27 February 2002.
10. James S. Frideres and Rene Gadacz, *Aboriginal People in Canada: Contemporary Conflicts*, 6th ed. (Toronto: Prentice-Hall, 2001).
11. Frideres and Gadacz, *Aboriginal People in Canada*.
12. Chief Constable Harry McLaughlin, quoted in "B.C. Gets Its First Aboriginal Police Force," B.C. Attorney General news release, available <http://turtleisland.org/news/news-policing.htm>, accessed 1 April 2006.
13. Adapted from John Steckley and Bryan Cummins, *Full Circle: Canada's Native People* (Toronto: Prentice Hall, 2001), pp. 237–38.
14. Angela Robinson, *Ta'n teli-ktlamsi Tasit (Ways of Believing): Mi'kmaw Religion in Eskasoni, Nova Scotia.* (Toronto: Pearson Education Canada, 2005).
15. Adapted from Brian Rice and John Steckley, "Lifelong Learning and Cultural Identity: A Lesson from Canada's Native People," in Michael Hatton, ed., *Lifelong Learning: Policies, Programs, and Practices* (Toronto: Asian Pacific Economic Cooperation Publication, 1997), p. 226.
16. Dickason.
17. Richard Wagamese, *One Native Life* (Vancouver: Douglas & MacIntyre, 2008), pp. 237–38.
18. R. Bell in Jean Barman, "Aboriginal Education at the Crossroads: The Legacy of Residential Schools and the Way Ahead," in D.A. Long and O.P. Dickason, eds. *Visions of the Heart: Canadian Aboriginal Issues* (Toronto: Harcourt Brace, 1996), p. 294.
19. James S. Frideres and René R. Gadacz, *Aboriginal Peoples in Canada: Contemporary Conflicts*, 6th ed. (Toronto: Prentice Hall, 2001), p. 37.

CHAPTER 6

Religion as Meaning and the Canadian Context

Mikal Austin Radford

A religion is a unified system of beliefs and practices relative to sacred things, that is to say, things set apart and forbidden—belief and practices which unite into one single moral community called a Church [sic], and all those who adhere to them.
—Emile Durkheim, *Elementary Forms of Religious Life*

Life is bigger,
It's bigger than you,
And you are not me. . . .
That's me in the corner,
That's me in the spotlight,
Losing my religion.
—R.E.M. (Berry/Buck/Mills/Stipe), "Losing My Religion"

Objectives

. . . .

After reading this chapter, you should be able to

- list the issues involved in finding a definition of religion

- distinguish the key differences between the world religious traditions

- describe how religion operates as an important component within the "cultural project"

- explain the importance of religion as part of socio-religious identity formation

- recognize how religion played an important role in the historical formation of Canada

- appreciate some of the concerns surrounding issues of religion by contemporary Canadians

INTRODUCTION

For most of us religion was one of *those* three topics—the others being politics and sex—that our parents cautioned against adopting as part of *any* casual conversation. Perhaps the idea was to avoid heated disputes and the loss of friends. What it has meant, however, is that the discussion of one's own religion or religious belief is very often relegated to either a myopic study of religion held in the privacy of one's own church, mosque, or temple, or a branch of learning undertaken by small, underfunded departments in our colleges and universities. As a result much of the public discourse of the past few decades has tended to think of religion in terms of something in opposition to the modern world—some quaint, antiquated curiosity that predates the Western "modernist experiment." In short, religion has often been treated as a cultural fossil, an antiquity that was to be replaced by science, economics, and modern statecraft. The events surrounding 11 September 2001 have dramatically changed the timbre of that conversation.

This chapter starts from the premise that to fail to understand the context, meaning, and *ethos* underlying the religions of the world is to fail to understand ourselves as we have developed, and continue to develop, both culturally and historically. The study of religion and religious belief provides three important components to understanding human diversity. The first is a lens into the great heritage of human civilization, what Ninian Smart calls "humankind's various experiments in living."[1] It can be argued, for example, that in order to understand the present context of capitalism or globalization, one should have more than a passing familiarity with the rise of the Protestant Reformation during that great period of "human experimentation," the European Renaissance. Max Weber was the first to state, more than a century ago, that to understand the "spirit" that underlies modern capitalism one must know the relationship between the religious radicalism of Calvinism and its interrelated concepts of Divine Providence, asceticism, and salvation. This background would enable contemporary culture to understand the West's march toward a capitalistic system with its cultic focus on "individualistic economic salvation."[2]

Secondly, to understand the world's religions within their cultural contexts and that of the Canadian multicultural mosaic gives us an opportunity for a new discourse that attempts to understand the meanings and values of the plural cultures both of the world and of those who come to Canada. For example, how is one to understand the passions surrounding current events in the Middle East and Central Asia, if one does not know something about the rise of Islam, and its cultural relationship to both Judaism and Christianity? More locally, how is one to understand why a young Muslim woman, born and raised in a primarily secular country such as Canada, would happily *choose* to wear the *hijab*? Why would a young Jain born into a North American culture so committed to a meat-based diet be so enthusiastic to advance the principles of vegetarianism? To understand these questions we must first understand the cultural contexts and associated sacred meaning underpinning their choices.

Thirdly, the study of world religions and their particular *ethos* gives us all the opportunity to individually reflect, shape, and articulate our own unique vision of reality. That is, in order to be adept in our own judgments about the range of philosophical and ethical choices in modern life, we need a comparative perspective.

This chapter is divided into two main sections. The first section will deal with the issues surrounding a working definition of religion, then with religion's importance within the "cultural project," and finally with religion as part of identity formation. The second section will deal with some aspects of the history of religion in Canada. This is obviously a broad topic, so there will be a focus on certain immigration patterns and the resultant political legislation. And finally, there will be a concluding statement on future challenges for religion in this country.

CRITICAL THINKING OUTSIDE THE BOX 6.1

If Weber was correct in drawing the connections between capitalism, economic progress, and Divine Providence, in which religious context do you think he would place the globalization model of today?

COMING TO TERMS WITH RELIGION

In the Lecture Hall: So What Is Religion?

Picture a small, darkened seminar room in Halifax, Nova Scotia. The theme of the seminar is "Religion and Meaning, and the Meaning of Religion." As the keynote speaker approaches the podium, the stage is bathed in an ethereal white light from the data projector. Block letters, filling the screen, pose the following question: "SO WHAT IS RELIGION?" Over the speaker system of the hall, the audience of religion students, academics, and the curious are treated to a rendition of the popular R.E.M. song, "Losing my Religion."

As the song fades, the speaker approaches the microphone and asks, "Interesting song? So, who knows what the title refers to?"

An awkward moment of silence, then a single hand from the back of the room. "Give it a shot," urges the speaker.

"The song is referring to an old saying," states a young woman who, judging by her eloquent inflection, is from the southern regions of the United States, "when someone *loses their religion*, it means they are losing their footing in the world. They are losing their mind, their grip on reality."

"Well done," responds the speaker. "So how, exactly, would you define the religion that the singer of our song appears to have lost?"

An anonymous voice from the darkened room: "I think he's lost his connection with God. It is like he has lost his bond with the transcendent, that thing that is bigger than you and me."

"Could be," responds the speaker. "Any other suggestions?"

"Perhaps he's feeling disoriented in the world. Maybe he's lost his sense of community, and his identity in that community. Perhaps his community is that thing that 'is bigger than you and me,' and he feels overwhelmed."

"Again, an excellent answer. Perhaps we should spend some time answering the question, 'What is religion?' and then maybe we'll have a better idea of what it is that the singer, Michael Stipe, might be losing. Today I want to start our discussion with the following definitions." The speaker offers a second slide, and reads to the audience:

> Durkheim's primary thrust in his sociological definition of religion is that "the idea of religion is inseparable from the idea of Church, it conveys the notion that religion must be eminently a collective thing."[3]

The speaker pipes in, "Perhaps this reflects what Michael Stipe has lost in his song—that somehow he has lost his sense of relationship to the collective community? After all, he appears to be all alone while under the spotlight. That somehow losing one's religion represents incredible loneliness."

After a short moment for audience reflection, the third slide appears on the screen:

According to Weber, the most elementary forms of behaviour motivated by religious or magical factors are oriented to this world. "That is, 'may go well with thee . . . and that thou mayest prolong thy days upon the earth' (Deut. 4:40) expresses the reason for the performance of actions enjoined by religion or magic. . . . Thus, religious or magical behaviour or thinking must not be set apart from the range of everyday purposive conduct, particularly since even the ends of the religious and magical actions are predominantly economic.[4]

Followed by the fourth slide:

Max Müller states that "Religion is an effort to conceive the inconceivable and to express the inexpressible, an aspiration toward the infinite."

There's an audible murmur in the crowd as the fifth slide is put on the screen:

According to Clifford Geertz, "A religion is (1) a system of symbols which acts to (2) establish powerful, pervasive, and long-lasting moods and motivations in men [sic] by (3) formulating conceptions of a general order of existence and (4) clothing these conceptions with such an aura of factuality that (5) the moods and motivations seem uniquely realistic."[5]

After a short pause, the speaker asks his audience, "So, are we satisfied with these definitions of religion? What is right with them, or what's wrong with them?"

A voice from the front row of the seminar theatre says, "Well, from a positive standpoint these definitions certainly appear to do their best to put all religions into a 'nutshell'; they appear to make the definition clear, concise, and to the point."

Another interjects, "I have a problem with that. As I see it, these definitions try to **essentialize** religion, to reduce all religious belief to some single common 'essence' or solitary universal definition. As I see it, by trying to search for the 'essence' of religion, we end up with a definition that in many ways is much too vague, too incomplete."

"Can you provide an example of what you mean?" asks the speaker.

"Well, for one thing, I consider myself very spiritual, but I don't belong to a particular church or religious community, and I certainly don't believe in some supreme transcendent being or the 'infinite' as your Müller slide tries to tell us. Instead, I follow what my grandmother and mother taught me. I find my spiritual connection with nature. I still view myself as being a religious person, but if I had to have a 'church' I would have to say it is being in the presence of nature."

The speaker concludes, "Obviously we're going to have to have another look at defining religion."

Attempting a Definition

Although many of us cannot provide a definitive answer as to why we think the following, most agree that Judaism, Christianity, Islam, Hinduism, Buddhism, Jainism, Taoism, Confucianism, Shinto, and the tribal belief systems around the world are part of a category we call "world religions." But that raises a question: So what makes a religion a religion? Is it a system or institution concerned only with metaphysical speculation? If this is the case, we might have a problem with including Confucianism in our list, in view of its early emphasis on social philosophy, social hierarchy, and societal harmony rather than religious conjecture and metaphysical speculation. We might have similar problems with the metaphysical atheism of Buddhism and Jainism. It is certainly a nuance that has to be taken into consideration.

From such public discussions as shown in the section above, it is clearly very difficult to come up with "one essential statement" that is true of, and defines, all religions. Taking Müller's attempt for a moment, he states that all religions are "aspirations towards the infinite." Although on the surface this seems a good starting point, it does present us with our first problem. To what "infinite" is Müller specifically referring? Is it some transcendent, Supreme Being such as the "Creator God" we have in the Judeo-Christian and Islamic traditions, a Godhead with which one can have a personal relationship? Or is he referring to some impersonal "**Ultimate Reality**" similar to the principle of Brahma as described in the mediaeval and contemporary religious texts of Hinduism? Or perhaps the *tao* and *chi* of early Taoism, in which there is something akin to "the Force" described in the film *Star Wars*, which permeates the universe, but is devoid of personality traits?

Coming to Terms with the Infinite

Certainly if we were to interpret Müller's definition, at least from one perspective, and apply it to the Jain and Buddhist traditions, we would run into some difficulties. In both these religious traditions, the concept of a **transcendent God**, an infinite Supreme Being, or some form of an Ultimate Reality that creates, and ultimately "judges" the universe, is absent. At best, if one did have to express an "ultimate concern" within these traditions, one would have to say that the primary focus is on the principles underpinning *karma*— that is, action-as-cause-and-effect. In a *karma*-based tradition, there is no Supreme Being judging the actions of the individual. Instead, *karma* is the accumulated sum of all actions in which one has participated, and the subsequent results of those actions that "bear fruit" in some future existence. It is the individual, therefore, who is solely responsible for his or her own future experiences, not some external divine entity. Therefore, if we define religion as something that must have a "Godhead," one has to ask: Are Jainism and Buddhism religions, or are they simply an interesting worldview that ignores metaphysical speculation and its concerns over a relationship with an "infinite Being"? See Have You Heard? 6.1.

General Categories of World Religions

. . . .

Although most introductory texts suggest there are eight major 'world religions' and a few major philosophies, the reality is there are more than six thousand distinct religions in the world today, each with their own rituals, practices, and distinct belief systems. Yet despite these seemingly overwhelming numbers it is possible to categorize these world religions and philosophies into a few core categories.

Table 6.1:

Philosophical Category	View on Reality	View on Human Nature	Understanding of Truth	Core Values
Empiricist (the belief that there is an empirical explanation for all things) Atheism Existentialism Agnosticism (open to possibility of a god or Ultimate Reality)	There is no metaphysical universe. Reality is seen as purely empirical, and is based solely on the "laws of nature." There is no such thing as a soul or spirit, or afterlife.	Human beings are the product of both chance and the "natural process" of evolution. We are products of our biology.	Truth exists only as an existential or empirical experience. Truth is only that which can be proved primarily through the five senses (a posteriori).	Morals tend to be viewed as preferences that usually manifest as socially useful behaviours. Morals are subject to change, and the "laws of nature," including evolution.
Pantheistic (the belief that every existing entity is, in reality, only one Being; all other forms of reality are either modes, or appearances, of this Ultimate Reality.	Emphasis tends to be on the metaphysical as the primary component of existence. The physical realm is often viewed as an illusion or	Ultimately human beings are to recognize that they are truly one with the "Ultimate Reality,"	Truth is beyond all rational description and empirical experience. It can only be experienced when in unity	In the pantheistic traditions awareness of the true nature of the uni- verse is the ultimate

(cont'd)

Philosophical Category	View on Reality	View on Human Nature	Understanding of Truth	Core Values
Hinduism Taoism Buddhism Jainism New Age	deception from the true nature of reality (e.g., *maya* in Hinduism). The metaphysical realm such as Brahman in Hinduism, or the *tao* in Taoism, is eternal and impersonal. In general terms, every-thing is part of the Godhead, and the God-head is a part of everything and everyone.	and there-fore are spiritual and eternal. The idea of an individual self is the "great illu-sion" to be conquered.	with the "oneness" of the *universal principle*, or "Ultimate Reality." In the case of Buddhism and Jainism the *universal principle* is the law of *karma*.	moral "goodness." Failing to under-stand the essential unity of all things is the "illu-sion" or "evil" that must be conquered.
Theistic (the belief in the existence and continuance of the universe is owed to one supreme Being.) Judaism Christianity Islam Sikhism	God is both an eternal and a personal entity who created a finite, material world that has both a beginning and an end. Reality is viewed as both material and spiritual.	Humankind is the unique creation of God. Therefore, human beings are *individuals* that are spiritual and biological beings who have a personal relationship with their creator.	The true nature of the Godhead is known prima-rily through revelation (personal expe-rience, sacred texts, etc.), the five senses, and rational thought.	Moral values are those put forth by "the Absolute Moral Being"— God.

(cont'd)

Spiritism (the belief that the dead communicate with the living) **and** **Polytheistic** (the belief in many deities, usually male and female) Thousands of folk religions Many new religious movements	Although there may be an initial "creator being," the universe is populated by many spirit-beings who govern and are the cause of all "natural events."	Human beings are just one of the many creatures brought about by the gods and goddesses. Often in tribal traditions, the group or clan will have a special relationship with one god or goddess, or spirit guardian (either for protection of the clan or to administer punishment).	Truth about the natural world is discovered through the shaman figure, who has visions telling him what the gods and demons are doing and how they feel.	Moral values take the form of taboos, which are things that irritate or anger various spirits. These taboos are different from the idea of "good and evil" because it is just as important to avoid irritating evil spirits as it is good ones.
Religious Postmodernism (a philosophical strategy that attempts to destabilize monolithic modernist concepts such as identity, historical progress, epistemic certainty, and the univocity of meaning)	Reality is seen as a "social construction" that must be interpreted through our language and cultural "paradigm."	Human identity is exclusively a product of social setting. The idea that people are autonomous and free is a myth; they are a product of society.	Truths are mental constructs that are meaningful only to individuals within a particular cultural paradigm. They do not apply to other paradigms. Truth is relative to one's culture.	Values are part of our social paradigms as well. Tolerance, freedom of expression, inclusion, and refusal to claim to have the answers are the only universal values.

We would run into a similar problem if we were to suggest that a religion, by its very nature, must believe in the existence of an immortal entity identified as the soul. Interestingly, the idea that something of each individual existing beyond death is very old, or at least the archaeological evidence appears to demonstrate that our earliest ancestor provided great care to their deceased some 200 000 years ago. And though we do not have a definition of what these ancestors believed existed after death, we do know they felt that something of the individual existed beyond the grave.

So, if the existence of something akin to a soul was a prerequisite to our definition of religion, many of the ancient tribal and indigenous traditions would certainly qualify. And if we continue with this as our operating definition, certainly the Judaic, Christian, and Muslim traditions would all qualify, though they have a different understanding about the nature of the soul. But despite these differences, there is also a commonality in the various traditions—they all maintain every individual has a soul, and that in some way this soul will be judged in the afterlife. That is, every soul is a uniquely individual component of personality that will be either punished or rewarded in the "afterlife" according to that individual's actions in this world. In most cases this judgment is final and eternal. See Have You Heard? 6.2.

Here, however, is where we run into problems with our definition. Though the Jains believe in an entity called the soul (**jiva**), in contrast to the traditional Judeo-Christian and Muslim definitions of soul, or the soul as ancestor spirit as described by many of the folk traditions around the world, both the Jains and many of the Hindu sects do not understand this entity to have any individual personality associated with it. In point of

HAVE YOU HEARD? 6 .2

World Religions by Population

. . . .

The following table includes both officially recognized organized religions that primarily adhere to a single orthodoxy of belief and those less formal in their social structure, religious hierarchy, or singular orthodoxy of belief. It is also interesting to note that most of these traditions have varying degrees of representation among the Canadian population. Unfortunately it is difficult to get exact percentages of population from Statistics Canada, as many fall under "Other" in the categories; however, a cursory glance at the telephone directory of any large urban centre or similar resources (e.g., the Multifaith

Council of Canada) provides insight into the number of different religions and sects represented in Canada.

World Religions by Population, 2006 (averaging of various sources)

Christianity	2 billion
Roman Catholicism	1.1 billion
Protestantism	360 million
Eastern Orthodoxy	220 million
Anglican	84 million
Other Christians	280 million
Islam	1.3 billion
Sunni	940 million
Shiite	120 million
Hinduism	900 million
Secular/nonreligious/agnostic/atheist	1 billion
Buddhism	376 million
Mahayana	185 million
Theravada	124 million
Chinese traditional religions[i]	394 million
Indigenous/folk religions[ii]	285 million
African traditional and religions that trace roots to African origins	95 million[iii]
Sikhism	25 million
Spiritism[iv]	14 million
Judaism	14 million
Bahá'í Faith	6.8 million
Jainism	5.3 million
Shinto	4.4 million
Cao Dai[v]	3 million
Tenrikyo[vi]	2.4 million
Zoroastrianism	2 million
Neopaganism	1.1 million
Unitarian Universalism	800 000
Rastafarianism[vii]	700 000
Scientology	550 000

[i]Not a single organized religion; includes all Chinese religions that contain elements of Taoism, Confucianism, and traditional indigenous folk religions.

[ii]Includes world folk traditions and Shamanism and Paganism.

[iii]Not a single organized religion; includes several traditions such as Yoruba, Santeria, and Vodoun.

[iv]Not a single organized religion; includes a variety of belief systems.

[v]A universal faith with the principle that all religions have the same divine origin, which is God, or Allah, or the Tao, or the Nothingness, and the same ethic based on love and justice, and are just different manifestations of one single truth.

[vi]A modern eastern religion based in concepts of the Japanese Shinto and Buddhist traditions.

[vii]Primarily an Ethiopian-based religion; prominent within the Jamaican community.

fact, the Jains would view those characteristics defined as personality more in keeping with those components that are the direct result of *karma*. The Jains understand personality to be *karmic* material that acts much like a ship's anchor holding the boat firmly to the ocean floor. It is karma that keeps the soul in bondage and away from liberation (**moksha**). Personality, therefore, is all those attachments and desires that manifest themselves within the material universe as either a human being, a god, a hell-being, an animal, or a plant, and holds the "pure soul" within the eternal cycles of reincarnation (**samsara**). Personality is one of the components of *samsara* (cycles of reincarnation) from which one should free one's self to gain liberation.

The Buddhists, on the other hand, would agree with the Jain philosophical position of *moksha*—that one must become free (**nirvana**) from the cycles of reincarnation (birth, death, and rebirth)—but would counter the Jain position stating that there is no such object, being, or eternal entity that one could call a soul. Would we be willing to say at this juncture that Jainism is a religion because it believes in an entity called "soul," but Buddhism is not because it does not believe in such an entity? To most scholars the answer would be inclusive: of course, both are religions.

"Big R" and "Little r" Religion

Before attempting to provide a descriptive template for religion, two more issues should be addressed. The first concerns those people who feel they are deeply religious, and yet do not participate within the framework of a formal religious movement or organization. In many cases, they belong to a group that is often marginalized outside the traditional mainstream religions (some may characterize these entities as "religious cults"). Many members of the Wiccan community across Canada, for example, have often stated to me in interviews that they do not recognize the imposed hierarchies of mainstream religions, nor do they accept the concepts of "the Infinite" or "the Transcendent" as used in the traditional senses. Instead, they often view "the Ultimate" in terms of both *unity with the forces of nature* and a unifying relationship they have with other members of their coven or local communities. For them, religion is not some essentialized doctrine or dogma, nor is it the hierarchical structure often associated with mainstream religious organizations; rather, it is an individual, internalized experience in relationship to an external spiritual and material world.

Secondly, it is apparent that when people talk about their religion, they do so in two different modes. On the one hand, there is **"big R" religion**—the type of religion one often reads about in introductory texts about religion and developed by either the religious specialist or academic. Then there is "little r" religion, which often refers to the area of study anthropologists describe as "that part of religion that becomes messy." This is the religion that is often passed from grandmother, to mother, to daughter, or from grandfather, to father, to son. **"Little r" religion**, then, is that religious practice that occurs *on the ground*—to coin an anthropological term—or in the home of an individual family unit. It is the traditional practices of our families, and not that which was conveyed by some religious specialist, academic, or religious institution. It is the type of religious practice that tends to be impossible to essentialize, because every family has a different practice or custom.

Religion as Builder of Worlds

In the opening pages of his text *The Sacred Canopy*, Peter Berger states, "every human society is an enterprise of world-building [, and] religion occupies a distinctive place in this enterprise."[6] Extending the social theories of such notables as Karl Marx, Emile Durkheim, and Max Weber, Berger contends that the phenomenal world, and how that world is perceived, understood, and acted upon by human beings is actually a **dialectical process** that constantly "creates" and "re-creates" the world through a procedure of **externalization, objectivation**, and **internalization**. Berger defines these terms as follows:

> Externalization is the ongoing outpouring of human being into the world, both in the physical and the mental activity of men. Objectivation is the attainment by the products of this activity (again both physical and mental) of a reality that confronts its original producers as a facticity external to and other than themselves. Internalization is the reappropriation by men of this same reality, transforming it once again from structures of the objective world into structures of the subjective consciousness. It is through externalization that society is a human product. It is through objectivation that society becomes a reality sui generis. It is through internalization that man is a product of society.[7]

CRITICAL THINKING OUTSIDE THE BOX 6.2

Despite Canada's guarantee to its citizens of religious freedom, can you think of examples of either "big R" or "little r" that should not be practised within the Canadian context? For example, if male circumcision is allowed based on religious belief and practice, should we also allow for the practice of female circumcision if performed in a sterile, hospital setting?

To try to put these definitions into context, externalization occurs when human perceptions and understanding of the universe become externally manifest as representations in both the things that we make (objects, tools, art, music, institutions, culture, etc.) and the things we do with those "products" within the public sphere. In short, human beings project meaning into the empty vastness of the universe by creating both a material and an institutional culture that reflects that meaning.

In turn these **products of the human cultural project** become the primary objects (*objectivation*) of our attention. That is, we begin to interact with the representations we have created as if they were the universe itself. Interaction with, and the subsequent internalization of, these objects begins to change us. For example, consider the institution of marriage. The roles of husband or wife are objectively defined by the existing culture to represent models for individual conduct within a particular culture. As Berger states,

> By playing these roles, the individual comes to represent the institutional objectivities in a way that is apprehended, by himself and by others, as detached from the "mere" accidents of his individual existence. . . . Society assigns to the individual not only a set of roles but a designated identity. . . . Internalization is . . . the reabsorption into consciousness of the objectivated world in such a way that the structures of this world [culture] come to determine the subjective structures of consciousness itself.[8]

From this perspective, culture is a project meant to bring order to a universe that may appear to the individual as both chaotic and sometimes meaningless.

Religion as Our Response to the Meaningless

On the surface, religion-as-dialectic-process appears to be both culturally stabilizing and self-contained. Indeed, if the individual finds resonance with these social roles and cultural institutions, he or she freely identifies with and participates within the "social project," as opposed to feeling society is forcing one to participate in a given role. This stable social environment is what Berger calls the **nomos**.

There is a problem, however, and this begins with the realization that the "dialectic" is actually a process, rather than an end. In other words, human culture is a project that is never "finished"—culture is inherently in a constant state of flux. Social environments change, in large part, because the "institutional programs are sabotaged by individuals with conflicting interests," or the "original" meaning underpinning the socially constructed world is simply forgotten from one generation to the next. Reaction to this change by the social collective, and the subsequent reabsorption of a newly reconstructed vision by both the individual and the consciousness of the social collective, can create "new worlds" of meaning and understanding, but it also gives rise to the identification of the primary human predicament—*culture is inherently volatile, unpredictable, and unstable.*

Religion, therefore, is the ultimate response to this predicament. In order to protect the individual, and ultimately society, from the breakdown of the existing social order, myths, rituals, and orthodoxy are established to help merge the internalized, humanly constructed *nomos* with that which is perceived to have been divinely constructed. In other words, to convince the social collective that society and its roles and institutions are not simply the construction of human beings that are prone to "human error," religion is used to sacralize the existing social order—to make it sacred, to set it apart as something divinely constructed, and therefore something both eternal and immortal. In this sense religion is "world maintaining."[9]

Religion as Destroyer of Worlds

There is, however, another side to religion. To use a cliché, religion is very much a two-sided coin. One side reveals religion as the ultimate response to the volatility of the cultural project. Religion is used to make sacred the cultural project, provide its members with social stability, and, in turn, provide the universe with meaning. But what happens when the cultural project begins to alienate its own participants? What happens when members of a culture discover that, instead of meaning and constancy, their sense of the universe and the state of the culture is actually in a condition of chaos and disintegration? To a large extent, history has provided the answer; it has shown us the other side of the coin, so to speak.

In contrast to religion being an enterprise that is "world building and world maintaining," it can also be the very organism that overthrows an existing social order. While religion can be initiated by an existing social order to maintain its way of life through claims that it was modelled after the diktat of some divine source, it can also challenge the very nature of this premise. It can pull back the veil of society's religious mystery, the **sacred canopy** protecting its cultural institutions from assault, and reveal that the status quo is nothing but a human construct, a project neither immortal, nor divinely inspired, nor immune to critical errors. Religion can also be the very mechanism of challenge and change to the social order with a new "divine message" or diktat.

Religion as Cultic Project

Throughout history, there are many examples of religion being the catalyst for social change: the Buddha (Buddhism) and Mahavira (Jainism) challenging the social and metaphysical hierarchies developed within the South Asian Vedic sacrificial culture; Jesus of Nazareth testing the priestly order in the Jerusalem Temple; Mohammed casting out the pagan idols contained within the Ka'ba and reinstituting monotheism in the Arabian peninsula (and beyond); St. Francis questioning the Christian monastic orders in Europe; Confucius addressing the chaos of the Warring States period in China; and in many ways, the religio-cultic political figures of Lenin, Mao, Castro, and Che in their struggle against the excesses described within Weber's model of Protestant theology and its new morality for entrepreneurial capitalist behaviour. Although we don't often think in terms of these new religious movements as being **cults**, these examples are in fact religio-cultic responses to a preexisting cultural order that has either marginalized or alienated (***anomie***) individuals within their midst. In response, the cult is born. That is, to paraphrase both Lorne Dawson and Steven Tipton, the reason for an individual or group's conversion to an alternative cultural paradigm is that people experience "ethical contradictions of unusual intensity" in the present cultural project, and therefore will gravitate to a new paradigm that provides a coherent solution.[10]

Within this paradigm, cults can be considered both beneficial and harmful. To the existing cultural order, any cult presents a challenge to their power and the ideals of the status quo. On the other hand, for those on the margins of society, the cult—whether it pays homage to a divine being, a charismatic leader, a cultural object or institution, or, in more modern times, an abstract ideal—can provide an alternative cultural project to restore order and meaning to their lives. See Have You Heard? 6.3.

Religion and Fundamentalism

Have you heard of that madman who lit a lantern in the bright morning hours, ran to the market place, and cried incessantly, "I seek God! I seek God!" As many of those who do not believe in God were standing around just then, he provoked much laughter. . . . "Whither is God," he cried. "I shall tell you. We have killed him—you and I. All of us are murderers. . . . God is dead. God remains dead. And we have killed him. . . .

—Friedrich Nietzsche, *The Gay Science* (1882), section 126.

Nietzsche made one of the most controversial declarations about the state of the modern humanist movement when he proclaimed that modernism's greatest accomplishment was to have finally "killed" God. This God, according to Nietzsche, was created and used as an instrument of social oppression, a cultural tool to redirect society's attention away from the potential freedoms of this world, and to point it toward some escapist other-world located in heaven (or hell). Much like Karl Marx, Nietzsche viewed religion as an anathema that oppressed the "masses," an illusion created by the social order to maintain social obedience among "the herd," and to curtail the full exploration of individual freedom. To kill off God was to clear the path to the experience of true freedom for the individual (even if that freedom includes the freedom to feel pain as well as joy).

HAVE YOU HEARD? 6.3

Cults and the Danger Signs

· ·

In many ways, the definition of "cult" has become so blurred it has lost any significant meaning. As shown above, cults can be the early form of life-affirming cultural movements whose intent is to replace social disintegration and anomie with order and meaning. In this sense, cults can be liberating, but they can also be a tool to oppress their members. Below are some of the cautionary danger signs of such cults.

Charismatic Leadership
- Most cults tend to be led by a charismatic leader, who is usually male. In many cases the leader has been married, but he or she tends to become "single" in conjunction with the growth of the cult.
- The leader dominates the membership, closely controlling them physically, sexually, and emotionally.
- The individual personalities of cult members are subsumed by that of the charismatic leader.

Apocalyptic Beliefs
- One warning sign is that the leader focuses heavily on the impending end of the world, often involving a great battle (e.g., images of Armageddon).
- Another sign is that the leader advocates suicide in order for the group to be transported to "another world" to escape the coming world devastation (e.g., the Solar Temple cult in Canada; the Heaven's Gate group).
- Members are expected to play a major, leadership role at and after the "end time."

Social Encapsulation
- Most cults tend to be small religious groups, and not an established denomination (although some may be "breakaway" groups).
- Most of the members, especially the "core members," live in communities isolated either physically or psychologically from the rest of society.
- Non-members are often demonized and considered "the enemy." There is often the sense within the cult that they are being closely monitored by the social authorities, and that these authorities are attempting to persecute the cult.
- Both information and contacts from outside the cult are severely curtailed.

Other Warning Signs
- In accordance with the social encapsulation process, many recent cults have been known to prepare defensive compounds and assemble a vast array of weapons and poisons (e.g., People's Temple, Branch Davidians, Solar Temple, Aum Shinrikyo, Heaven's Gate).
- Theologically many cults appear to be associated with a familiar religious tradition, but they often have some unique deviation from it. They often stress this as "the new Revelation" with a focus on end-time prophecies.

Important note: Though they may exhibit some of the characteristics listed above, some cult communities may not be considered dangerous. For example:

- Some of the factors may not be practised to such an intense degree, or may be absent altogether. For example, some groups may have a charismatic leader, and promote an "end times" theology, but not present a danger or advocate violence to either the "outsider" community or its own members.
- Some cults may "advocate" hatred toward the "outsiders" or minority groups (e.g., homosexuals, ethnic groups, or those with a particular political affiliation), but not call for direct or immediate violence against them. The problem, of course, is that they may impel others associated with the cult to take action.
- Some religious groups, although not a threat to the larger society, may risk the health of their own members. For example, groups such as the Jehovah's Witness recommend that their members refuse blood transfusion, and members of the Christian Science Church ask that their members refuse all medical help, and seek healing through prayer. Also, issues surrounding the treatment of children and corporal punishment have been raised in recent years.

CRITICAL THINKING OUTSIDE THE BOX 6.3

Often cults are considered only within a religious context. But they can also be applied to political ideologies. Can you think of cults that might be political in nature? Using the model for cultic warning signs, how much do these political ideologies resemble religious cults?

The problem of secularizing the social order—and this concept was not really developed by Nietzsche and other existentialists—was that it took away the *sacred canopy* of society. On a surface reading, "killing God" was seen as an opportunity to be truly free, an opportunity to break the yoke of an outdated social construct that no longer provided meaning and order to the world. But for those who valued the role of the sacred canopy, its removal exposed secular society as a "Godless society" with a "Godless morality," a society constructed by human beings alone, very much prone to the "evils" of human error. For this group "killing God" meant killing a divine order and, more importantly, a disintegration of its divine morality. One response to the failures of the modernist state—viewed as a morally bankrupt political system—was the rise of religious **fundamentalism** during the 19th, the 20th, and now the 21st, centuries.

In North America this renewed religio-cultural project tends to be associated with a wide spectrum of traditional evangelical (both Protestant and Catholic) and Christian fundamentalisms, many of which are associated with the political conservative right-wing of both American and Canadian politics. Interestingly, this development in North America has come in response to what has been perceived as the steady decline in the influence of the more traditional religious denominations, and the increase of the control of the public sphere by the modernist state. In Quebec, for example, the "Quiet Revolution" took place during the 1960s with the election of the Liberal Party. The result of this election was that the church no longer held sway over education, social services, and health care (Newfoundland was to follow this path a bit later)—the *curé* in Quebec was replaced by the modernist state. In Ontario we see a similar "revolution." The traditional domination of Anglo-Protestantism, particularly in the urban centres such as Toronto, was quickly losing its grip as it found itself adapting to the federal government's policy of multiculturalism (1971). For many, religious conservatism was losing out to the "revolutionary" ideals of social liberalism.

CRITICAL THINKING OUTSIDE THE BOX 6.4

Do you see a Canadian politician's declaration of being a Christian fundamentalist a concern for our multicultural political and social stability?

Fundamentalism in the World

These movements are not confined, however, to either Europe or North America. On an international level we see the rise of fundamentalist forms of Hinduism in South Asia, new religions in China, evangelical movements in South Korea, the Orthodox church in both the former Soviet Union and its subject states, and various fundamentalist factions of Islam throughout the world—most a response to the corruption, social chaos, and meaninglessness created by the human secularization of the cultural project. In other words, the fundamentalist perceives the modernist ideal of the secular nation-state as a system of **failed states**—a system that is morally bankrupt because of the secularization project. In response then, religion and its "sacred canopy" is very much reentering the global cultural discourse. And to some extent, understanding this trend, however distasteful we may view the extremist outcome produced by these sentiments, may provide some insight into the events leading up to "9/11."

When I first heard this joke about thirty years ago, I didn't realize the importance of the statement: "God is dead—Nietzsche / Nietzsche is dead—God." In the light of recent events around the world, I wonder if this statement of humour has even more relevance today, as it raises the important question: How is the modernist cultural project to deal with religious groups that understand God to be, despite Nietzsche's claim, very much alive and meaningfully guiding their lives? One response might be Canada's *Multiculturalism Act*, an act meant to provide equality to all religious points of view, yet ensuring no domination by one group over another.

CRITICAL THINKING OUTSIDE THE BOX 6.5

Canada's Solution—The Multiculturalism Act of 1985

Using the material excerpted from the Act quoted below, choose one of the following areas of discussion:
- With an eye to the *Multiculturalism Act*, discuss or write your views on the best way to integrate religion with the secular.
- Is Canada's multicultural policy a good solution to issues of religious conflict? Why or why not?
- Canada was the first country in the world to actually legislate multiculturalism. Should all countries in the world follow Canada's lead? Why or why not?
- Should students/citizens be given provision/locations in the public arena in which to conduct prayers or religious services?

From the *Multiculturalism Act*:

*An Act for the preservation and enhancement of multiculturalism in
Canada [1988, c. 31, assented to 21st July, 1988]*
Preamble

- WHEREAS the Constitution of Canada provides that
  every individual is equal before and under the law and
  has the right to the equal protection and benefit of the
  law without discrimination and that everyone has the
  freedom of conscience, religion, thought, belief, opinion,
  expression, peaceful assembly and association and guarantees those rights and freedoms equally to male and female
  persons;
- AND WHEREAS the Constitution of Canada recognizes the importance of preserving and enhancing the
  multicultural heritage of Canadians;
- AND WHEREAS Canada is a party to the International
  Convention on the Elimination of All Forms of Racial
  Discrimination, which Convention recognizes that all
  human beings are equal before the law and are entitled
  to equal protection of the law against any discrimination and against any incitement to discrimination, and
  to the International Covenant on Civil and Political
  Rights, which Covenant provides that persons belonging
  to ethnic, religious or linguistic minorities shall not be
  denied the right to enjoy their own culture, to profess
  and practise their own religion or to use their own
  language;
- AND WHEREAS the Government of Canada recognizes the diversity of Canadians as regards race, national
  or ethnic origin, colour and religion as a fundamental
  characteristic of Canadian society and is committed
  to a policy of multiculturalism designed to preserve
  and enhance the multicultural heritage of Canadians
  while working to achieve the equality of all Canadians in
  the economic, social, cultural and political life of
  Canada;. . . .[11]

CANADA AND ITS RELIGIOUS EXPERIENCE

It has been four centuries since the arrival of the Europeans and the establishment of their permanent settlements in Canada. And although the arrival of the French and its Roman Catholic faith may initially have been on good terms with the indigenous First Nations Peoples—a focus more on trade and commerce than religious conversion—this peace was not to last. Native spirituality as the dominant religion in Canada was, by the early 1600s, supplanted by the Franco-Europeans, whose focus shifted from trading commodities to imposing their cultural values on the religious landscape. The template for Canadian history had been formed.

As we look back at Canada's rich cultural tapestry, the threads of religion have always been located front and centre. Whatever the origin of its peoples—First Nations, French, British, American, Irish, Scottish, Asiatic, South Asian, Ukrainian, Italian, African, Arab, or Russian—religion has always provided these new Canadians with both a sense of meaning and an awareness of order and justice. Like a double-edged sword, however, religious belief and practice has also been one of the leading causes of conflict throughout Canadian history. As Robert Choquette states,

> [T]he arrival of the Europeans in Canada [has] often been characterized by rivalry, acrimony, and conflict among the leading religions in place. European Christians worked to eradicate Amerindian spiritualities, Protestants fought Catholics and vice versa, Jews were frequently the victims of discrimination by Christians, and Asiatic Chinese and Japanese were the targets of repressive legislation. That has been because each religion considered that it had the monopoly of truth; all others were in error. Therefore, the religious group that was dominant usually made life difficult for all religion minorities.[12]

For the most part, religious conflict in the first 250 years of the European presence in Canada was primarily fuelled by the religious and political hostility centred in Europe—the fighting between Roman Catholics (French, Spanish, and later the Irish) and Protestants (British and Dutch). These religious wars continued in the lands the Europeans colonized, and in the case of Canada and North America they meant a battle for souls by "evangelizing" the peoples of the First Nations. North America was seen by the Europeans as a land not only of economic opportunity (politically and economically based colonialism), but also one in which to develop their religious vision of a "New Jerusalem"—a religious experiment in which a religious community could practise their particular tradition freely.

Between the years 1600 and 1760, the British and French fought for the sovereignty of Canada; however, with the end of what several historians call the "first true world war," France was to cede the Canadian territories to the British in 1763 with the signing of "the Treaty of Paris." For the next six years a series of treaties were signed with one of the major components being the establishment of a religious policy in the *new* Canada—a policy that was to last more than 150 years (but one not to be severely challenged on many fronts). For the most part these treaties spoke of a policy of religious freedom for Canada's Catholics, an unusual policy by the British-as-conqueror, and a unique policy experiment for its time. This was, however, only a surface reading of the British intent in Canada. The "unofficial" message given the governors of Quebec was quite different. For the most part they were directed to "hold the church on a tight leash, to restrict its freedom as much as possible, and to do everything they could to promote the interests of the Protestant religion."[13] Between the 1760s treaty-years and the 1800s both the British Crown and its Protestant émigré population undertook a project to make Protestantism the official religion of Canada. The British largely succeeded in this venture—Upper Canadian and Maritime politics was to be dominated by Protestantism, but Lower Canada and parts of Newfoundland were to be dominated by Roman Catholicism (a power that was not seriously challenged in Quebec until the rise of the sovereigntist movement in the 1960s). As the British pushed westward, so did the domination of its pro-Protestant political and social policies. See Have You Heard? 6.4 and 6.5.

HAVE YOU HEARD? 6.4

Top 10 Religions in Canada, 2001

· ·

Group	Identified Membership	Percentage of Population
Roman Catholic	12.8 million	43.2%
No religion	4.8 million	16.2%
United Church of Canada	2.8 million	9.6%
Anglican	2.0 million	6.9%
Apostolic, Evangelical	780 thousand	2.6%
Baptist	729 thousand	2.5%
Lutheran	607 thousand	2.0%
Muslim	580 thousand	2.0%
Other Protestant	549 thousand	1.9%
Presbyterian	410 thousand	1.4%

Note: Census data on religions in Canada is collected every ten years (i.e., 2011 Census).

Source: Adapted from Statistics Canada, "Top Ten Religions in Canada," adapted from the Statistics Canada publication "Highlight tables, 2001 Census," Catalogue No. 97F0024XIE2001015, released 13 May 2003, available at: <www12.statcan.ca/english/census01/products/highlight/religion/Index.cfm?Lang=E>.

The First Challenge to British Canada and Protestant Domination

Despite travelling a rather "rocky road," it appears that by the 1850s there was a relative religio-political equilibrium between the dominant Protestant ruling class and Roman Catholicism. Perhaps one of the major factors contributing to this was the relative singular ethnicity of its peoples. That is, most new Canadians were arriving from the land of western and northern Europe. By the 1860s, however, the constancy of this "European ethno-culture" was to be challenged, and for the next 100 years the ethnic, cultural, and religious composition of Canada was to become one of the most diverse in the world. As space is too short to thoroughly outline the details of this diversity, we will focus on two non-European immigrant groups, the Chinese and South Asians, as an example of this new immigrant pattern and the dominant culture's reaction to it.

The First Major Wave of Non-European Immigrants to Canada: The Chinese

Although Captain John Meares, a retired British naval officer, noted the presence of people of Chinese origin on the western shores of Canada (British North America) as early as 1788, most sources indicate that it wasn't until 1858, with the beginning of the Fraser Valley Gold Rush, that we see large-scale immigration to Canada of the Chinese from both California and China—in the period of 1858 to 1884 entry into Canada as either labourer or prospector was unrestricted. By the 1860s, and particularly after Confederation (1867), pressure from a land-hungry United States forced an exacting effort by the newly formed Canadian government to push into the Canadian West in order to maintain sovereignty from coast to coast. This required building a national railroad. Despite considerable efforts by the Canadian government of its day to increase immigration from Europe, labour shortages in the underpopulated West, especially for the building of the railroad, continued to plague the government.

In China during this period, increases in both population and taxes forced many off the land. Industrialists in Canada saw an opportunity—Canada needed labour, and those Chinese who chose to leave their homeland saw economic opportunities in Canada. Between the years 1881 and 1884, 17 000 Chinese arrived in Canada, most under contract to the Canadian Pacific Railway to complete the connection between British Columbia and the rest of Canada.[14]

With the completion of the railway in 1885, the West was finally opened to "the rails" and the need for Chinese labourers had all but disappeared. The "white society" of British Columbia looked upon members of the Chinese community as competition for the few jobs remaining in the region. The government's response was to impose a $50 "head tax" on all Chinese immigrants. The "head tax" policy, continued well past World War I, in time had increased from $50 to $500 per person. Despite this enormous tax, and the fact that many Chinese were excluded from industry and commerce in the West and forced to move eastward as far as Toronto, immigration from China still continued until the early 1920s. However, compounding the demise of the Chinese labour market was the return of the Canadian soldiers from the war. The situation became so tense between the "white community" and the Chinese community that the government was "forced" to bring two acts before Parliament: the *Dominion Elections Act* of 1920, which took away the federal franchise rights of both the Chinese and South Asian Immigrants and the *Chinese Immigration Act* of 1923, which virtually prohibited any Chinese immigrant from entering Canada.[15]

South Asian Immigration to Canada: The Problems of Identification

In many ways the immigration pattern of the South Asian community parallels that of the Chinese immigrant population, as did the response by the dominant "white" culture in Canada to this group. It was Canada's relationship with Great Britain and the other Commonwealth nations, however, that was profoundly different from the Chinese experience and facilitated the first wave of South Asian immigrants to continental North America.

Members of the British Commonwealth were initially granted special access to other Commonwealth countries. South Asians, especially those who served in the British Army (i.e., the Sikhs), were considered "full members" of the Commonwealth nations and given limited preference in consideration for immigration. However, the host countries did not necessarily appreciate this special status, and many supported laws that discriminated again non-white members of the Commonwealth. In time, this movement to ban South Asian entry into Canada grew exponentially. The Chinese, on the other hand,

---

CRITICAL THINKING OUTSIDE THE BOX 6.6

Both the Chinese and Japanese had private property either destroyed or confiscated during different periods of their Canadian experience. In the light of Canada's present policy of multiculturalism, is it the duty of its current citizens to make reparations for these past transgressions?

were never members of the Commonwealth (with just a few colonial exceptions); they were never considered for special status, and therefore were the first to feel the effects of discriminatory laws in Canada. Eventually, these laws were passed to include both Asians and South Asians.

Unfortunately, existing documentation in the early days of Confederation (1867) can provide only a meagre glimpse into South Asian immigration and visitation patterns between 1867 and 1899.[16] For example, according to Roger Daniels there were a total of 491 "Indian entries between 1871 and 1899 . . . but this data reflects place of birth as well as race," and in many cases, unlike in the Chinese example, race and place of birth were often confused. Immigrants might be of British, French, Dutch, Persian, or African ancestry, but if they were born within the colonial jurisdiction of British India they might be incorrectly classified as "Indian" by birth—or vice versa.[17]

Keeping these descriptions in mind, there are some Canadian studies that attempt to paint a slightly more definitive picture of the early South Asian immigrant and visiting patterns to Canada. For example, C.I. Petros concludes that although specific names of the first South Asian immigrants to Canada are not known, it is clear from the early records and reports that there "had been visits of Indian dignitaries and Indian seamen, to Vancouver, in the west coast of Canada, especially after the opening of the trans-Canada rail route to the eastern ports."[18]

Patterns of South Asian Immigration to Canada: The First Wave

Although the historical context of the story varies, the first wave of South Asians to establish themselves in Canada were largely members of the Sikh community both from India (retired army officers who had served under the British Raj) and "from established Indian communities in Hong Kong."[19] According to George Kurian (1993) and web publications by both the Government of Canada and members of the Canadian Sikh community,[20] the event that marked the genesis of South Asian immigration from the Indian subcontinent to North America was the visit of Sikh soldiers to British Columbia on their return journey (to Hong Kong and India) after participating in Queen Victoria's Diamond Jubilee celebrations in 1897. The visiting group initially received a friendly welcome from their "official" Canadian hosts, particularly from prospective employers. As Buchignani states, highly placed officials within the Canadian government did not share the local concerns that South Asian immigrants might not be "warmly received" and cited "the beneficial effect of South Asians in British Guyana, Trinidad, and elsewhere.[21] Thanks in large part to the various rumours of job availability (particularly with regard to the expansion of the national railway, the west coast lumber mills/logging camps, and farming), offers of Canadian farmland to any British subject, and compelling sales tactics by shipping companies hoping to cash in on any migrants willing to book passage on their ships, the soldiers returned to India (particularly the Punjab) to "spread the news."

A variation on this story states that the single incident that fuelled immigration of Indians to Canada was the visit of a group of soldiers under Sergeant Major Kadir Khan Bahdur who were on their way back after attending the coronation of Edward VII in 1902. Although both versions of the story are acknowledged by the Sikh community and the Canadian governmental sources, a greater emphasis is placed on the first (with Captain Kesur Singh being the first Sikh soldier to arrive in Canada). Records with Citizenship and Immigration Canada mention both versions, but again, they lean toward the "Queen Victoria version." What all sources agree upon is that the first permanent South Asian immigrants arrived in British Columbia in 1903–04, and totalled 45 "Hindoos"[22] (an obvious misnomer, even though a few were in fact members of the Hindu religious tradition) who had mortgaged their land at 10 to 12 percent interest to raise the $65 they needed for their ship fare and the amount dedicated for the immigration (head) tax.

HAVE YOU HEARD? 6.5

Religious Trends in Canada by Percentage of Total Population

Religion	1981 Census	1991 Census	2001 Census
No religion	7.4%	12.3%	16.2%
Buddhism	0.2%	0.6%	1.0%
Catholic	47.5%	45.2%	43.2%
Protestant	41.2%	34.9%	29.2%
Eastern Orthodox	1.5%	1.4%	1.6%
Other Christian	—	1.3%	2.6%
Hinduism	0.3%	0.6%	1.0%
Judaism	1.2%	1.2%	1.1%
Islam	0.4%	0.9%	2.0%
Sikhism	0.3%	0.5%	0.9%

Note: Census data on religions in Canada is collected every ten years (i.e., 2011 Census).

Source: Adapted from Statistics Canada publications: *Religions in Canada, 2001 Census*, Catalogue 96F0030XIE200 1015, page 18 www12.statcan.gc.ca/English/census01/products/analytic/companion/re/pdf/96F003X1E2001015.pdf; and *The Muslim Canadians: A Profile*, 1981 Census, Catalogue 99-958, page 15.

In contrast to racial issues surrounding the earlier "wave" of Chinese and Japanese indentured labourers brought to the west coast of Canada, the initial reception of the South Asia migrants (who were already British subjects, and in many cases either educated professionals or retired members of the British army) was relatively "warm." This "warmth" was particularly demonstrated by one segment of Canadian society, the industrialists and railway company executives who had lobbied the government to increase the immigration numbers of inexpensive, unskilled, and semiskilled workers. What is interesting here is that these immigrants were not indentured labourers. They paid their own ship fares and immigration "taxes." It is arguable that many of the South Asian immigrants—those who were former members of the British Army or landowners from the Punjab region—were "underemployed" and that their skills were "underutilized" by those seeking the services of cheap, immigrant labour.

The "warm greeting" was short-lived, however. In contrast to the sentiments expressed by business owners and industrialists, many labour, political, and religious organizations raised objections to all forms of immigration whether the source of individuals was Asia, or South Asia, or northern or eastern Europe. On the Prairies, for example, suspicion and hatred of this kind were focused mainly on the first wave of Ukrainian (Roman Catholic and Orthodox) immigrants and the Doukhobors (Anabaptist) from Russia. For example, we have the following from the archives of Citizenship and Immigration Canada:

> Organized labour, of course, took a very jaundiced view of the hiring of unskilled immigrant labour by railways and manufacturing companies. One spokesman who did not hesitate to speak bluntly on the subject was James Wilks, a vice-president of the Trades and Labour Congress. In 1900, he wrote to Prime Minister Wilfrid Laurier about the impact that an influx of Scandinavians and Finns from Minnesota had on the Canadian labour market. Wilks beseeched the Laurier government to enforce the *Alien Labour Act*, a piece of legislation designed to prevent the importation of contract labour. Only rigorous enforcement of this law, claimed Wilks, would prevent Canada from being inundated with "ignorant, unfortunate . . . non-English-speaking aliens" who would do irreparable damage to the community. There was also widespread opposition to western pioneers from central and southeastern Europe. Excellent farmers they might have been, but in the eyes of many westerners this did not qualify them as desirable settlers. Only those who assimilated readily into the dominant Anglo-Saxon society were welcome.[23]

Despite these strenuous objections, Sir Clifford Sifton, who became Minister of the Interior in Sir Wilfrid Laurier's Liberal government in 1896, instituted a relatively tolerant immigration policy and simplified regulations to meet the economic needs of business, trade, manufacturing, and farming. Sifton actively persuaded immigrants, particularly from both eastern and western Europe, to come to Canada. He did this by appointing immigration agents in many countries, and advertising aggressively though handbills, newspapers, and periodicals. According to the archives of Statistics Canada, 2 500 000 immigrants from around the globe came to Canada between 1904 and 1913. The numbers of immigrants from India (almost exclusively male) were as follows:

1904–04	45
1905–06	387
1906–07	2124
1907–08	2623

Opposition to Asian and South Asian Immigration Rises: Legislation and the Riot

By 1907 the public outcry associated with perceptions of rising unemployment contributed to the problems of racial hatred, particularly against the Japanese and Chinese immigrants in British Columbia and the eastern Europeans in the Prairie provinces.[24] Headlines in the newspapers of the day demanded politicians act against the "rising tide" of immigrants, and the papers in British Columbia focused on the "crisis" created by the Chinese and South Asian immigrants "flooding the country" and working for "half the wages of a white worker." To keep these settlers out of Canada, the federal government increased their "head tax" on all Chinese immigrants from $50 in 1885 to $100 in 1900 and to $500 in 1903.[25] Immigration continued, however, and racial tensions came to a boil when white rioters in Vancouver (British Columbia), fuelled by racial propaganda supplied by hate groups such as the San Francisco–based Asiatic Exclusion League, attacked members of the Asian immigrant community in 1907 and destroyed property worth thousands of dollars (again, animosity focused largely on the Japanese and Chinese community).

Fortunately, members of the South Asian community were located in a different section of Vancouver and spared the brunt of the rioters' actions; however, they did receive the full impact of the British Columbia legislature. In 1907 the right to vote in provincial elections was denied to all Hindus (S.B.C. 1907, c. 6) and persons from India, and in 1908 the Municipal Elections Act (S.B.C. 1908 c. 14, s.13(1)) denied any "Chinese, Japanese or other Asian or Indian person the right to vote in any municipal election."[26]

Federally, with Sifton's resignation in 1905, Laurier's government began to bow to pressure from the majority "white population"—one that was steadily growing with a new influx of immigrants from the British Isles—fellow politicians, various labour organizations, and members of the Christian clergy, and by 1907–08 introduced a federal Order-in-Council demanding all Indian and Asian immigrants have at least $200 in their possession before entering Canada.[27]

Feeling the federal Order-in-Council was not sufficient to stop immigrants of South Asian origin who could readily afford the entry requirements, the Laurier government under the direction of Sifton's successor, Frank Oliver, amended the 1906 *Immigration Act* and introduced a "continuous journey" regulation in 1908, which more than any other legislation was specifically directed to stem the flow of South Asian immigration into Canada. From the archives of Citizenship and Immigration Canada we have the following:

> Would-be immigrants, who all traveled by ship unless they were coming overland from the United States, were now required to arrive in Canada from the country of which they were natives or citizens, and on a ticket purchased in that country. The government, wanting to stop the flow of immigrants from Asia, had signed an agreement with Japan in 1907 limiting the number of male immigrants from that country to 400 per year, but no such agreement was in place with the government of British India. Since no shipping company provided direct passage from India to Canada, the new 1908 continuous-journey regulation effectively banned immigrants from India.[28]

What was particularly draconian about this legislation was that it meant that neither wives nor family members could immigrate overseas to join their husbands or fathers who had established themselves in Canada. The new legislation had, therefore, achieved its desired objective of limiting the establishment of a religio-cultural community. This legislation was certainly challenged by members of the South Asian community who were resolved to claiming their right to equal treatment as "white" citizens of the British Empire. For the most part these challenges failed. One of the more glaring examples of mistreatment was the incident starting 21 May 1914 and involving the S.S. *Komagata Maru* and 376 South Asian immigrants (330 Sikhs, 24 Muslims, 12 Hindus). In the "spirit" of Gandhi, the voyage was meant to challenge the "continuous journey" legislation, but they were still refused entry to Canada and forced to stay anchored off Vancouver for over two months. Eventually, a Navy gunboat escorted the ship from the port of Vancouver.[29]

By 1908, the South Asian population in Canada (primarily in British Columbia) was over 5000 individuals, but in the years 1909–10 the total number of South Asian immigrants allowed to enter Canada had fallen to ten people, to five individuals in the following year,[30] and to one in the years between 1914 and 1917. In large part this was due to the passage of the *Immigration Act of 1910*, which, unlike the 1906 *Act*, conferred on the Cabinet the authority to exclude "immigrants belonging to any race deemed unsuited to the climate or requirements of Canada." The *Act* also strengthened the government's power to deport individuals, such as anarchists, on the grounds of political and moral instability. Compounding the situation, an Order-in-Council required that all immigrants arriving in any season other than winter have $25 on them. This last measure ignited a storm of protest in Great Britain, because it meant that prospective immigrants would need to have $25 in addition to their ocean and inland transportation fares.

As mentioned above, by the year 1917 the total population of South Asian immigrants in Canada had dwindled through out-migration (primarily to the United States or back to India) to under 2000 individuals, and as Sampat-Mehta notes, "between 1914 and 1917 only one Indian successfully entered Canada as an immigrant."[31] Although these were the years of World War I, it is little excuse for such blatant inaction. The only positive legislation regarding South Asian immigration in the early part of the 20th century was initiated in 1919. As the result of political pressure from the remaining members of the Sikh community, a federal Order-in-Council was passed to allow "British Hindus residing in Canada" to bring to Canada their immediate family members (wives and children). Between 1904 and 1920, however, only nine South Asian women were allowed to immigrate to Canada (a similar pattern of oppression was applied to the Chinese community as well). The "continuous journey regulation" stayed in effect until 1947 and was finally repealed in 1977.

The Struggle and the Legislation

The year 1947 was important for both Canadian nationals and those who had immigrated to Canada. The war had confirmed Canada as a sovereign nation, and this led, thanks to the *Canadian Citizenship Act* passed in June 1946 (effective 1 January 1947), to the legal recognition of Canadian citizenship to those living in Canada (Order-in-Council P.C. 4849), eliminating the official designation of Canadians as solely British subjects. This meant that a few immigrants of South Asian descent who met the criteria outlined in the *Act* (those who had "lived here for many years") were given the right to vote in Canadian elections; however, the reality is that for most (particularly those of Asian or South Asian origin or persons of colour) the qualifications continued to be both restrictive and discriminatory.

Although there had been significant revisions to the *Immigration Act of 1910*, it was not until 1952 that a new *Act* was finally introduced to Parliament. Unfortunately for both the South Asian community and other potential immigrants of colour, the wording meant that "Cabinet could prohibit or limit the admission of persons by reason of such factors as nationality, ethnic group, occupation, lifestyle, unsuitability with regard to Canada's climate, and perceived inability to become readily assimilated into Canadian society"[32]—provisions that were clearly designed to exclude non-white and non-Christian immigrants.

Although slow in coming, significant changes began to occur within the prevailing Canadian psyche by the late 1950s. For example, Prime Minister John Diefenbaker introduced a Bill of Rights in 1960 that rejected any discrimination by reason of race, colour, national origin, religion, or sex. The passage of the Bill meant that pressures were exerted on members of the federal government who attempted to justify the selection of immigrants on the basis of race, national origin, or "types perceived to be radicals." Ten years after the passing of the *Immigration Act of 1952*, Ellen Fairclough tabled new regulations to amend it, which prohibited the use of race, religion, colour, and national origin as criteria for the selection of new immigrants to Canada providing "(1) they had a specific job waiting for them in Canada or were able to support themselves until they found employment, (2) they were not criminals or terrorists, and (3) they did not suffer from a disease that endangered public health."[33]

The introduction of the "point system" in 1967—100 years after Canadian confederation—allowed all potential immigrants to be "given entry points" based on merit, language, and professional skills that eliminated the sole discriminatory provision in the *Act* and allowed European immigrants and immigrants from the Americas to sponsor a wider range of relatives. Former Prime Minister Pierre Trudeau's adoption of a policy of multiculturalism on 8 October 1971 institutionalized the idea that to be Canadian is to share a proud heritage of diverse cultural and religious backgrounds—the idea of the "Canadian cultural mosaic" had finally been articulated. In 1988, both Houses of Parliament unanimously passed the *Multiculturalism Act* first introduced in 1985 (see above) and Canada became the first country in the world to legislate specific goals for cultural and religious harmony.

CONCLUSION: WHERE DID WE COME FROM, AND WHERE DO WE GO FROM HERE?

Although our snapshot of Canadian history has shown fleeting moments of religious tolerance, for the most part the first 300 years of her history has been marked by religious, legislative, and social intolerance, starting with the treatment of First Nations Peoples and the destruction of their religion and culture through the process of missionary conversions (and later, the infamous residential schools run by various Christian denominations). The religious landscape of Canada had been dominated first by the Franco-Europeans, then by the Anglo-Europeans. With Britain's acquisition of the Canadian territories in 1763, we see a shift from economically based military aggression to cultural domination by the British over the French. This conflict was largely based upon the differences between the Protestant religious culture and that of the Roman Catholics, and continued with the Roman Catholic Irish immigrants of the late 1840s. Compounding the societal tension during this period, all three Christian groups discriminated against the growing Jewish communities in both Upper and Lower Canada.

As the "new Canada" developed during the late 1800s, and her populations pushed westward across the prairies to meet with the communities of British Columbia, the diversity and numbers of her ethnic populations also grew—and so did the cultural and religious conflict. During the 1870s, for example, there is the Métis Rebellion, and during the late 1880s and early 1900s we see specific social movements, often supported by legislation, directing their wrath against the Asian, South Asian, and Eastern European communities as they tried to establish themselves in the new Dominion of Canada (1867).

And these hostilities were not confined to the 19th century. Along with the legislation covered in the section above, we also observe cases of incarceration of her citizens along with the confiscation of their private property—one of the more infamous examples of this injustice being that visited upon members of the Japanese community during World War II. And though many arguments were made for this action, it might be said that part of the reason for this tragic miscarriage of justice was religious discrimination. That is, it was based on the pretext that these Canadians might somehow be loyal to the Japanese Emperor—a rationalization that appears to be fuelled by a limited understanding of the Japanese Shinto tradition, in which it is held that the Emperors are direct descendants of Japan's first Emperor Jimmu, a descendant of the Sun Goddess, Amaterasu.

Another group that was imprisoned solely for their religious beliefs were the Doukhobors of western Canada. This group of Anabaptists, originally from Russia, practise a strict form of religious pacifism and were imprisoned because of their protests against war. In fact, their pacifism and non-compliance with militarism led the Canadian authorities to confiscate Doukhobor farmland twice: once in Saskatchewan and once in the Kootenay region of British Columbia.

In other cases where the state disagrees with a particular religious practice or religio-political position, rather than confiscating property or imprisoning members of the community we find the state either removing a child or children from the homes of a particular individual or removing several children from the religious community at large. A more recent example occurred when a parent of a particular religious community refused to allow a child to be given a lifesaving blood transfusion.

Despite this mottled past, Canada has certainly matured during the past fifty years. Starting with Prime Minister John Diefenbaker's Bill of Rights (1960), and continuing with Prime Minister Pierre Trudeau's push for a multiculturalism policy (1971) and the establishment of the Canadian Constitution (1982), Canada has gained the status of a world leader in the multiculturalism project—a project that enshrined the concept that no one ethnic or religious group would dominate the cultural or political landscape.

For the most part these changes in political policy have been positive. From a religious perspective the recognition of multiculturalism has meant a rapid growth of the ecumenical movement, by increasing dialogue not only between the many Christian denominations but also between the diverse faith communities now represented in Canada. Organizations such as the Multifaith Council of Canada have significantly opened the lines of communication and social cooperation between many religious groups and denominations that seek mutual understanding and the sense of a common social cause.

On the other hand, many religious groups in Canada are beginning to view the modernist multicultural experiment as impotent, and consequently we have also seen the rise of the more conservative forms of fundamentalism in recent years. The question must be asked: Does this newly revived religious conservatism unite or divide the larger multicultural community? In some circumstances—the fundamentalist opposition to the gay marriage legislation being the most recent example—there appears to be unity among the conservative religious groups, but it certainly was not a rallying point for communities across this nation, or one that sought political or social consensus. And this brings us to a final question: If liberal religious views allowed for the rise of the social and religious ecumenical movement in this country, a movement that asks religious communities to put aside their own interests for the greater good of all communities—then will the rise of conservative fundamentalism (of all religions) return this country to a point where one religious viewpoint will dominate? Only time will tell.

CHAPTER SUMMARY

With the arrival of the new millennium, and the subsequent events surrounding 11 September 2001, it becomes apparent that religion can no longer be thought of as some antiquated cultural fossil made extinct by such commodities of modernism as science, economics, and modern statecraft. Instead, religion has come forth from the shadow of modernism to show that it is still very much a vital and significant cultural entity, an entity that continues to operate as part of the complex human condition.

The first part of this chapter illustrates that religion not only provides us with a lens into the great heritage of human civilization, but also provides Canadians with both a new discourse with which to understand the meaning and values of others within our multicultural mosaic and a distinctive opportunity to individually reflect, shape, and articulate our own unique vision of reality. But religion goes beyond the experience of the individual and individual identity formation. It also plays an important part in the human "cultural project"—that social enterprise or dialectic process that projects meaning into the empty vastness of the universe by creating a material, institutional, and, more importantly, religious culture reflecting that meaning.

The second part of this chapter shifts focus to the issues of religion as present within the rich cultural tapestry of the Canadian context. Whether the peoples be First Nations, French, British, American, Irish, Scottish, Asiatic, South Asian, Ukrainian, Italian,

African, Arab, or Russian, religion has always provided them with both a sense of cultural meaning within their Canadian experience and an acute awareness of order and justice. However, it has also been the basis of socio-religious intolerance and political bias. To outline the experiences of each immigrant group would be too vast an undertaking for this chapter, so the remainder of the section pays particular attention to both the Chinese and the South Asian immigration patterns, and the consequent political legislation. In the light of this historical content, the chapter concludes not so much with answers as questions concerning some of the future challenges for religion in this country.

KEY TERMS

anomie, p. 174

"big R" religion, p. 170

cults, p. 174

dialectical process, p. 171

essentialize, p. 163

externalization, p. 171

failed states, p. 178

fundamentalism, p. 177

internalization, p. 171

jiva, p. 168

karma, p. 164

"little r" religion, p. 171

moksha, p. 170

nirvana, p. 170

nomos, p. 172

objectivation, p. 171

products of the human cultural
    project, p. 172

sacred canopy, p. 173

samsara, p. 170

transcendent God, p. 164

"Ultimate Reality," p. 164

DISCUSSION QUESTIONS

1. The Multiculturalism Act states not only that we should condone various religious practices, but also that we should enhance these practices. How actively should government agencies enhance religious practice within Canadian society?

2. The recent events surrounding the "cartoon issue" in which a Danish newspaper produced cartoons depicting the Islamic prophet, Mohammad, has raised some very serious issues (and violence) around the world. One particular issue concerns the right of free speech versus the right of a religious community to not to have its religious belief debased. The balance between these two premises is perhaps one of the greatest challenges of a multicultural society. In small groups, discuss the following: (a) Should the right of religious belief and practice supersede the right of free speech (e.g., should publication of the Danish cartoons be forbidden because all depictions

of the Prophet are considered sacrilegious by Muslims)? (b) Are there responsibilities associated with the right of free speech? What are they? (c) Do individuals or members of a particular group have the right to say anything they wish no matter how offensive it may be to another group?

3. Discuss the advantages and disadvantages of having one religious tradition dominate a particular culture. What are the advantages and disadvantages of granting all religions equal status within a particular culture?

4. Many religions, such as Roman Catholicism (Canon), Judaism (*Halacha*), and Islam (*Shariah*), have their own religious codes, traditions, and sacred laws—some of which, such as those governing marriage and the rights of inheritance, might conflict with Canadian law. Discuss when the application of these codes, traditions, and laws would be appropriate or inappropriate in the light of the Canadian context.

5. In both Canada and the United States, the rise of religious fundamentalism has created some concerns over this form of religious philosophy entering the political arena and influencing legislation. Though Canada recognizes and supports religious freedom of expression, should its legislative process involving such issues as abortion, gay marriage, evolution, etc. be influenced by religious doctrines?

6. As you understand religious fundamentalism, can you appreciate the relationship between the social theory of *anomie* and the concept of the sacred canopy? Is this a proficient response? As a group can you envisage other, alternative responses to *anomie*? Are they as successful and effective as the religious response?

NOTES

1. Ninian Smart, *The World's Religions* (Cambridge: Cambridge University Press, 1998), p. 10.
2. Max Weber, *The Protestant Ethic and the Spirit of Capitalism* (New York: Charles Scribner's Sons, 1958).
3. Emile Durkheim, *The Elementary Forms of Religious Life* (New York: Free Press, 1995), p. 44.
4. Max Weber, *The Sociology of Religion* (Boston: Beacon Press, 1964), p. 1.
5. Clifford Geertz, *The Interpretation of Cultures* (New York: Basic Books, 1973), p. 90.
6. Peter L. Berger, *The Sacred Canopy* (Toronto: Doubleday, 1967), p. 3.
7. Berger, p. 4.
8. Berger, pp. 14–15.
9. Berger, p. 100.
10. Lorne L. Dawson, *Comprehending Cults* (Toronto: Oxford University Press, 1998), pp. 52–53.
11. *Canadian Multiculturalism Act*, R.S., 1985, c. 24 (4th Supp.), available Canadian Heritage site <www.canadianheritage.gc.ca/progs/multi/policy/act_e.cfm>, accessed 4 April 2006.
12. Robert Choquette, *Canada's Religions* (Ottawa: University of Ottawa Press, 2004), pp. 433–434.
13. Choquette, p. 145.
14. Denise Kupferschmid-Moy, *Across the Generations: A History of the Chinese in Canada*, 2005, <http://collections.ic.gc.ca/generations/index2.html>, accessed 4 April 2006.

15. "A Tale of Perseverance: Chinese Immigration to Canada," *Life and Society*, CBC Archives, 2006 <http://archives.cbc.ca/IDD-1-69-1433/life_society/chinese_immigration>, accessed 4 April 2006.

16. Norman Buchignani, Dorren Indra, and Ram Srivastiva, *Continuous Journey: A Social History of South Asians in Canada* (Toronto: McClelland and Stewart, 1985), p. 113.

17. Roger Daniels, "The History of Indian Immigration to the United States: An Interpretive Essay," in Jagat Motwani, Mahin Gosine, and Jyoti Barot-Motwani, eds., *Global Indian Diaspora: Yesterday, Today and Tomorrow* (New York: Global Organization of People of Indian Origin, 1993), p. 440.

18. C.I. Petros, "Indo-Canadians" in J. Motwani, M. Gosine, and J. Barot-Motwani, eds., *Global Indian Diaspora: Yesterday, Today and Tomorrow* (pp. 475–484) (New York: Global Organization of People of Indian Origin, 1993), p. 475.

19. Petros, p. 475.

20. Government sources include: Citizenship and Immigration Canada <www.cic.gc.ca/english>; Statistics Canada, *The Daily*, February 17, 1998, available <www.statcan.ca/Daily/English/980217/d980217.htm>; Department of Justice of Canada <http://canada.justice.gc.ca/en>; Heritage Canada <www.canadianheritage.gc.ca>.

21. Buchignani et al., p. 8.

22. R. Sampat-Mehta, "First Fifty Years of South Asian Immigration: A Historical Perspective," in R.N. Kanungo, ed., *South Asians in a Canadian Mosaic* (Montreal: Kala Bharati, 1984), p. 13; Subash Ramcharan, "South Asian Immigration: Current Status and Adaptation Modes," in Kanungo, p. 33.

23. "The Arrival of the Europeans," *Forging Our Legacy*, October 2000, available Citizenship and Immigration Canada site <www.cic.gc.ca/english>, accessed 4 April 2006.

24. Sampat-Mehta, p. 24.

25. *Chinese Immigration Act*, S.C. 1900, c. 32, s. 6; *Chinese Immigration Act*, S.C. 1903, c. 8, s. 6.

26. Department of Justice of Canada site <www.chrc-ccdp.ca/en/timePortals/milestones/9mile.asp>, accessed 9 April 2006.

27. C.I. Petros, "Indo-Canadians," in J. Motwani, M. Gosine, and J. Barot-Motwani, eds., *Global Indian Diaspora: Yesterday, Today and Tomorrow* (New York: Global Organization of People of Indian Origin, 1993), pp. 475–484. Available <www.chrc-ccdp.ca/en/timePortals/milestones/8mile.asp>, accessed 9 April 2006.

28. Citizenship and Immigration Canada, "Chapter 1: Across by Boat, Overland by Train," *The Role of Transportation in Canadian Immigration 1900–2000*, March 2001, available <www.cic.gc.ca/english/department/transport/chap-1a.html>, accessed 10 May 2006.

29. For more details on this incident see Hugh Johnston, *The Voyage of the Komagata Maru: The Sikh Challenge to Canada's Colour Bar* (Vancouver: UBC Press, 1989).

30. Petros, p. 476.

31. Sampat-Mehta, p. 27.

32. "Towards the Canadian Citizenship Act," *Forging Our Legacy*, November 2000, available Citizenship and Immigration Canada site <www.cic.gc.ca/english/department/legacy/chap-5b.html>, accessed 4 April 2006.

33. "Trail-Blazing Initiatives," *Forging Our Legacy*, October 2000, available Citizenship and Immigration Canada site <www.cic.gc.ca/english/department/legacy/chap-6.html>, accessed 4 April 2006.

CHAPTER 7

Disability as Difference

Nancy Nicholls

[We make disability] in impersonal encounters, in school, on the job (and long before a job is gotten on), in the media, in human service agencies, within self-help groups, through governmental policy, within cultural belief (nurtured and displayed through all of the above and more), through technology, through sweeping societal changes, and even through the writings of observers of disability.

—Michelle Fine and Adrienne Asch, quoted in Higgins, 1992

Objectives

. . . .

After reading this chapter, you should be able to

- clarify the relationship of historical ideas and the history of disability in Canada

- appreciate the role institutions, especially government, church, education, and family, have on issues affecting people with disabilities

- know and analyze the different models and theories for studying disability

- explore the importance of the theory of "normalization" in the treatment of individuals with disabilities

- recognize critical social policy issues for people with disabilities in Canada

INTRODUCTION

When people used to talk about **inclusive societies**, it was assumed that they were referring to issues of race and ethnicity. Increasingly, however, the notion of inclusivity also incorporates **disability**.

Disability is not a new phenomenon in Canada. To appreciate the issue of disability in the 21st century and beyond, we will begin with some background discussion about how people with disabilities were treated in the past. This historical perspective will (1) help shed light on the definition of disability, (2) outline the role institutions have played in the lives of those who have disabilities and in shaping the view others have of people with disabilities, (3) show how public interest has shaped the development of policies in the area, and (4) show how government has responded.

Not all disabilities affect all people the same way. We will look at the types of disabilities—physical, intellectual, and mental—and attempt to identify how differently they have been treated over time and how the various disabilities raise different issues for equality. We will highlight the major theoretical perspectives on the study of disability, with particular emphasis on the theory of "normalization."

HISTORICAL CONTEXT

The Early Years

Historically the view of those with disabilities was that they were being punished for their sins or those of their ancestors. Many felt that people with disabilities were possessed of "evil spirits." Often they were ridiculed and certainly they were ostracized by society—they were seen as outcasts and were unwelcome. In time, the view changed from a concern about evil spirits to one of seeing people with disabilities as weak, as less worthy, as persons in need of charity. Originally, the person's family was expected to provide this charity. The family was seen as the major institution to provide health, educational, and social care for all its members. In the early 16th century, people with disabilities were thought of as noncontributing members of society and as individuals who needed to be provided with only basic care (minimal food and shelter). If their families were unable to provide this care, then it would sometimes be provided by more fortunate members of society.

European settlers brought with them to Canada the views of individuals with disabilities that they had held in Europe. Individuals with disabilities were seen as weaker members of society in need of the protection of stronger members, and their family and friends were expected to care for them. For these settlers, life in the new land often involved physical hardship and physical strength; individuals who could not be adequately protected in the new country were sent back to Europe for care.

In Europe, the major provider of care outside the family had been the church, so it was natural, in terms of both culture and tradition, for the church to assume the same responsibilities in the new land. From about the mid-18th century, as the population grew in New France (now Quebec), the Roman Catholic Church began to provide care for individuals requiring special assistance. Even after Britain assumed control of New France, the Roman Catholic Church maintained this role as the major institutional provider of care in Quebec. This lasted until the 1950s, when the provincial government assumed more responsibility and as the Quiet Revolution began to take root.

The Church provided care for individuals with mental disabilities. One of the earliest known institutions for the care of those with disabilities was a hospital founded by the Sisters of Charity (Grey Nuns) in Montreal. In the late 18th century, Quebec's Legislative Assembly authorized expenditures for the care of "insane" persons in Quebec, and a per diem rate was given to the Grey Nuns to provide care for the "insane" in their existing institutions in Trois-Rivières, Quebec City, and Montreal. This is the first example in Canadian history of government expenditure for people with disabilities.

Services were expanded in the 19th century, largely because of increased population growth. An example of this expansion is the establishment of a hospital for the "insane" in Saint John, New Brunswick.

It was very difficult for those with severe physical disabilities to survive the hardships and challenges of the new country, and those that did not return to Europe often died young. In the 19th century, in response to population growth but also because of two major epidemics of cholera and smallpox, services for the physically ill were also expanded. Similar medical crises, polio and the effects of thalidomide, had a major impact on the treatment of people with disabilities in the 1950s. Events such as these touched many lives and brought the issues of people with disabilities to the forefront.

Confederation and the *British North America (BNA) Act*

Pivotal to an understanding of the Canadian government's role in caring for people with disabilities is the *British North America Act*, now called the *Constitution Act*, of 1867. This *Act* established that health care and education, as well as what we now term "social services," are the responsibility of the provincial governments. It is important to note that the federal government retained the responsibility to provide health care to the Inuit populations and to veterans of the armed forces. Policy issues about the provision of services to people with disabilities often are entrenched in the division of powers as outlined in this *Act*.

New Services in the 19th Century

An important player in the development of most services is the public. Without public pressure and interest, governments tend not to expand services. For people with mental disabilities, the public was satisfied with the government providing institutional care—citizens were not only concerned about the care given people with mental disabilities, but they were also equally, and some would argue more, concerned about the safety of the public. Institutional care provided in isolated areas, far from the public view, was considered best.

Public concern for people with physical disabilities, however, was growing, primarily for those who were deaf or blind. Sending such individuals back to Europe was no longer feasible or practical, as many of them were now a few generations removed from the "old country." In response to the pressure to provide special education to the deaf and the blind, asylums for the blind were funded in Halifax and Montreal, and the Ontario School for the Deaf was established in 1872 in Toronto. Alexander Graham Bell, who is well known for his invention of the telephone, was a major contributor both financially and in terms of public pressure to developing and influencing the provision of special education services to the deaf. This notion of education for individuals with physical disabilities influenced those concerned about other kinds of disabilities. In 1888 an institution was built in Orillia, Ontario, to provide education to the "**mentally deficient**."

It is sad to note that what started out as a movement for special education in many instances resulted in institutions that provided merely housing, often in less than adequate conditions.

Along with public pressure for the government to provide services came an impetus from the public to offer volunteer services. Volunteer organizations were established, such as the Canadian Red Cross in 1896 and the Victorian Order of Nurses in 1898. Volunteer services both increased the provision of care to people with disabilities and had a significant impact on the quality of care provided. As more people worked with individuals with disabilities through these volunteer efforts, public awareness grew about the issues facing people with disabilities, as did public support of increased financial and moral support.

The epidemic outbreak of serious diseases has often been the impetus for demanding services; another major impetus is civilian disaster. In 1917 an ammunition ship, the *Mont Blanc*, exploded in the port of Halifax. More than 1900 people were killed instantly, and within a year more than 2000 had died. Around 9000 more were injured, many permanently, 1000 with eye injuries alone. Virtually all of north-end Halifax was destroyed. The impact of this incident focused the public's attention on the needs of those with physical disabilities.

The voluntary sector saw children as "innocent victims" and thus the only ones deserving of help. Public pressure to care for children led to the establishment of institutions such as the Toronto Hospital for Sick Children and, later, the Ontario Society for Crippled Children.

The World Wars

World War I had an enormous impact on the delivery of services to people with physical disabilities in Canada. For the first time in Canadian history, many Canadians were faced with major physical problems, as soldiers returned from the front with a variety of serious illnesses and "**handicaps**," among them tuberculosis, blindness, mental illnesses, paralysis, and amputated limbs. The notion of who "deserved" help shifted. People with disabilities were no longer the unfortunate and the weak, but some of our "brightest and strongest"—our country's "hope for the future."

Because these disabilities had been incurred by our men in fighting for our country, the country felt an obligation to help them. And because, according to the *BNA Act*, the federal government was responsible for veterans, the federal government was obliged to take a leading role. Thus, help for people with disabilities took on a federal perspective with regard to government policy. Help also took on a federal perspective with regard to the voluntary sector: in 1918 both the Canadian Mental Health Association and the Canadian National Institute for the Blind were established.

Care for people with disabilities shifted from being merely the provision of food, shelter, and some educational services to the provision of rehabilitation services. The policy was to help veterans get into the labour market, and thus vocational training was seen as critical.

In 1915 the Military Hospitals Commission was created. On the basis of experience gained from World War I, a subcommittee of government workers and civilians was established shortly after war broke out in 1939 to develop a comprehensive plan for assisting veterans.

Another important result of the wars was the vast medical experience gained and the resulting innovations in **rehabilitation medicine**, including the development of "wonder drugs." After World War II, a group approach, now known as the "**rehabilitation team**" approach, was developed in Montreal to combat the many issues facing returning veterans. Team conferences and team planning are now standard practice in working with individuals who have disabilities, whether physical, mental, or intellectual. This approach recognizes that treating the effects of disabilities also includes the social aspects such as education, vocational training, housing, and employment and that professional expertise and access to a variety of services are needed.

The services developed in the war years for veterans were extended to include all Canadians. In 1948 national health grants were established by the federal government to assist all the provinces in providing rehabilitation services. These grants were also to be used for the training of medical personnel and for rehabilitation equipment. This initiative led to many services and facilities that we still have today, including Toronto's Variety Village, which was originally a school for children with disabilities and today offers a wide range of services including recreational activities for people with disabilities.

CRITICAL THINKING OUTSIDE THE BOX 7.1

In what way did World War I affect the public's view of people with disabilities?

Rehabilitation Planning and the Labour Market

In the early 20th century, the new **social movement** of organized labour pushed for protection of injured workers. This resulted in the Ontario *Workmen's Compensation Act* of 1914. At first the *Act* dealt with giving injured workers lost wages, but later it provided medical assistance and rehabilitation benefits as well. Today all provinces have such legislation, and in response to the position of women in the labour market, most such acts have changed their wording from "workmen" to "workers."

A major breakthrough in the rehabilitation field was the 1951 Touchstone Conference. This national conference saw the provinces reassert their role in the field of rehabilitation, at the same time encouraging a continuing presence of the federal government in planning and in coordinating a national rehabilitation program. The most significant outcome of the conference was the Federal–Provincial Vocational Rehabilitation of Disabled Persons (VRDP) initiative, which led to the *Vocational Rehabilitation of Disabled Persons Act* in 1961. The major tenet of this *Act* is that the federal government makes cost-sharing arrangements with the provinces for the provision of services to help people with disabilities enter or reenter the workforce. The *Act* also requires that there be a special section in the federal and provincial employment services for placement in the workforce of (primarily) people with physical disabilities.

Medicare

The federal *Hospital Insurance and Diagnostic Act* was passed in 1957. It provided people who have disabilities with free treatment and rehabilitation for insured services. In 1961 Saskatchewan established what has been called the first Medicare program in North America. This was followed in 1966 by the federal *Medical Care Act*, and with this legislation, a 50 percent cost-sharing arrangement for medical services was made between the federal government and the provinces. By 1971 all Canadians had medical coverage under this *Act*.

The *Canada Pension Plan Act* (1965) was another major breakthrough in this area. It stipulates that for those who have contributed to the plan and who are later deemed unlikely to be able to work because of a "severe" disability, a pension will be paid.

In 1964 a conference, similar in importance to the Touchstone Conference, was held for the "mentally retarded." Since the early 1960s there have been major breakthroughs for people with what are now called **developmental disabilities**. In 1963 a National Institute on Mental Retardation was founded together with York University in Toronto. Today, other such foundations exist at universities throughout Canada, which has greatly enhanced research and consultation in the field.

Parents of children diagnosed as having developmental disabilities have arguably had the greatest impact on care for any disabled group in Canadian history. The first such parents' council was formed in 1951; similar associations are in evidence throughout the country today, and there is a national association. These groups have successfully lobbied for services and for **antidiscriminatory** legislation. It is they who are largely responsible for the present-day inclusion, or mainstreaming, in many schools of children with special needs. Another major facilitator of changes in the treatment of those with developmental disabilities is the theory of "normalization" (to be discussed later in this chapter).

Human Rights Codes

Rehabilitation is not only an issue in Canada. Over the years the international community has put great emphasis on the prevention of various disabilities and on the integration of people with disabilities into society. This has manifested itself in a variety of ways, including international conferences such as the one dedicated to people with disabilities sponsored by the United Nations in 1981, the International Year of Disabled Persons. In part this was in reaction to lobbying by people with disabilities themselves, through a variety of self-help groups, in particular by Vietnam War veterans in the United States. Canada's response to the dedicated year was to table a special committee report entitled *Obstacles*.

In 1980, in Canada, a special committee was created to deal with issues affecting people with disabilities, including the effect of programs and services in the government and in the voluntary sector and the overlap and interlocking of such services. Perhaps most important, however, this committee addressed the issue of human rights. It strongly recommended that these people should have full and equal protection under the law. Today, individuals with mental or physical disabilities are protected in human rights documents in Canada.

Care for the people with mental illnesses has developed along similar lines to those outlined for people with physical disabilities and for those with developmental disabilities. However, many would argue that the stigma is often greater for mental illness. The development of psychoactive drugs in the 1970s led to the discharge of vast numbers of patients from psychiatric institutions and allowed for care on an outpatient basis. These drugs did much to decrease the number of individuals getting custodial rather than rehabilitative care.

Advocacy

A major shift in the treatment of all individuals with disabilities has been "the consumer movement." No longer are people with disabilities unable to speak for themselves, and the 1980s trend toward self-help groups was critical in bringing about this change. This increased involvement is a result of several things, including better medical treatment and thus improvement in the mental and physical well-being of consumers; numerous improvements in assistive devices brought about by advanced technology; changes in expectations on the part of people with disabilities themselves and society as a whole; and increased access to and involvement in education and the workforce. To appreciate this change it is important to consider not only the historical changes that have occurred, but also the changes in theoretical perspectives. See Have You Heard? 7.1.

THEORETICAL PERSPECTIVE

Three distinct models of disability have been developed, and each produces its own expertise and experts: (1) the biomedical model, (2) the economic model, and (3) the sociopolitical model. The operation of these models is reflected in the historical perspective, that is, throughout certain periods of Canadian history, implementation of one or the other model appears to have dominated.

Biomedical Model

The biomedical model emphasizes **impairment**, which the World Health Organization (WHO) in 1980 defined as "any abnormality of physiological or anatomical structure or function." Disablement is divided into respective varieties, and, according to Canadian lawyer and philosopher Jerome Bickenbach, social action concerns itself with issues of "prevention, cure, containment, pain management, rehabilitation, amelioration, and palliation."[1] This view largely resembles the medical model of treatment, and the individual is seen as a patient who is "sick" or hurt or, in some cases, a victim of bad luck. This model lends itself to social goals that focus on accommodation, that is, society is obligated to provide a basic level of medical care and health services. This model also had a role to play in concerns about eligibility criteria and the emphasis on assessment in determining need. Much of the early history of disability in Canada and society's reaction to disability before World War I can be understood by using this model.

Economic Model

The economic model emphasizes the economics of disablement. How does one's impairment affect one's capabilities? This model is concerned with the effects of a disability

HAVE YOU HEARD? 7.1

Canadian Human Rights Act, 1985

∙∙

Section 2. Purpose

The purpose of this Act is to extend the laws in Canada to give effect, within the purview of matters coming within the legislative authority of Parliament, to the principle that every individual should have an equal opportunity with other individuals to make for himself or herself the life that he or she is able and wishes to have, consistent with his or her duties and obligations as a member of society, without being hindered in or prevented from doing so by discriminatory practices based on race, national or ethnic origin, colour, religion, age, sex, marital status, family status, disability or conviction for an offence for which a pardon has been granted....

(g) Discrimination Based on Handicap

Handicap was added as a ground of discrimination in 1981 (S.O. 1981, c. 53, ss. 1, 2, 4: now ss. 1, 2, 5). While boards of inquiry had recognized an employer's duty to make reasonable accommodation of an employee's characteristics as a requirement of the Code, the 1986 amendments (S.O. 1986, c. 64, s. 18(15) introduced into section 23(2) (now s. 24(2)) an express reference to reasonable accommodation and a provision (s. 16(1)(a); now s. 17(2)) dealing specifically with the duty of accommodation in relation to the handicapped (S.O., 1986, c. 64, s. 18(10)).

Source: *Human Rights Legislation: An Office Consolidation* (Toronto: Butterworths, 1991).

not only on the individual, but also on society as a whole and on the individual's ability, or inability, to contribute to society. Concerns are framed as labour market issues. Any disability is significant in that it limits a worker's productive potential and skills. Using a cost–benefit analysis, people with disabilities are seen as an economic cost. Policies must take into account that people with disabilities may not be able to work to their full potential and thus not contribute fully to the labour market. These people are also a cost in terms of the provision of health and other services such as housing. This view of people with disabilities emphasizes the need to address any barriers that prohibit full participation of people with disabilities in the workforce, and it leads to the development of social policy that strives to fully integrate people with disabilities into the economic market.

The economic model can serve to explain the shift to rehabilitative services that occurred after World War I. Also, from this perspective many of the policies toward people with disabilities adopted by Canada in this century can be explained—for example, the establishment of vocational services, social insurance programs, and social assistance programs.

Sociopolitical Model

The third model is the one most representative of current trends in the area of disability policy. From this perspective, disability is viewed as a type of social injustice. This social injustice stems from the way people with disabilities are stigmatized in society and from the way they are treated, that is, from discriminatory practices. This sociopolitical model blends sociological theories and psychosocial theories about disability with an advocacy and civil rights perspective. It is society that determines disability; it is discriminatory social attitudes that become part of the social fabric, part of how institutions are organized and operated, and it is these institutions and their practices that often disadvantage and marginalize people with disabilities. In this model, society disables people.

The sociopolitical model holds that disability needs to be destigmatized and that respect and rights must go hand in hand in shaping policy for people with disabilities. Thus, disability issues resemble other equality issues, such as racial discrimination and women's issues.

The sociopolitical model is reflective of the rise of self-help groups and the increased participation of people with disabilities in the sociopolitical realm. The independent living movement stands as a clear example of a shift toward **empowerment**. This model is the one most concerned with reform.

As with most theories and models, social policy is often explained by a combination of models. The policies developed for people with disabilities are extremely diverse. Jerome Bickenbach cites fourteen policy areas for people with disabilities. These include biomedical services (research, therapy, chronic care), independent living (group homes, the deinstitutionalization movement), employment issues, housing concerns, communication (media) issues, and human rights. In part because of the diversity of issues and

---

CRITICAL THINKING OUTSIDE THE BOX 7.2

As a blind child today, how would your life be different from what it would have been in the 1980s?

---

concerns and because of the variety of disabilities (physical, mental, and intellectual), much of the policy development has been fragmented and is ad hoc in nature.[2]

Obstacles (1981), mentioned above, discussed three goals sought by disabled persons, and these have marked policy development in Canada for people with disabilities ever since. Individuals and groups representing disabled persons have differed on which goal they want emphasized. Some goals have been emphasized more than others at particular times. Nevertheless, the three goals are as applicable today as they were in 1981. People with disabilities want

1. *to be treated with respect.* This includes the idea that people with disabilities should participate in decision making and in developing their own services and agencies.
2. *to have the same opportunities as other Canadians to participate socially, economically, educationally, recreationally, and in all other ways in the social life of the country.* Participation should not be limited by discriminatory acts or practices, and the means necessary to achieve this participation should be provided.
3. *services and assistance to ensure that their needs are met.* Environments, including the workplace, should accommodate people with disabilities so that full social participation can be achieved.[3]

One issue that has complicated the development of consistent social policy in the area of disability is the conflict between programs that discourage people with disabilities from working with programs that encourage them to work. For example, is a person with a disability actually unable to work and thus in need and deserving of financial assistance? Or could he or she work if certain accommodations were made in the workplace? The needs of people with disabilities are as varied as their disabilities, their capabilities, and their skills. Much of the confusion around policy stems from the various definitions of disability.

Normalization Theory

A milestone in the treatment of people with disabilities is the "theory of **normalization**," developed in the 1970s. This theory led to the belief that all individuals are entitled

CRITICAL THINKING OUTSIDE THE BOX 7.3

The sociopolitical model argues that society disables people. In what ways might society disable an individual?

to lives that are "as normal as possible." In many ways this theory explains the massive **deinstitutionalization** of those with developmental disabilities and mental illnesses. With the move of many individuals with disabilities from institutions and asylums to group homes and other forms of independent living, people with disabilities are better able to participate in the daily social life of society. Deinstitutionalization has allowed many people with disabilities to have more participatory lives, but some argue that the real impetus behind this normalization was to save public money. Governments often moved people with disabilities out of institutions without providing them with adequate community programs and financial resources. Especially in urban areas, this policy has led to many people, particularly those with mental illnesses, becoming homeless.

Inherent in the theory of normalization is that "normal" is a desired outcome and that it is possible to determine what normal is. If what is normal can be determined, it

---

HAVE YOU HEARD? 7.2

Case Scenario

. . . .

Judith Snow, a woman with disabilities who lives in Ontario, describes how society's view of people with disabilities and of their potential—and not her physical disability itself—sustained her disadvantages. Snow describes how after completing university, her world became limited by the practices of government and their institutions, who seemed insensitive to her needs as an individual.

Over a three-and-a-half-year period, Snow was bounced from one chronic care hospital to another because each facility was unable to provide her with the minimum five hours of daily attendant care that she required.

In an effort to preserve her mental health and to keep active and connected with life outside the institution, she continued to work four days a week at York University. However, Snow states, "The money I earned was used up in paying for a semi-private room, a private nurse in the mornings and my transportation ... my health began to break down because of the institution, its policies, atmosphere and staff. No matter how hard I worked to explain how I needed to be active, I was always pushing against the life of the institution."

Source: Judith Snow, "Imprinting Our Image on the World," in Diane Driedger and Susan Gray, eds., *An International Anthology of Women's Disabilities* (Charlottetown: Gynergy, 1992), pp. 81–82.

---

follows that we can also determine what is not normal. Sociologists have written at great length about how a dominant group regards its experience as "natural," as "normal," and experiences that differ from these are considered less than normal. Therefore, when it comes to disability, it is society that socially constructs the difference. Paul Higgins points out[4] that **learning disability** is a new term for a condition that in earlier times was called "word blindness." This example illustrates how views of people with disabilities are ever-changing and that the issue of disability is an ongoing one. The example also helps to remind us that throughout history, "normal" has been a narrow concept and because of that, society has been able to shut out many from the mainstream, be it an ethnic group, women, or people with disabilities. Individuals with disabilities have often said that it is not the physical, mental, or intellectual disability that represents the major obstacle in their lives, but the barriers that society creates. See Have You Heard? 7.3.

WHAT ABOUT THE FUTURE?

Individuals with a variety of disabilities now take part in the day-to-day life of Canadian society. Much remains to be done, and some accomplishments are being threatened. As Carol Goar states in the *Toronto Star*, 24 March 2010, when talking about federal initiatives, such as the Registered Disability Savings Plan, "they do little for the majority of disabled Canadians who can't get basic services, can't get into federally funded job training programs, and live in poverty."[5]

The 1990s saw the cancellation of many programs for the disabled, as major cuts to government spending occurred in all areas of health care in response to shifting policy priorities and a downturn in the economy. Twenty years later, cuts continue, in part related to a recent recession, as evidenced by decreases in Ontario in provincial funding for services for the developmentally disabled.

In 2006, it is reported that 4.4 million people were disabled in Canada.[6] Many, of the over 4 million disabled individuals in Canada, still experience the stigma of a disability and are afraid to acknowledge learning disabilities and mental illness. As with many developments, change takes place when people are aware of and become involved in issues. As our population ages, more and more Canadians are going to face physical disability and this, in turn, will increase awareness of the needs of people with disabilities. Since women have a longer life expectancy than men do, the needs of disabled women will increase in disproportion to those of men. Women report more limitations to their participation in society due to a disability than men report (see Figure 7.1).

Great strides have been made in the way disabled individuals are viewed and in terms of increasing the participation of people with disabilities in decision making that affects their own lives (**self-determination**). The inclusion of individuals with disabilities

Figure 7.1 Percentage Reporting a Participation or Activity Limitation, by Age Group and Sex, Household Population Aged 12 Years or Older, Canada, 2008

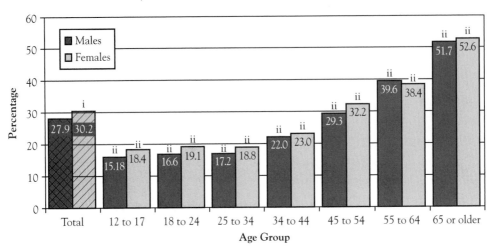

[i] Significantly different from estimate for males (p < 0.05)

[ii] Significantly different from overall estimate for same sex (p < 0.05)

[iii] Respondents who reported being limited in home, school, work, or other activities (sometimes or often versus never) because of a physical condition, mental condition, or health problem that has lasted or is expected to last six months or longer.

Source: Adapted from Statistics Canada, *The 2006 Participation and Activity Limitation Survey: Disability in Canada* 89-628-XIE 2007003, no. 3, Released December 3, 2007.

CRITICAL THINKING OUTSIDE THE BOX 7.4

Think of a particular disability (physical, mental, or intellectual) and describe two obstacles that the person who has this disability faces because of the disability itself. Now think of three obstacles the person faces that represent barriers imposed by society.

---

in advertisement, television, and the arts although still minimal, would not have been thought of years ago.

In the early years of Canadian history, as our pioneers fought for their very existence, no one thought much about any individual's recreational needs—let alone the needs of any individual with a disability. The history of sport and of the Olympics is a

Table 7.1   People with Disabilities: Most Difficult Goal to Achieve

	Responding Organizations (65)	Mobility/ Agility (39)	Emotional/ Mental (32)	Hearing/ Speech (32)	Vision (27)	Multiple Disabilities (40)
Ensure equality of opportunity and access	23%	26%	19%	25%	22%	25%
Help people with disabilities to integrate into communities	15	13	19	13	15	8
Ensure full range of services for people with disabilities	11	5	9	6	0	8
Help disabled persons enter and succeed in workforce	9	13	13	13	22	15
Help disabled persons to be independent	9	10	13	9	11	8
Make sure that people with disabilities receive a fair share of government services and funding	9	8	16	13	7	13
Promote acceptance of people with disabilities among the general public	5	8	3	9	7	8
Develop sense of community among those with similar disabilities	3	3	3	3	4	3
Reach as many as possible who have same disabling conditions	3	5	0	0	7	3
Obtain parallel or separate services	2	3	0	3	4	3
Don't know or no answer	11	8	6	6	0	10

Note: Totals may not add up to 100 percent because of rounding.

Source: "Most Difficult Goal to Achieve," adapted from the Statistics Canada publication "Adults with Disabilities, Their Employment and Education Characteristics," Catalogue No. 82-554, released 28 July 1993, page 87.

relatively new one, yet just recently many disabled Canadians actively participated in the Vancouver Paralympics.

In 1989 in Ontario, the then Office for Disabled Persons engaged Environics Research Group Limited to conduct a survey of the needs and attitudes of disabled Ontarians. The major findings are representative of a significant number of individuals with disabilities and organizations serving them. Most of all, the surveys provided people with disabilities with an opportunity to share their views. It remains one of the most comprehensive studies of the views of the disabled, and thus, although it is over twenty years old, it remains relevant and is applicable to policy initiatives (see Table 7.1).

It is significant to note that little has changed in terms of goal achievement for people with disabilities since this 1993 table was completed. A research project of the Canadian Council on Rehabilitation and Work, Diversity Planning for Inclusive Employment (DPIE), looked at trends in employer attitudes in terms of hiring and retraining individuals with disabilities. Over 700 responses were obtained from identified employers across Canada by e-mail surveys and focus groups. The research found that "little or no progress" had been made in terms of employer attitudes concerning hiring and retaining individuals with disabilities. See Have You Heard? 7.3.

In addition to major advances in technology and assistive devices and in the overall inclusion of individuals with all forms of disability in society as a whole, there have been

---

HAVE YOU HEARD? 7.3

Highlights of the Findings of DPIE Project

. . . .

Highlights of the findings of DPIE project included that:
- attitudes and cultural biases continued to be a barrier to the hiring of persons with disabilities
- awareness of statutory obligations under the *Employment Equity Act* (EEA) of 2003/2004 to recruit, hire, and employ persons with disabilities was low
- accountability for achievement of EEA targets was mostly poor

Source: Halifax Global Inc., "Diversity Planning for Inclusive Employment (DPIE) Employer Survey," 7 September 2005, available Paths to Equal Opportunity site (Government of Ontario) <www.equalopportunity.on.ca/eng_t/subject/index.asp?action=search_7&page_id=788&file_id=26146>, accessed 6 April 2006.

---

some significant changes and shifts in social policy. One of the most significant occurred in 2005 when Ontario finally passed the *Accessibility for Ontarians with Disabilities Act*.

The Americans with Disabilities Act came into effect in 1993, and it was in advance of much work in Canada. The Ontario *Act* announced the need to develop, implement, and enforce accessibility standards in all areas of social life, including accommodation, services, and employment, by the year 2025, and ensured the provision of involvement of disabled individuals in meeting the standards. It also deals with enforcement issues.

One positive aspect of the *Act* is that it formerly recognizes that the disabled have historically faced discrimination in the province. Another encouraging aspect is the fact that the *Act* covers all forms of disability including learning disabilities and mental illness. A major criticism of the *Act* is that its full implementation is staged over twenty years and every year without change limits the potential of disabled individuals to fully participate in Ontario.

The extent of participation that individuals with disabilities desire was perhaps, best expressed in a speech by the president of the Treasury Board of Canada to the Disabled People's International Conference in 2004:

> We want a Canada in which citizens with disabilities have the opportunity to contribute to and benefit from Canada's prosperity—as learners, workers, volunteers, and family members.[7]

2010 and Beyond

Decades from now, it may be determined that the most significant historic moment for the disabled will have resulted from Canada's ratification of the *United Nations Convention on the Rights of Persons with Disabilities*. Article 1 of the *Convention* states that the purpose is:

> To promote, protect, and ensure the full and equal enjoyment of all human rights and fundamental freedom by all persons with disabilities, and to promote respect for their inherent dignity.

> Persons with disabilities include those who have long-term physical, mental, intellectual or sensory impairments which in interaction with various barriers may hinder their full and effective participation in society or on an equal basis with others.[8]

The *Convention* recognizes that rights apply to *all* aspects of life and all forms of disability. In addition the *Convention* outlines a paradigm shift in that it comments on the capability of the disabled to make decisions about their own lives. The *Convention* also pays attention to the increased risk disabled women face in terms of violence, abuse, and exploitation.[9] Further to the point of exploitation the *Convention* addresses the need for the media to treat the disabled with respect.[10]

CRITICAL THINKING OUTSIDE THE BOX 7.5

Think of a recent television show, movie, or newspaper article you have seen or read in which a disabled individual was portrayed. Was the disabled individual treated with respect? Was the individual exploited? How could the portrayal have being changed to show increased respect for the disabled individual?

It is important to note that Canada was not a leader in the signing of the Convention but was in fact the 82nd country to sign.[11]

Unfortunately, ratification of a UN document does not always lead to action but it does formally commit the country to working towards fairer treatment of its citizens with disabilities. It might also move Canada to developing national policies in the area of disability. A major strength of the *Americans with Disabilities Act* is that it applies across the country. To date, in Canada social policy in the area of disabilities varies greatly depending on the province where the disabled individual resides.

CHAPTER SUMMARY

The issue of disability is not simple, and the interplay of both historical events and theoretical perspectives affects the day-to-day lives of people with disabilities. In Canada generally there is a move to greater empowerment of individuals with disabilities. Yet, in many ways, people with disabilities are still not accorded full participation in our society. They are not fairly represented in the workforce, in the arts, and in postsecondary education. Canada lags behind many countries as exemplified by the fact that Canada was the 82nd country to ratify the *United Nations Convention on the Rights of Persons with Disabilities*.[12]

Wars, the labour movement, public disasters, epidemics, recessions, and the resultant changes in social policy and social programs have had an impact on policies that affect people with disabilities.

The initial institutional provider of services to people with disabilities was the Church. This responsibility shifted to the government, especially because of World Wars I and II. The rise of the voluntary sector and increased participation and awareness of the needs of people with disabilities among the Canadian public at large led to a sharing of responsibility between the government and the private sector. Now, with reduced government funding, the role of the voluntary sector is likely to increase.

A major trend in the past two decades has been for greater involvement in all aspects of social policy and programs for people with disabilities by people with disabilities.

Three models help to explain the direction of policy initiatives: (1) the biomedical model, (2) the economic model, and (3) the sociopolitical model. The theory of normalization has led to fuller participation of people with disabilities in all areas of everyday life (work, recreation, and housing), and yet this same movement, many would argue, accounts for there being vast numbers of individuals who need care and have no place to go for help.

As with other issues of equality, acceptance and attitudinal change must occur before practice changes. The needs, issues, and demands of people with disabilities resemble those of other groups in Canadian society who are disadvantaged or marginalized or **oppressed**. There are parallels with the fight of people with disabilities for empowerment and equality with various Aboriginal and ethnic groups, with immigrants and refugees, and with women. The experience of people with disabilities, however, is unique in this country, as is reflected in the history and in the development of theories related to disability.

KEY TERMS

antidiscriminatory, p. 203

deinstitutionalization, p. 208

developmental disability, p. 203

disability, p. 198

empowerment, p. 206

"handicaps," p. 201

impairment, p. 204

inclusive societies, p. 198

learning disability, p. 209

"mentally deficient," p. 200

normalization, p. 207

oppressed, p. 215

rehabilitation medicine, p. 201

rehabilitation team, p. 201

self-determination, p. 209

social movement, p. 202

DISCUSSION QUESTIONS

1. Compare and contrast three major theoretical perspectives about people with disabilities.
2. What accounts for the great changes in social policy toward people with disabilities that were brought about by the two world wars? In other words, why did the wars have such a great impact on the lives of people with disabilities?

3. From the perspective of the sociopolitical model, what indicators are there for increased empowerment of people with disabilities in the 21st century? Consider the fields of health, education, and welfare in your answer.

4. What might be some negative consequences to the "theory of normalization"?

5. What would be the advantages of a national disability policy?

NOTES

1. Jerome Bickenbach, *Physical Disability and Social Policy* (Toronto: University of Toronto Press, 1993), p. 12.

2. Bickenbach, p. 12.

3. Special Committee on the Disabled and the Handicapped, *Obstacles*, First Session, Thirty-Second Parliament, 1980–81, The Third Report, February 1981, available Department of Human Resources and Social Development site <www.sdc.gc.ca/asp/gateway. asp?hr=/en/hip/odi/documents/obstacles/00_toc.shtml&hs=vxi>, accessed 6 April 2006.

4. Paul C. Higgins, *Making Disability: Exploring the Social Transformation of Human Variation* (Springfield, IL: Charles C. Thomas, 1992).

5. Carol Goar, "Tories Earn Mixed Grades at Best from Disabled," *Toronto Star*, 24 March 2010, p. A23.

6. "Indicators of Well-being in Canada, Canadians in Context." People with Disabilities: Statistics Canada at: <www.4.hrsdc.gc.ca/.3indic.lt.4r@-eng:jsp?iid=40>.

7. Reg Alcock (President, Treasury Board of Canada), "The World Needs More Canada: Strengthening Support for People with Disabilities," speech to Disabled People's International Summit, Winnipeg, MB, 10 September 2004, available president of Treasury Board of Canada Secretariat site <www.tbs-sct.gc.ca/media/ps-dp/2004/0913_e.asp>, accessed 6 April 2006.

8. United Nations Convention on the Rights of Persons with Disabilities and Apparent Protocol, 2007, Article 1: Purpose, at: <www.un.org/disabilities/document/Convention/convoptprot-e.pdf>.

9. United Nations Convention on the Rights of Persons with Disabilities and Apparent Protocol, 2007, section (g), at: <www.un.org/disabilities/document/Convention/convoptport-e.pdf>.

10. United Nations Convention on the Rights of Persons with Disabilities and Apparent Protocol, 2007, Article 8, Awareness Raising, at: <www.un.org/disabilities/document/Convention/convoptport-e.pdf>.

11. Carol Goar, "Historic Moment for Nation's Disabled," *Toronto Star*, 17 March 2010, p. A15.

12. Ibid.

CHAPTER 8

Diversity and Conformity: The Role of Gender

Leslie Butler

> *I now see the women's movement for equality as simply the necessary first stage of a much larger sex role revolution. . . . What had to be changed was the obsolete feminine and masculine sex roles. . . . It seemed to me men weren't really the enemy—they were fellow victims, suffering from an outmoded masculine mystique that made them feel unnecessarily inadequate when there were no more bears to kill.*
>
> —Betty Friedan, *The Feminine Mystique*

> *God created men and women different—then let them remain each in their own position.*
>
> —Queen Victoria

Objectives

....

After reading this chapter, you should be able to

- define gender identity and gender spheres

- describe the different spheres men and women occupy

- give social and biological explanations for why men and women choose or are channelled in different life directions

- discuss the ways in which gender divisions are positive or negative for individuals and society

- form opinions about what, if anything, to do about the gender issues raised in this chapter

INTRODUCTION

The differences between men and women are perhaps the most celebrated of all human diversities. Poets and philosophers have probed the mysteries of love and the wonders of sexual difference for centuries, but only recently have sex and gender become the subject of scientific study. These studies confirm what many might already have known intuitively: your sex and gender influence every aspect of your life. Whether you are born a boy or a girl will affect everything from what kinds of jobs you will have and how frequently you want sex with your partner, to whether you are likely to be poor and how long you might live. Our masculinity or femininity is a physical and psychological lens that filters our very perception of reality. Knowing something about how sex and gender influence our personal and social lives can help us to better understand our experiences. But first, we need to understand what these terms mean.

To begin with, sex and gender are two different things, even though the terms are sometimes used interchangeably. Your **sex** is determined at conception and refers to the reproductive organs you are born with and your hormonal makeup. Your **gender** is a social role governed by how your culture defines masculinity and femininity. Sex is therefore something unchangeable, whereas gender changes as cultures evolve. (Twenty-first-century Canadian women wearing suits or playing sports would seem terribly unfeminine to their 19th-century counterparts.) This distinction between sex and gender is important, because if we want to build a fair and equal society we need to have the wisdom to know what we can change and what we cannot.

WHAT IS GENDER?

Gender Identity

Despite the many changes of the last century, there are still clusters of traits we designate masculine and feminine. These clusters of traits make up our conception of masculine and feminine **gender identity**, or what it means to be a man or a woman. In North American culture, a truly masculine person is, above all, competent. He is physically strong and sexually virile, aggressive, logical, unemotional, decisive, and protective. A feminine person is, above all, warm and nurturing. She is physically "soft," intuitive, emotional, indecisive, and in need of protection. Women talk, men act; women conciliate, men confront. These associations are powerful determinants of how we feel and how we act as men and women. Some feminists have pointed out that masculine and feminine traits are not valued equally, that society pays lip service to the value of nurturing and warmth but actually rewards masculine traits more concretely than feminine ones.

These clusters of traits are **gender stereotypes**, or generalizations, about the way most men and women are expected to behave. Individuals certainly deviate from these stereotypes, and modern Canadian society tolerates a much wider range of opposite gender behaviour than in the past. However, despite the many social changes of the past century, statistical evidence shows there is a surprisingly high degree of conformity to traditional roles.

It is tempting to believe we are unaffected by stereotypes, that we are free to look and behave as we choose. But think of the penalty a man pays for being effeminate and a woman pays for being "butch." Penalties such as ridicule, ostracism, and workplace discrimination are called **social controls**, and they help enforce rigid gender behaviour codes. When men are feeling emotional or vulnerable, they may feel conflicted about feeling "feminine" and may suppress those feelings for fear of being ridiculed. Women may similarly suppress their masculine side. Enforced by social controls, the gender stereotype becomes a self-fulfilling prophecy. Biology, too, may limit our freedom to choose our gender identity. We will discuss the social and biological influences on gender in more detail later in this chapter.

Diversity or Conformity?

It is interesting to note here that because gender is a social role and controls are in place to make sure most people play the right role, gender may actually enforce conformity rather than encourage diversity. In other words, gender may limit rather than liberate us.

Consider for a moment the expected attitude of men and women toward sex. Men are expected to (and do) initiate sex, to want it frequently, and to value sex over other kinds of intimacy; women are expected to value love over sex, to desire sex less frequently, and to see love as a prerequisite for sex. Because our very identity as men and women includes these messages about sex, these role definitions may profoundly affect and perhaps limit our sexual freedom. Women may feel unfeminine, and thus uncomfortable, if they are sexually aggressive; men may feel unmasculine, and thus uncomfortable, if they prefer submissive roles in sexual interplay. Women may feel guilty or conflicted about having purely sexual relationships that do not have emotional commitments. It is finally okay for women to want sex, but they must not want it too much for fear of being labelled "easy" or a slut. There is simply no male equivalent in our language for slut. Manwhore still carries a congratulatory connotation. Apparently, only women can be too easy and are far more likely than men to feel the guilt or shame associated with sexual promiscuity. Alternatively, men who are anything less than obsessed with sex may find themselves ridiculed or questioning their own masculinity. These powerful messages about appropriate sexual feelings and behaviour are one example of how gender identity may be restrictive rather than liberating.

Challenges to Traditional Gender Identity

It has become more commonplace to see people openly challenging these behaviour codes. **Transvestites** are those men and women who adopt the dress and behaviour of the opposite sex. Their refusal to behave in a gender-appropriate way challenges cultural definitions of masculinity and femininity. The often-harsh reaction to transvestites is a measure of how deeply ingrained is the idea that women should behave like women and men like men. **Transsexuals** are genetically of one sex but have a psychological urge to belong to the opposite sex. Some transsexuals seek surgery to modify their sexual organs to bring their biological self in line with their psychological self.

Gay sexuality has become so openly expressed in North American society that early tentative attempts to portray homosexuality in a sensitive rather than denigrating ways (movies such as *The Kiss of the Spider Woman* and *The Crying Game*) have been followed by mainstream sitcoms such as *Will and Grace*. Gay marriage was a defining issue in the 2004 and 2006 federal elections in Canada, and continues to be a major issue in American politics. *People* magazine announces gay celebrity breakups as casually as straight ones. Since Canada legalized gay marriage in July 2005, nearly 17 percent of gay couples report being married. The number of same-sex couples surged 32.6 percent between 2001 and 2006, five times the pace of opposite-sex couples, though same-sex couples still account for only 0.6 percent of all couples in Canada.[1]

Although the challenges to rigid gender identity and traditional sexual behaviour continue and even move into the mainstream of our culture, they are still the exception rather than the rule. The strict definitions of masculinity and femininity persist, along with the expectation that most people will adopt the "right" kind of behaviour. And, in fact, the vast majority do.

Gender Patterns

Both your sex and gender have a powerful influence on the kinds of experiences you will have in your life. When parents gaze at their children, for example, they may not know that compared with her brother, their daughter is more likely to

- live longer and be widowed
- earn less
- live in poverty
- marry younger
- be a single parent

Their son, on the other hand, is more likely than his sister to

- commit suicide
- be a victim of violence
- remarry if divorced
- lose custody of his children in divorce
- get cancer or AIDS

Canadian statistics continue to bear out these patterns. A woman can expect to live to age 82, whereas a man can expect to live to age 80.[2] At all ages Canadian women are more likely to be widows than men, and when women reach age 80, two-thirds will be widows in contrast with just less than half of men aged 80.[3] Women who work full time continue to earn only 71 percent of what full-time male workers earn,[4] and when women have children, the wage gap widens further. Women have part-time jobs much more often than men, and they continue to shoulder a greater share of the childcare and domestic work.[5] In Canada, women head four out of every five single-parent households,[6] and 38 percent of those households headed by single women have incomes that fall below the poverty line.[7]

HAVE YOU HEARD? 8.1

Feminist and Feminine?

In her groundbreaking book of the early 1960s *The Feminine Mystique*, Betty Friedan chronicled women's struggle to break out of the confines of their domestic straightjacket. But Friedan also argued that the new role of women didn't mean they had to hate men or give up fulfilling romantic and sexual relationships with men. Much of the backlash against feminism in the past thirty years has centred on feminists as man-haters. Some believe being a feminist means women have to hate men or give up on marriage. Others say simply that the idea of romantic love is so entwined with traditional gender roles that it dies when those roles change and overlap. Still others say men react to the feminist challenge with a powerful backlash that includes violence. Friedan herself believed that feminism was not incompatible with romantic love and that the liberation of women would also liberate men.

The patterns for men are equally compelling. It may surprise some readers to know that Canadian men are more likely to experience violence than women are, especially in the light of our heightened awareness of the frequency with which women are abused. In Canada in 2008, men are were three times more likely to be murdered than women.[8] Men of all ages commit suicide more frequently than their female counterparts, and men over 65 are five times more likely to commit suicide than women.[9] In the work world, men are still much more likely than women to be employed in senior managerial positions. This tendency for women to be shut out of high-level jobs is sometimes called the **glass ceiling**. At all ages men as a group are more likely than women to be employed and they make more money. [10]

Individual men and women will not always follow these patterns. Nevertheless, there is striking consistency in the kinds of experiences men and women can expect to have. Let's look at some in more detail. See Have You Heard? 8.1.

WHAT ARE GENDER SPHERES?

Because people conform to fairly well-defined notions of masculinity and femininity, patterns of male and female behaviour emerge. These patterns create what we might call **gender spheres**. By this, we simply mean there are areas of work, school, and play in which men dominate and areas in which women dominate. Although there has been a lot of social change in Canada, these traditional divisions between what men and women do are surprisingly persistent.

Occupational Spheres

In the area of work, men still dominate in administration, technology, the professional fields, and jobs requiring physical strength. Women still find themselves dominating in the "caring" professions such as nursing, social work, and teaching. Women also predominate in the clerical and service sectors. "In 2004, two thirds of all employed women were working in teaching, nursing and related health occupations, clerical or administrative positions and sales and service occupations."[11] Table 8.1, which is based on data from the year 2006, compares the percentage of men and women employed in selected industry sectors. The data show clearly that men and women still find themselves in predictably male and female occupations.

Educational Spheres

Like the workplace, education also has its gender spheres. We might expect this, because educational institutions feed the labour market and as such are a kind of gate that young men and women pass through on their way to jobs. If men and women self-select or are

Table 8.1   Distribution of Employment by Gender, 2006

Industry/Sector	Percentage of Men in Occupation	Percentage of Women in Occupation
Transport and construction	93.5 %	6.5 %
Forestry, fishing, mining	79.5	20.5
Manufacturing	68.9	31.1
Management	63.7	36.3
Doctors, dentists	44.7	55.3
Teaching	36.1	63.9
Clerical and administrative	25.0	75.0
Nursing, therapy, health	12.6	87.4

Source: Adapted from Statistics Canada, *Women in Canada: Work Chapter Updates* 89F0133XIE 2006000 2006, Released April 20, 2007, table 11.

selected out (through gender-biased admissions criteria) of certain educational programs, the gate to jobs requiring that training will close. Data from the 2001 Census show that Canadian men are far more likely than women to study architecture, engineering, and applied sciences. Women predominate in secretarial, community and social services, nursing, and the humanities. Women significantly outnumber men in education, health professions, social sciences, and the humanities; men are far more likely than women to enter engineering, mathematics, and physical science.[12] Women have dramatically closed the gap in postsecondary education in recent years. In 2001, 15 percent of Canadian women had a university degree compared to 16 percent of Canadian men.[13]

Leisure Spheres

Men and women have different amounts of free time, and they often choose to spend it differently. Although men spend more time than women doing paid work, they have slightly more free time than women because women do more unpaid work such as childcare and housework.

As the gender stereotype would predict, men are more physically active at all ages than women. In 1998, 44 percent of Canadian men reported that they regularly participate in sports, in contrast to only 26 percent of women.[14] Men are far more likely than women to choose competitive and physically rough sports such as football and hockey; women are more likely to choose swimming, cross-country skiing, and bowling.[15]

To summarize, men and women continue to choose or be forced into separate work, school, and leisure activities. Figure 8.1, compiled from 2006 data, gives a clear illustration of where masculine and feminine spheres remain separate and where they have begun to overlap.

The Issue of Equality

Once we recognize that men and women occupy different occupational and educational spheres, it is natural to wonder whether these spheres are separate but equal, or separate but unequal. In fact, the issue of equality is central to most questions surrounding sex and gender, and we will return to it several times in this chapter.

It is hard to ignore the economic inequality between the sexes in Canada: women simply do not get an equal share of the pay rewards, whether they work outside the home or inside. The work of raising children and maintaining a household goes unpaid. Women's occupations—childcare, clerical work, nursing, service jobs—for the most part pay less

Figure 8.1   Gender Spheres

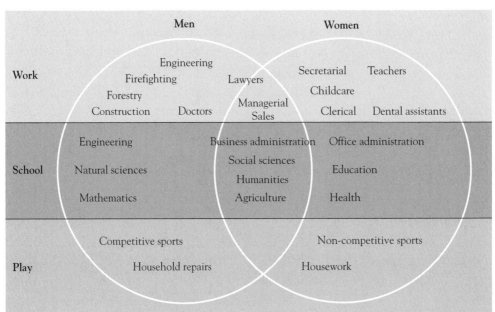

Sources: Adapted from the Statistics Canada CANSIM database http://cansim2.statcan.gc.ca 282-0008; *The Daily: Women in Canada* 11-001 Tuesday, March 7, 2006; *Highest Degree, Certificate or Diploma (12), Major Field of Study (122), 2000 Employment Income (3), Work Activity in 2000 (2), Age Groups (13B) and Sex (3) for Total Population 15 Years and Over, for Canada, Provinces and Territories, 2001 Census - 20% Sample Data* 97F0018XIE2001043, Census year 2001, July 3, 2003.

CRITICAL THINKING OUTSIDE THE BOX 8.1

Superiority in Sports

Is male superiority in athletics a result of nature or nurture? Consider how women have closed the gap in world record time for the marathon. In 1964 the men's world record marathon time was 1 hour and 22 minutes faster than the women's. In 2003, only 10 minutes and 30 seconds separated the men's record from the women's. With more women participating, better training for women, and larger monetary rewards, will women one day close the gap altogether?

than men's—business, manufacturing, and professional jobs. Is it just a coincidence that women's work is less valued than men's? Is childcare, for example, inherently less valuable than janitorial work? Did men simply take an unfair share of the material rewards? Or does having a pool of cheap and even unpaid (female) labour simply benefit employers? (Wages are kept down when there is a reserve army of labour ready and waiting to fill jobs.)

A stark example of economic inequality between the sexes can be found in Table 8.2, which shows what men and women can expect to earn after graduating in different fields of study. The survey compared men and women who achieved the highest degree, certificate, or diploma in each field, and found that men make more than their female counterparts in every field, including teaching and nursing, which have traditionally been female-dominated. So even when men venture into nontraditional roles they can still expect to earn more than their female colleagues.

If women are the losers in the economic sphere, there is strong evidence that men are losers in the interpersonal sphere. As breadwinners forced to be absent from the home, they are more likely to forgo close relationships with their children. Confined by rigid definitions of masculinity, many men may be unable to achieve emotional and intellectual intimacy with their partners. Men rarely get sole custody of their children in divorces, and often play a secondary role in raising children after divorce (see Have You Heard? 8.2). For many men, the stress of having the family's material well-being thrust on their shoulders results in mental and physical health problems. The bare fact is, men die younger than women, and more men than women suffer from chronic stress-related diseases such as heart disease and alcoholism. Being valued as a meal ticket is probably every bit as confining for men as being valued as a sex object or a mother figure is for women. A picture of two solitudes continues to emerge, with men cast in the role of provider and women in the role of caregiver.

Table 8.2   Wage Gap by Selected Field of Study

Major Field of Study	Average Employment Income ($)		Difference for Men
	Men	Women	
Medicine	121 010	75 003	+46 007
Dentistry	112 512	60 932	+51 580
Law and jurisprudence	93 458	52 196	+41 362
Business and commerce	64 447	35 275	+29 172
Civil engineering	57 564	34 090	+23 474
Primary education	32 742	23 770	+8 972
Nursing	42 458	35 524	+6 934
Hairdressing and other applied arts	27 632	17 043	+10 589

Source: Adapted from Statistics Canada, *Highest Degree, Certificate or Diploma (12), Major Field of Study (122), 2000 Employment Income (3), Work Activity in 2000 (2), Age Groups (13B) and Sex (3) for Total Population 15 Years and Over, for Canada, Provinces and Territories, 2001 Census - 20% Sample Data 97F0018XIE2001043,* Census year 2001, July 3, 2003.

HAVE YOU HEARD? 8.2

Child Custody Awards

. . . .

A 1998 survey of 5000 Canadian divorce cases showed women get sole custody of children in 80 percent of Canadian divorces. Men get sole custody only 8.4 percent of the time. Some would say this is concrete evidence of gender discrimination against men. Intentionally or unintentionally, the courts may assume that men are unsuited for nurturing and raising children, leaving men with the pain of losing their children. Men's rights groups and websites devoted to promoting men's interests in custody awards have proliferated in recent years.

Source: Lorne D. Bertrand, Joseph P. Hornick, and Nicholas M.C. Bala, "The Survey of Child Support Awards: Preliminary Analysis of Phase 2 Data (October 1998–May 1999)," 25 August 2000, available at: <www.justice.gc.ca/eng/pi/fcy-fea/lib-bib/rep-rap/2000/rap/index.html>, accessed 13 June 2010.

Sexual Politics

Women who have historically found themselves on the short end of the economic stick have nonetheless achieved some degree of equality through what might be called *sexual politics*. This is the delicate, usually unacknowledged, power struggle between men who desire, or appear to desire, sex more than their female partners, who have the power to give or withhold sex. The fact that men have a greater sexual appetite than women, or at least a more openly acknowledged sexual appetite than women, is evident in sex trade statistics. The job market for female prostitutes, strippers, exotic dancers, and pornographic subjects far exceeds the demand for their male counterparts. This apparent difference in the sex drives of each gender has caused many feminists to observe that the only two professions in which women are able to out-earn men are prostitution and fashion modelling.

Whether men hire prostitutes, exchange their paycheques for regular sex in marriage, or merely use money (along with flattery and favours) when courting and wooing, men's apparently greater need for sex gives women some leverage in negotiating with their partners. Before women could advance themselves in paid work outside the home, they could improve their socioeconomic standing by being sexually desirable to a wealthy man. Today, the process of sexual negotiation is much more subtle, and may even be invisible to those involved in it. But in the day-to-day give and take of male–female relationships, sexual politics continues to play an often unacknowledged role in determining who gets what out of the partnership.

The Idea of Progress

It may surprise some of you to see such stark evidence of persisting gender spheres. After all, aren't the bad old days gone?

Much *has* changed. The days when women were prevented by law from entering politics, and when no man would choose to be a secretary or nurse for fear of total ostracism, are gone. Economic imperatives, such as the need for two-income families, have resulted

---

CRITICAL THINKING OUTSIDE THE BOX 8.2

Sexual Politics

How real is the issue of sexual politics in most relationships between men and women? Do women use men's more openly acknowledged desire for sex to get some of the things they want out of a relationship (e.g., financial security, help around the home)?

---

in real changes in the workplace and the home. Attitudes about what is acceptable for men and women have also changed. Women now have professional hockey and basketball leagues, and some men choose to be nurses and secretaries.

But the majority of men and women are still channelled into "acceptable" roles by powerful social controls. It may be that our liberated attitudes toward gender have changed much faster than social reality has.

We may have trouble accepting that gender spheres persist because deeply ingrained in our consciousness is the notion of progress. Our worldview is dominated by the idea that things are getting better and that this inexorable force will march ever forward and never backward. But the number of women in politics, for example, goes up and down, and sometime just stands still. Federally, women have held roughly 20 percent of the seats in the House of Commons since the mid-1990s, with virtually no progress. Despite the absence of "natural" progress, some people think that very little should actively be done to eliminate the inequalities between the sexes because things will just get better in the not-too-distant future.

WHY GENDER SPHERES EXIST

Nature and Nurture

Once we recognize that gender spheres exist, and that men and women do find themselves playing fairly predictable roles, it is natural to wonder why. Do we behave as men and women because we were born that way or because we learned how to behave? When a man is masculine, is he strong, aggressive, and unemotional because of biological factors or social factors? Does testosterone make him so? Or is he merely conforming to rigidly maintained social definitions of masculinity? Does a woman's biological makeup lead her to be nurturing, emotional, and conciliatory? Or does she learn there will be penalties if she behaves in an unfeminine way? You will recognize this as the **nature/nurture** debate central to most questions about human behaviour, a debate that rages on. Although it is not likely to be resolved any time soon, the debate is worth looking at, because it reveals some interesting ideological alignments and helps us understand how politically charged is the issue of sex and gender.

Progressivism and Conservatism

Biological explanations for why men and women seem to behave differently and occupy different social roles have a **conservative ideology** because nothing can be done to change the status quo. Taken to its extreme, the biological argument would say there is little point in trying to make men more nurturing, compassionate, and conciliatory because men are driven by their biology to adopt exactly the opposite behaviour. Similarly pointless are attempts to make women more aggressive, logical, and decisive. Going a step further in the conservative position, most men will be less effective than women if they move into occupations such as childrearing and nursing that require traditionally feminine nurturing qualities. Women who move into politics and business will be hampered by their emotional nature. It is therefore sensible, when we are building our social world, to exploit the natural abilities of men and women rather than trying to buck the natural trend.

Social explanations for why men and women seem to behave differently demonstrate a **progressive ideology** because they include the possibility that the status quo can be changed. In other words, if behaviour is learned and not forced on us by unchanging laws of biology, then we can simply learn differently and change will happen. If we want to broaden the range of acceptable masculine and feminine behaviours, we can change the social environment in which we raise boys and girls: dolls for boys and trucks for girls.

It is, however, unlikely that very many people side wholly on the nature or the nurture side of the question (and are therefore entirely progressive or entirely conservative). This is probably because in reality, we know people with both masculine and feminine traits. There is a widely held notion, probably based on the work of psychologists such as Carl Jung, that all men and women have both a masculine and a feminine side to their psyche. This mixing of masculine and feminine traits is what probably leads many people to conclude that a combination of biological and social factors shape human behaviour. Therefore, most people probably lean toward one side or the other rather than believing entirely in either nature or nurture.

It is worth noting here that whether you lean toward the nature or the nurture side may depend more on self-interest than on how logical you find the arguments on that side. For example, women who are dissatisfied with rigid role definitions that they perceive have relegated them to low-status, low-paying jobs may align themselves with the progressive, nurture position. At least hope for change exists there. Similarly, men who like their positions of relative prestige and power might align themselves with the conservative, nature position and believe that they are merely living out an inevitable role thrust on them by laws of nature. Alternatively, men who are denied custody of their children may also find themselves looking to break down rigid gender roles through social change.

TWO THEORIES ABOUT GENDER SPHERES

Sociologists also have pondered why gender spheres exist. They tend to examine the behaviour of men and women in groups, rather than as individuals, and they look primarily to the social world, not the biological world, for explanations. The two theories that follow reflect two common divisions in the way people explain why men and women occupy distinct spheres: (1) gender spheres either result naturally and provide a useful way to organize our social world or (2) they result from one group trying to maintain advantage over the other.

Structural–Functionalist Theory

The theory that says that gender spheres evolved naturally because of the fact that men and women had different biological strengths and weaknesses is called **structural–functionalism**. Men hunted because of their physical strength and women could not hunt because they were tied to the children by their capacity to bear and breastfeed them. As societies became more complex, male and female roles grew out of this fundamental division of labour: women at home, men out hunting and protecting the family. This perspective stresses that the roles played by men and women are natural and serve to help society function more or less smoothly. Men and women have clear roles and those roles stay the same over time. The idea is that societies, like organisms, evolve to survive. Social structures evolve to serve different purposes in the functioning of society. Structural–functionalists would point to the fact that it makes sense, from a group survival standpoint, to have men do dangerous work such as hunting, firefighting, or mining because they are reproductively expendable. (We only need one man to produce twenty babies in a year if he impregnates twenty women, but we need all twenty women to produce twenty babies.)

For structural–functionalists, the exclusion of women from paid work or the devaluing of women's work also serves a useful function in distributing wealth fairly. At first glance this may seem absurd, but consider that the family is the basic unit and each family has a male breadwinner. Paying only the men makes it more likely that each family will have access to at least one of the scarce good jobs. When both men and women can take the good jobs, it is easier for families to "hog" wealth by taking two good jobs. This phenomenon is evident today when a male doctor marries a female lawyer.

Conflict Theory

In contrast, another sociological theory takes a different view of gender spheres. **Conflict theory** sees society as consisting of many different groups that have competing, or conflicting, interests. Each group is busy pursuing its self-interest even if it means disadvantaging or even exploiting another group. Conflict theorists would say that having clear male and female spheres and excluding women from the paid work sphere effectively cuts the competition for good jobs and monetary rewards in half. This was no doubt good for men, who used every means to maintain this advantage. But as economic necessities brought women into the workforce in large numbers, the competition for good jobs intensified. Much of the backlash against feminism in North America results from the fact that

---

CRITICAL THINKING OUTSIDE THE BOX 8.3

Segregated Schools?

Recent work by American psychologist Leonard Sax points to research showing boys are falling behind girls in early education. Classrooms are girl-friendly, and boys' need for more physical stimulation leads them to become disaffected as they become marginalized. Are segregated schools that cater to boys' needs the answer? Or is this a regressive step?

---

males today face much greater competition from females than their fathers faced. If you are male, you may face nearly twice the competition for jobs that your father did.

Because men benefited from limited competition, they would naturally use any means at their disposal to maintain the status quo. Conflict theorists might look at the means by which men maintained their advantage over women historically. These means are called instruments of social control and are seen not as natural but as "man"-made phenomena. Laws that prevented women from owning property, for example, were an important means by which men kept women out of the competition. Because owning property was a necessary criterion for just about any political or economic activity, women were effectively excluded from anything that shaped society. For conflict theory then, the law becomes a social institution that does not benefit all equally, but rather an instrument used by one group to gain advantage over another.

It is vital to point out here that conflict theorists do not see gender as the only, or even the most important, distinction in understanding who dominates whom. Equally important are differences in social class. When women's work is undervalued, it is not necessarily men controlling women, but rather people with power and money (the ruling class) controlling those without power and money (the working class). An underemployed man earning a fraction of a professional woman's salary can more directly relate to class difference than gender difference. Employers can be, and are increasingly, women. These women may even benefit from sexual discrimination against their sisters.

Conflict theorists might similarly identify ways women benefited from gender division of labour and used their biological childbearing roles to exert power over men. Some feminist scholars have unearthed evidence of ancient matriarchal societies in which women's central role as procreator put them in a position of power over men. A concrete modern example of how men are excluded from childrearing is seen in the disproportionate number of child custody suits that are won by women (see Have You Heard? 8.2).

CRITICAL THINKING OUTSIDE THE BOX 8.4

The Disappearance of Men's Work

Since men have occupied the sphere of hard physical work, what will happen to men as the physical work in society increasingly is done by machines or disappears altogether? Will men lose their traditional territory as blue-collar jobs disappear and white-collar jobs—which women are equally or better qualified for—make up the majority of work?

So gender spheres may simply serve a function in the smooth operation of society by ensuring that jobs get done by those best equipped to do them, or gender spheres may be evidence of an ongoing battle of the sexes and social classes.

Merit versus Social Connections

Whether gender spheres evolved in order to help society function or because of conflicting gender interests, why do they persist, especially in a society that prides itself on providing equal opportunity for all? If people are free to choose their destiny, if they can truly be whatever they want to be, why do men and women mysteriously want to choose gender-appropriate activities? Why do they behave so predictably? Or could it be that people are not as free as they think, that strong social, economic, legal, and psychological controls steer men and women into predictable destinies?

If you believe that people are free to choose their path in life, that individual character and hard work can help women overcome barriers preventing them from entering a male sphere and men from entering female spheres, then you believe in a **meritocracy**. This simply refers to the idea that people get their rewards in life on the basis of their individual merits (say talent, skill, or intelligence). In a meritocracy, skills and talents are rewarded fairly and equally regardless of factors such as gender, race, or social class. Therefore, women who manage to acquire the talents and skills necessary to do a job will ultimately get that job. Along this line of reasoning, it would be foolish and ultimately self-defeating for employers to turn away well-qualified women just because they are women. Therefore, if women find themselves ghettoized in low-paying, low-status jobs, the way out is to get the skills and education necessary for better jobs. Those skills will be rewarded. Similarly, men who are barred from female spheres also need to get the right qualifications to compete equally with women. Therefore, those who buy into the idea that we have a meritocracy would say gender spheres persist because individual men and women have not applied themselves to getting the right kinds of qualifications.

Others, however, doubt that a meritocracy can or does exist. They believe that the competition for jobs, money, and status is not a fair one at all and that the rewards are not given out to those with the most merit but instead to those with social connections to the group that controls hiring. Therefore, if women control the selection of candidates for early childhood education in schools, men will be excluded by virtue of their sex. Women simply will not value the kinds of qualities men bring to the job. Those who doubt we have a meritocracy tend to believe that women and men are prevented from entering some fields of education and occupation because of often-invisible **systemic barriers**, not because they lack the skills or talents. These barriers are built right into the system in the form of laws, discriminatory hiring practices, and psychological barriers.

Laws

An example of how law works as a built-in barrier preventing women from entering the male sphere can be seen in the fact that in some countries women are still prohibited from combat roles in the military. History is crammed with examples of laws that prevented women from entering male spheres. For example, in the early 20th century, women were not defined as persons under the law in Canada and therefore could not hold political office.

Discriminatory Hiring

Discriminatory hiring practices might include a host of subtle or not-so-subtle ways to screen out the wrong gender. An experienced male primary-school teacher in Ontario was privately told by the principal to stop applying for the kindergarten job at his school because parents were simply not ready to have a man take their daughters to the washroom.

Gender-biased hiring standards can be another form of discrimination in hiring. Recently, women have challenged the high value placed on height or physical strength in screening applicants to police academies, arguing that the vast majority of police work requires skills such as mediation, conciliation, and communication (feminine strengths). To the men who created the tests, the gender bias would probably not even be visible, and they may see any attempt to change the standards as "lowering" the standards for women.

Psychological Barriers

Psychological barriers are less tangible but may be no less powerful in preventing men and women from being free to choose their path. Girls and boys may never even want to do nontraditional jobs because of powerful messages given to them about what is an appropriate activity for males and females. Education officials may wonder why social work

CRITICAL THINKING OUTSIDE THE BOX 8.5

Girls spend increasing amounts of their time on social networking websites such as Facebook, causing concern that girls are becoming more and more "outer-directed." Instead of developing a strong sense of inner self and identity, the reasoning goes, these girls are busy creating images of themselves through photo galleries, status updates, and online quizzes. A recent New York Times article called this starvation of the inner self "anorexia of the soul."[16] Is this concern justified?

still attracts very few males, and they may even institute a program to attract more male applicants to social work programs. But if boys sense that social work, with its emphasis on interpersonal skills and its relatively low pay reward, is an inappropriate activity for them, no amount of "affirmative action" will bring more men into the programs.

WHY IT ALL MATTERS AND WHAT TO DO ABOUT IT

Individual Choice

We know that men and women are different, that they are expected to and do behave differently, and that as a result they occupy different spheres in our social world. We might even have some ideas about why gender divisions exist and persist. The logical next question is: Why does it matter?

It matters to individuals because men and women suffer when they are forced into rigid masculine and feminine roles that limit their potential or simply do not fit them. Stereotypes about how people should behave restrict people's freedom to act the way they want to and to pursue their real interests and strengths. Men who want to take a secretarial job and who have no desire for promotion or further responsibility are deterred from doing so by a disapproving society. (Does he have enough testosterone?)

It is difficult to overstate the profound infringement this is on a person's individual liberty. If the state were to pass a law prohibiting men from staying home to raise children, for example, Canadians would be outraged and challenges to the *Charter of Rights and Freedoms* would abound. But we quietly tolerate a powerful set of social controls that virtually guarantee men and women will "self-censor" their activities and conform to society's expectations. Although challenges to accepted gender roles have always existed and may over time change our conceptions of masculinity and femininity, they are still peripheral and cause the challengers much pain.

But conforming to society's expectations might cause as much pain as challenging them. Feminist scholars are now looking at the high rate of mental illness among women historically as evidence that some women literally lost their minds when they were prevented from using their talents in the world outside the home. Some were brilliant women who were forced into mundane domestic chores for which they were wholly unsuited.

Men, too, have suffered terribly, because the masculine stereotype left them unable to communicate their emotions or achieve intimacy. Literature has many examples of emotionally crippled men who are isolated from their loved ones because they cannot communicate their feelings.

Constructing a Fair Society

On a societal level, our construction of society along rigid gender lines may not be as functional as we think it is, nor may it be very fair. What a waste of talent and potential we have created if we exclude talented men and women from certain jobs simply because they are men and women! It is an even greater waste if they exclude themselves by never even wanting to do other than what men and women have always done. What should we do to try to open up opportunities for individuals and to ensure that society uses its human resources to the best potential? How do we stop gender from limiting our life choices?

Education

One popular notion about how to break down gender barriers is to educate people. The assumption is that education will erase many gender stereotypes that restrict human potential. If we teach people that men and women have a very broad range of skills and talents that often do not conform to traditional male and female stereotypes, we may liberate the potential of men and women alike. An enlightened population is presumably more open to change than an unenlightened one.

Equity Laws

Another way to remove gender barriers is to simply cut to the chase and engineer the result we want through laws and regulations (see Critical Thinking Outside the Box 8.6). If we want more men in secretarial fields or childcare, simply establish hiring quotas. If we want women to enter firefighting or engineering, make rules forcing educational institutions and employers to bring in more women. This is, of course, very controversial. In Canada, we have not gone as far as establishing quotas, but we have had employment equity legislation at both the federal and the provincial level. These laws promote the hiring of not just women but also minorities and people with disabilities by requiring

---

CRITICAL THINKING OUTSIDE THE BOX 8.6

Are Employment Equity Laws Necessary?

Employment equity laws are designed to engineer changes in our workplaces to ensure that certain groups (women, people with disabilities, racial minorities, and Native people) are fairly represented in Canada's workplaces. But some people believe hiring quotas will cause reverse discrimination against qualified white males and could lead to unqualified women and minorities getting jobs. Advocates of equity laws counter by saying there are plenty of well-qualified women and minorities and there is no need to lower hiring standards. What do you think?

---

employers to set their own hiring targets and to meet them. The debate about equity laws can be inflammatory at times. Some believe laws are necessary to balance out existing systemic barriers and overt discrimination against these groups; others believe these laws cause reverse discrimination by excluding qualified males and lowering hiring standards. Those who favour employment equity also argue that gender stereotypes and the psychological barriers that prevent people from choosing nontraditional roles will be broken down most effectively when young children see male daycare workers and female engineers as role models.

Proportional Representation

Along these same lines, another way to eliminate gender spheres is to have proportional representation of women (and other disadvantaged groups) on hiring committees and educational selection committees. This approach admits that consciously or unconsciously, we will value the attributes of those most like ourselves. Proportional representation (e.g., the number of women on any committee should mirror the percentage of women in that community) would then lead to more qualified women being selected for employment or postsecondary programs. If women help define hiring standards, it might also lead to less-gender-biased selection processes. In the case of police academies, this might lead to a higher valuing of communication and mediation skills and a deemphasis on physical strength. If women made up 51 percent of the House of Commons, women's concerns would be more urgently addressed by government. Proportional representation would also help open the doors for men in fields in which they have suffered systemic discrimination.

Chickens and Eggs

Employment equity and proportional representation raise an interesting point that divides many people about how change happens. Those who want to cut to the chase with hiring quotas and proportional representation believe that you have to change reality first and then changes in people's attitudes and behaviour will follow. In other words, only *after* people see that women can be aggressive decision makers and men can be excellent nurturers will gender stereotypes break down. This view stresses that our attitudes are shaped in response to what we see around us. The opposite view stresses that we must change people's attitudes first, and then social change will follow. This view stresses the role of education in social change. If we teach boys and girls to be open-minded about gender and to question traditional stereotypes, those attitudinal changes will lead to the kinds of real changes contemplated by employment equity.

The Wisdom to Know the Difference

There may be some facts about gender that we simply cannot change, or we cannot change any time soon. Perhaps we need to find the wisdom to know what they are. For example, we know women must bear children, and they suffer economic penalties as a result. We know men pay dearly in health and longevity for their role as primary breadwinners. Whether gender divisions are caused by biological or social forces, we may want to build a society that accommodates these facts about gender rather than a society that denies them. For example, society could accommodate women's childbearing imperative by requiring all employers to have decent maternity leave programs, job-sharing provisions, and fewer pay and promotion penalties for women who have interrupted careers. Similarly, measures for men such as more frequent vacations, voluntary unpaid leaves, and flextime working hours might help reduce the incidence of stress-related diseases such as alcoholism and heart disease that men suffer and die from.

CONCLUSION

Do gender divisions help society function smoothly or do they lead to conflict between the sexes? How you answer this question probably depends on the kinds of experiences you have had as a man or woman. The existence of a strong feminist movement throughout most of the past century in Canada may be evidence that some women find gender restrictive. Men, too, may want to free themselves from restrictive male stereotypes.

If we want to make changes, we must begin to understand how gender affects men and women individually and in groups. Only then can we make the kinds of changes that will enable men and women to live out their destinies as freely and as fully as they can.

CHAPTER SUMMARY

Despite many changes in Canadian society, men and women are still encouraged to adopt a fairly rigidly defined masculine or feminine gender identity. Gender identity is a socially defined role for men and women. When men and women consistently adopt traditional male and female roles, gender spheres are created. Gender spheres are simply areas of work, school, and play that tend to be dominated by either men or women.

Whether gender identity and the resulting gender spheres are created mostly by unchangeable biological factors or by changeable social factors is still hotly debated. Also at issue is whether the creation of male and female territories helps society to function smoothly overall or whether it creates conflict between the sexes. Some people believe men and women are free to choose their gender identity. Others believe it is forced on them by powerful social controls that reward proper masculine and feminine behaviour and penalize nonconformity.

Issues of freedom of choice and social equality are central to the gender question. Is individual freedom severely limited by rigid gender stereotypes and the social controls that enforce them? Do women lose out in the economic sphere when women's work is undervalued? Do men lose out in the interpersonal sphere when they are barred from nurturing roles? As you further your education and life experiences, you will form your own views on these important gender issues.

KEY TERMS

conflict theory, p. 230

conservative ideology, p. 228

gender, p. 218

gender identity, p. 218

gender spheres, p. 222

gender stereotypes, p. 219

glass ceiling, p. 222

meritocracy, p. 232

nature/nurture, p. 228

progressive ideology, p. 229

sex, p. 218

social controls, p. 219

structural–functionalism, p. 230

systemic barriers, p. 233

transsexuals, p. 220

transvestites, p. 220

DISCUSSION QUESTIONS

1. In small groups, discuss the gender roles of men and women in the culture your family originated from. How do the roles differ from culture to culture? How are they the same? Consider some other cultures, such as Afghanistan and the Taliban's laws regarding women.

2. Discuss the question of how rigid our gender roles are. Would the men you know be turned off by a sexually aggressive, dominant woman who works in a construction job? Would the women you know be attracted to or turned off by a submissive man who loves his secretarial job and has no desire to move up the ladder?

3. Do you agree with employment equity laws? Why or why not?

4. Parents frequently remark that their male and female children were different from the moment they were born. Despite their attempts to treat their boys and girls the same, the children seem to follow predictable patterns of male and female behaviour. Which is more significant in forming our gender identity, nature or nurture?

5. Discuss some of the penalties people pay for violating society's expectations of them as men or women. Consider minor deviations such as men wearing long hair and major ones such as transsexualism.

6. Do you think the ability of men and women to form happy, lasting relationships is made more difficult by the gender inequalities in our society?

NOTES

1. Statistics Canada, "2006 Census: Families, Marital Status, Households and Dwelling Characteristics," *The Daily*, 12 September 2007, available <www.statcan.gc.ca/daily-quotidien/070912/dq070912a-eng.htm>, accessed 12 June 2010.

2. Statistics Canada, "Deaths," *The Daily*, 20 December 2006, available <www.statcan.gc.ca/daily-quotidien/061220/dq061220b-eng.htm>, accessed 12 June 2010.

3. Statistics Canada, "Population by Marital Status and Sex," 6 December 2009, available <www40.statcan.ca/l01/cst01/famil01-eng.htm>, accessed 15 June 2010.

4. Statistics Canada, "Women in Canada," *The Daily*, 7 March 2006, available <www.statcan.gc.ca/daily-quotidien/060307/dq060307a-eng.htm>, accessed 15 June2010.

5. Statistics Canada, "Women in Canada."

6. Vanier Institute of the Family, "Family Facts," *Virtual Library*, available <www.vifamily.ca/library/facts/facts.html>, accessed 15 June 2010.

7. Statistics Canada, "Women in Canada."

8. Statistics Canada, "Victims and Persons Accused of Homicide by Age and Sex," 28 October 2009, available <www.ojp.usdoj.gov/bjs/homicide/gender.htm>, accessed 15 June 2010.

9. Statistics Canada, "Suicides, and Suicide Rate, by Sex and by Age Group," available <www40.statcan.gc.ca/l01/cst01/perhlth66a-eng.htm>, accessed 15 June 2010.

10. Statistics Canada, "Women in Canada."

11. Statistics Canada, "Women in Canada."

12. Statistics Canada, "Education in Canada: Major Fields of Study," 2001 Census, 97F0018XCB2001043, available <www12.statcan.ca/english/census01/products/standard/themes>, accessed 17 June 2010.

13. Statistics Canada, "Chapter 4: Education," Women in Canada," 2005, available <www.statcan.gc.ca/pub/89-503-x/2005001/chap4-eng.htm>, accessed 22 June 2010.

14. Statistics Canada, "Sports Involvement by Sex," *General Social Survey, 1998,* available <www40.statcan.gc.ca/l01/cst01/arts18-eng.htm>, accessed 18 June 2010.

15. Statistics Canada, "Most Popular Sports," *General Social Survey, 1998,* <www40.statcan.ca/l01/cst01/arts16.htm>, accessed 23 April 2006. (Table is noted as discontinued from 25 February 2005.)

16. Sarah Rimer, "Driven to Excel, For Girls It's Be Yourself, and Be Perfect, Too," *New York Times,* 1 April 2007, available <http://query.nytimes.com/gst/fullpage.html?res=9E03E3DC1E30F932A35757C0A9619C8B&sec=&spon=&pagewanted=3>, accessed 22 June 2010.

CHAPTER 9

Sexual Diversity in Canada

Shane Gannon and Lee Easton

The realm of sexuality also has its own internal politics, inequities, and modes of oppression. As with other aspects of human behaviour, the concrete institution forms of sexuality at any given time and place are products of human activity. They are imbued with conflicts of interests and political manoeuvre, both deliberate and incidental. In that sense, sex is always political.

> — Gayle Rubin, "Thinking Sex: Notes for a Radical Theory of the Politics of Sexuality"

Sex was not something one simply judged; it was a thing one administered.

> — Michel Foucault, *The History of Sexuality: An Introduction*

Objectives

. . . .

After reading this chapter, you should be able to:

- articulate the connection between an individual's sense of self as a sexual person to larger social contexts

- understand the different ways that sexuality has been framed/discussed/defined in both Canadian and global contexts

- situate the Canadian experience of sexuality in global and historical context

- describe different ways of understanding sexuality and placing yourself in them

- discuss the differences between biological and social constructivist ways of defining sexual identity

- outline how the process of normalization has constructed the Canadian experience of diversity of sexualities

INTRODUCTION

Sexuality profoundly shapes every facet of our lives. Despite our often elaborate explanations about reproduction, evolution, or romantic love, human sexuality still baffles us. Perhaps its elusiveness explains why the last two decades have seen an explosion of interest in trying to understand sexualities since, as it turns out, sex and sexuality is not just about biology or even just about our private, individual choices about what we do with our bodies and with whom and how. As our awareness of the meaning of sexual differences has increased, we've come to see that sexuality informs how we think about our everyday lives as individuals who have families, shop in malls, maintain friendships, participate in sports and of course, with whom we fall in love and have sex.

Sexuality is also a political issue. Canada's debates about same-sex marriage and about whether Medicare should cover gender reassignment surgeries have underscored how closely connected politics remains to issues of sexual diversity and equality. And, as much as progress has been made in Canada, the global picture suggests that tolerance, let alone acceptance of sexual diversity, remains an elusive goal. In 2010, for example, two gay men in Malawi were sentenced to fourteen years in jail for trying to marry and were spared only when international pressure led the Malawian president to issue them a pardon. Malawi is only the most recent example of nations who criminalize homosexuality and homosexual relationships. At least eighty-five countries have laws regulating what sex acts between men are legal and those which are illegal. Interestingly, forty-four countries have similar laws restricting illegal sex acts between women.

The emergence of sexual diversity can be traced to changes in how sexualities have been conceived through science and medicine. In the1950s, for example, homosexuality in Canada, as elsewhere, was illegal and often viewed as a medical condition requiring medical and psychiatric interventions. Individuals were dismissed from their jobs while others were subjected to electroshock treatments and even lobotomies to cure "the problem." Today intersexed and transgendered people often endure similar kinds of prejudice despite better understandings of gender and sexuality. Parents of intersexed children are encouraged to have their children undergo surgery to make their infant bodies fit the conventions of the male/female sex-gender system. In order to qualify for sex reassignment surgery, transgendered people must undergo rigorous psychiatric testing and evaluation.

Certainly sexual diversity in Canada is more evident than ever. From a time when James Klippert was jailed for having sex with other men, major changes have occurred both socially and politically to move towards tolerance and acceptance of sexual minorities. There are about 46 000 same-sex couples in Canada today, many of whom are married.

And yet, at the same time, 10 percent of hate crimes in Canada are linked to sexual orientation.[1] In March 2009, for example, Shawn Woodward attacked Ritch Dowrey, leaving him with permanent brain damage. When asked why he did it, Woodward is reported to have stated, "He's a faggot. He deserved it." This example is one of many, which demonstrates the uncomfortable fact that gay men are still at risk of violent attacks that may end in death.

This dichotomy between social change on one hand and the continuing intolerance of sexual diversity on the other informs the approach we take in this chapter. Sex and sexuality are not just individual private matters. They are also political in the sense that as feminists have shown, personal choices have political implications for everyone. And, although sex has been around for eons, our cultural frames regarding sexuality shift from time to time and from culture to culture. Our focus is on sexual diversity in Canada, so we will examine the **cultural frames** that our nation-state has used to interpret sexuality and then show how those interpretations underpin legislation, social practices, and beliefs that ultimately shape our lives as "Canadian" citizens today. **Gays** and **lesbians** in Canada have acquired more rights as they've joined the mainstream but at the same time these gains are not necessarily as progressive as they appear. Larger social structures still restrict and contain individual freedom and keep us from genuine acceptance and real equality. At the same time, as we discuss in the last section of the chapter, sexual diversity has created forms of community and celebration that resist these still powerful social forces of inequity.

THINKING SEXUALITY

Sex is not new: humans have been exploring and explaining it for millennia. Sexuality, on the other hand, is a more recent interest that emerged alongside the desire to use reason and science to explain an all natural process. The word "sexuality" was first coined in the 1700s to name the property of organisms that possessed sexual attributes. Over

CRITICAL THINKING OUTSIDE THE BOX 9.1

Why do you think that it is significant that the invention of the word "homosexual" preceded the creation of the term "heterosexual?"

time, the term came to talk about the physical sex differences between men and women. Then, as more studies focused on 'aberrant' forms of desire, such as that between members of the same sex, sexuality became linked to sexual attraction to others. Although both **heterosexuality** and **homosexuality** are translated into English in 1892, homosexuality was invented in 1869 before the term, heterosexuality! And yet until recently, homosexuality was considered a disorder which required treatment.

Human sexuality has proven notoriously difficult to categorize. For example, how do we explain the fact that some people have claimed to have been aware of their sexual orientation from a very early age while others come out much later in life after having married and raised children? People are able and often do have sex with members of the same sex even if they don't identify as gay, lesbian, or even bisexual. Among Canadian male sex workers who have sex with men, 23 percent of the workers reported that they identified as heterosexual or straight and 31 percent reported they were bisexual.[2] Sometimes individuals in prisons will engage in on-going same-sex relationships even though they actually see themselves as heterosexual. Some forego any sexual activity and intimacies. In the attempt to explain these observations, two frameworks have come to shape our understanding of sexuality. Many focus on biological explanations of **sexual orientation** while the other has focused on the cultural and sociological reasons that shape **sexual identity**. The dialogue between supporters of these two positions is commonly known as the **nature/nurture** debate.

Biological Roots of Sexuality: It's Only Natural!

While scientists agree that heterosexual reproduction offers the evolutionary advantage of developing immunity against diseases, there are other ways of reproducing a species than heterosexual sex. Homosexual and heterosexual activity has been recorded in human societies as well as in species other than humans. What has differed is how these acts have been incorporated or excluded differently in various societies across cultures and over time.

Biological arguments about sexual orientation have tended to support the lesbian and gay rights arguments about adopting and raising children. As some activists ask, if sexuality is learned or taught, how is it that heterosexuals have given birth to and raised homosexual children? Given the levels of **homophobia** that pervades society, why would a person choose homosexuality? To answer such questions, science has attempted to locate the 'cause' of homosexuality (and not that of heterosexuality). Twin studies, for example, have been an important focus since it was hoped having identical subjects might resolve the question whether homosexuality is a biological fact or a product of up-bringing. The results of these studies are mixed without any clear resolution. In the 1990s, partly as a consequence of the AIDS crisis and the concomitant pressure for gay and lesbian equal rights, a flurry of studies emerged examining the biological roots of sexual orientation. Simon Levay examined the brains of gay men and reported size differences between a section of the hypothalamus in gay and heterosexual men. Other studies have looked at birth order to determine if indeed homosexuality might be a result of natal development and the role of hormones. For example, it is noted that the chances of being gay are much higher if a boy is born after a brother while a woman is more likely to be lesbian. One widely viewed study in 1993 reported Dean Hamer's argument that "Xq28" was the **gay gene**, which formed the genetic basis for homosexuality. There have been more recent studies that suggest gay and lesbian identities can be detected through either finger prints or finger size. We might note that while much of the research has focused on gay men, less research has been done on lesbian women and the roots of same-sex attraction between women.

The dogged attempts to locate biological roots for homosexual behaviour are partly driven by the desire to show that homosexuality is not a choice or a 'lifestyle,' but an orientation based on biology or genetics. For many, if sexual orientation is biological then there can be no basis to deprive lesbians and gays of basic human rights. But the biological approach has not been entirely successful. Many criticisms were laid against Levay's research; Hamer's findings have not been replicated in other experiments. Although the media and some activists used these findings to assert that homosexuality is innate, Levay, a gay man himself, cautioned against using his work to support such views since brain differences can emerge as result of interactions with the environment.

Social Constructivism

In contrast to those who seek to find an answer in biology, others prefer to think about sexuality as connected and constructed through social institutions including the family, the church and, of course, the media. What does it mean for identity to be socially constructed? To start with, social constructivist argue that **identity**, or the sense of self that people have, is not anchored in a fixed and unchanging source. Instead, they suggest that we come to know ourselves through the already existing ways of thinking about ourselves. Language plays a central role here since it's through the meaning of the words that we begin to tell ourselves and others about our identity. For example, if I claim that I have a particular identity (whether it be white, male, queer, academic, etc.) then the meanings of these designations determine who I am. That is, the ways that we classify ourselves do not reflect who we are, but determine who we are. So, language does not simply reflect who we are, but actually defines and constructs our identities.

In this framework, identity is also contextual, shaped by the social context within which people find themselves. And more importantly, we have various identities that we draw upon not always consistently. Given that identity is contextual, a person might identify one way in one context, and in a contradictory way in another context. For instance, a woman might identify as heterosexual in the context of her marriage and children, and homosexual in the context of her desire. Instead of seeing these identities as contradictory and therefore impossible, social constructionists argue that identity is often contextual and inconsistent. This means that people can hold many different identities, some seemingly contradictory, and it is not a matter of which identity is correct; instead, they are all equally valid, but different. Social constructivist theories underline how heterosexuality is seldom questioned or challenged since opposite-sex attraction is presumed to be natural while other forms are seen as aberrant.

UNDERSTANDING SEXUALITIES

Anthropological studies and archaeological findings have shown that societies expended considerable resources understanding human sexuality. Ancient civilizations often focused on female fertility and reproduction. From *buller bois* in the Caribbean to the *travesties* of Brazil to *onnabes* in Japan, the understanding of sexuality around the world varies greatly from the often-glamorous representations of lesbians and gays that circulate in the advanced industrial countries. Here in Canada, our understanding of sexualities is deeply informed by the way sexuality was studied in Europe starting in the early 18th and 19th centuries. As we discuss below, many colonial laws were based on these understandings and shaped Canadian laws about sexuality.

Prior to the European **Enlightenment**, homosexuality was viewed as a series of 'acts' that were sinful and perhaps criminal. But according to historian Michel Foucault, whose work traces the different ways that sexuality has been thought about from ancient Greek to the present, the 1800s saw a major shift in how sex practices were conceptualized in Europe. As we discuss below, before the Enlightenment, specific sex acts—anal sex, in particular—were seen as undoubtedly sinful and subject to punishment. But as science began to enquire into the mysteries of sex and, as we noted above, sexuality, these acts were no longer sinful acts that anyone might do. Rather, they became the hallmarks of a particular type of person, one who had a past, a childhood, and maybe even had been treated as a case history. As Foucault famously stated about this shift, "The sodomite had been a temporary aberration; the homosexual was now a species."[3]

Making Aberrant Sexualities: 19th-Century Sexology

Foucault's reference is to the emergent field of scientific study of sexuality that became known as **sexology**. The 1700s had seen investigations into sexuality, but as science itself became more organized, sexology became a kind of sustained scientific examination of human sexuality. Our current thinking about sexuality remains connected to several figures in this discipline, of whom arguably the most important are Richard von Krafft-Ebing, Havelock Ellis, Carl Westphal, Karl Heinrich Ulrichs, and Magnus Hirschfeld. Since they tended to focus on sexual variations rather than sexual regularities, their work and the themes in them quickly positioned homosexuality, lesbianism, and other forms of sexual desire as aberrant and sources of potential illnesses subject to medical intervention. As their studies became better known, heterosexuality quickly became normalized, while other kinds of sexuality were seen as forms of illness or sources of criminality. Indeed, this process of **normalization** positions sexual variation of many kinds as aberrations, something that should be studied and understood, even though heterosexuality itself remains mysterious and unexplained.

The Viennese psychiatrist, Richard von Krafft-Ebing (1840–1902), was one of the first to study sexuality through a scientific lens and exemplifies this process of normalization. While he focused on various forms of sexual variance, he is perhaps best known for his work on homosexuality. He asserted that homosexuality was a form of degeneracy. According to his most famous book, *Psychopathia Sexualis*, civilization is based on love and monogamy; any deviation from this mode of sexuality is representative of a degenerate stage of evolution. Moreover, he understood homosexuality as a particular type of **sexual inversion**, or when a person has the psyche of one gender in the body of another. In addition, through his examination of skull shapes, postures, gestures, and mannerisms, he argued that same-sex desire was based on biological factors.[4] Consequently, while it was similar to a disease, it was not a sin. For this reason, Krafft-Ebing advocated the examination of homosexuality through a medical perspective.

Like Krafft-Ebing, British physician, Havelock Ellis (1859–1939), viewed homosexuals as a category of sexual inverts and shared Krafft-Ebing's belief in the biological nature of sexuality. However, even though he argued that hormonal irregularities played a factor, Ellis thought that sexuality could also be affected by non-biological factors. Yet, sexual inversion, for Ellis, was incurable and, although not a disease, he asserted homosexuality was an abnormal behaviour. Ellis was not an activist, but he did oppose the criminalization of homosexual acts occurring in Britain during the late 1800s.

The reoccurring theme of sexual inversion is no better seen than in the works of the German psychiatrist, Carl Friedrich Otto Westphal (1833–1890). In fact, he coined the term 'sexual invert' from the German; the term literally means 'contrary sexual feeling.' Not only did he think of sexuality as biologically determined, but Westphal felt that it was a deviation and a psychiatric disorder. Thus, it should be treated under the medical system.

Another significant theme in the works of early sexologists is the idea of sexual inverts as being a third or intermediate sex. Originally theorized by the German lawyer, Karl Heinrich Ulrichs (1825–1895), this idea not only captures the notion that people whose mind is of one gender can be trapped in the bodies of another gender, but that such people constitute a separate sex. Ulrichs coined the term 'urning' to designate a female mind that is in the body of a male; in fact, Ulrichs thought himself to be an urning.

A final 19th-century sexologist of note is Magnus Hirschfeld (1868–1935). Like Ulrichs, he originally thought of sexual inverts as a third or intermediate sex, he eventually changed his mind, advocating for infinite sexual variation. He was an early leader of the German gay rights movement, and whose activities could be, as some argue, considered one of the first examples of gay pride activism.[5]

Despite their differences, these five sexologists exemplify several themes around sexuality that are present in the period. First, the notion of sexual inversion is significant. The prevalence of this conception indicates that gender and sexuality were not clearly differentiated. That is, the two were not separated in the way that we understand them now. Second, the medicalization of sexuality was predominant. Sexologists agreed that homosexuality should be treated as a medical condition. In fact, this approach is evident in the references that various sexologists made to sexuality as being in the scope of disease, evolution, and curability.

The positions of the sexologists relied on the classic debate between nature and nurture. Whether sexuality was biological or socialized was a common question, usually with the writer allying himself on the side of the former. Part of the reason for this philosophical positioning was that, by arguing that sexuality is based largely on biology, these thinkers could argue against punishing homosexuality. After all, if sexuality is biological, then one has no choice how it is manifest.

A final theme is that of homosexuality as an intermediate sex. This notion demonstrated how the sexologists of the time could not think outside of the rigorous sex binary. So rigid was the construction of the two-sex model that the only way that sexual variance could be imagined was by positing a third sex, one that was separate from the categories of males and females.

ALFRED KINSEY AND THE KINSEY REPORT

The legacy of these writers can be seen in the work of a mid-20th century sexologist, Alfred Kinsey (1894–1956). He is considered to be the Father of modern sexology. He is best known for his development of a measure of sexual orientation. Rejecting the biological determinism of previous sexologists, he created a measure of orientation that had at one end of the spectrum homosexuality and at the other homosexuality. Any person could be located within this seven-point scale (see Figure 9.1). Aside from his methodology, his results were also important for the study of sexuality. When he interviewed 4275 white males, he found that 37 percent of them had at least one homosexual experience in their lives.[6]

Such a methodology and findings were significant. First, Kinsey's dismissal of biology as determining sexual orientation represented a challenge to the conceptions of the 19th-century sexologists. By challenging biological determinism, he called for sexuality research to be outside of the domain of medicine. In addition, by defining

Figure 9.1   Two Models of Sexual Orientation

1. Original Two-Point Typology

Heterosexual ◄——————— or ———————► Homosexual

The typology model places heterosexuality and homosexuality on polar opposites and mutually exclusive points.

2. Kinsey's Seven-Point Continuum

0	1	2	3	4	5	6
Exclusively heterosexual experience	Mostly heterosexual, with incidents of homosexual experience	Primarily heterosexual, with substantial homosexual experience	Equal amounts of heterosexual and homosexual experience	Primarily homosexual, with substantial heterosexual experience	Mostly homosexual, with incidents of heterosexual experience	Exclusively homosexual experience

Kinsey's model proposes a continuum between heterosexuality and homosexuality. People in category 0, who accounted for the majority of Kinsey's subjects, were considered exclusively heterosexual. People in category 6 were considered exclusively homosexual.

Source: A.C Kinsey, W.B Pomeroy, and C. E. Martin. *Sexual Behavior in the Human Male.* (Philadelphia: Saunders, 1948.) Reproduced with permission of The Kinsey Institute for Research in Sex, Gender, and Reproduction, Inc.

heterosexuality and homosexuality to be on a spectrum, he challenges the view that one is either one or the other. That is, the difference between them is fluid, rather than static. Moreover, since so many men had homosexual experiences, he contests the belief that one is normal and the other abnormal. Quite the opposite, Kinsey's findings indicate that homosexual experience is far more common than many have thought. Indeed, when he repeated his studies with women, he found similar findings.[7] Finally, the conflation of sexuality and gender, which was so ubiquitous with the 19th-century sexologists, had been replaced. Now, gender and sexuality were considered to be two different facets of human experience.

The scientific study of sexuality, then, directed the investigations of the topic into specific directions. However, by the mid-20th century, these directions had changed. Instead of begging questions of determinism, sexual inversion, and the dualistic logic of homosexual versus heterosexual, the inquiry of sexuality had transformed itself into a different field. However, it remained somewhat descriptive. What was missing, at least at this early point, was an appreciation of how power has influenced our conceptions of sexuality.

Feminist Interventions

In the accounts of many of the sexologists, the role of power in sexuality was not central. In the 1960s and 1970s, this changed. In this period, various feminist writers gained recognition in academic circles. With the growing popularity of the texts of such thinkers, sexuality came to be thought of as an issue that was intimately related to concerns with power.

As highlighted in Table 9.1, there are three general types of feminist thought that influenced how sexuality was linked to power. **Liberal feminism** centres on the relationship

Table 9.1 Feminist Approaches to Sexuality

	Liberal Feminism	Socialist/Marxist Feminism	Radical Feminism
Time period	1960s and 1970s	1970s	1970s and 1980s
Representative writers	Millett Firestone	Mitchell Eisenstein	Rich Rubin
Main concepts	Patriarchy Female Reproduction	Economy–Production Patriarchy–Reproduction	Compulsory Heterosexuality Lesbian Continuum
Role of power	Male dominance lies in their control of women's reproductive capacity	Patriarchal family and men's control over women's reproduction essential to supplying labour for production	Patriarchy is essentially heteronormative and silences diverse sexualities as a way of maintaining power
	Heteronormative		Sexual diversity starts to emerge

of women's sexuality to patriarchal control; that is, sexuality is constructed as political. The domination of women by men in a patriarchy is, among other things, sexual. Consequently, women's reproductive capacity—and the sexuality that accompanied it—served as the very basis for this patriarchal domination. **Socialist/Marxist feminism** examines the relationship between patriarchy and sexuality through the lens of how economies organize their production. Arguing that the control over women's bodies and sexuality is a control over the relations of production, writers such Eisenstein and Mitchell emphasize how biological reproduction overlaps with capitalist forms of production. From their Marxist feminist perspective, capitalism requires men to control women's reproduction so that property can be passed to other men and to ensure a steady supply of new workers for economic production. Insofar as women give over their control of their reproductive capacity to men, they relinquish control over their labour. It is difficult to work outside of the home when your place is within it. Equally important, the nuclear family with the father in control served as a training ground for reproduction of patriarchy.

These schools of feminist thought took heterosexuality for granted. Not until the late 1970s and early 1980s did feminists, especially those associated with **radical feminism**, tackle the issue of non-heterosexual forms of sexualities in mainstream contexts. Radical feminist writers Adrienne Rich and Gayle Rubin both challenged the **heterosexist** bias of both liberal and Marxist feminism. Rich was critical of the cultural context of sexuality. Focusing on the idea of 'compulsory heteronormativity,' she understands heterosexuality as a political institution, in which the personal has been colonized by the political. Women live in the context of a **lesbian continuum**. This captures the notion that women's experiences are unified, not in terms of female/female sexuality, but against patriarchy. In fact, Rich argues that heterosexuality for many women is compulsory; therefore, she evokes the notion of **compulsory heteronormativity**. Within this framework, lesbians are not just ignored, but stigmatized; since they challenge compulsory heteronormativity, lesbians are silenced and punished. However, lesbian existence is not just about being victims. It serves as a political challenge to the system that dominates women through compulsory heteronormativity (i.e., patriarchy).

Rubin's goal is similar, which is to address the problem of erotic injustice and sexual oppression. Through an examination of aspects of our cultural milieu, such as the existence of 'sex law,' she argues that sexual stratification has been created that understands male–female sexual relations within marriage as the pinnacle of the pyramid of sexuality. Below this apex are other forms of sexuality that are ranked based on their deviation from reproductivity and respectability. In other words, sexual relations between two gay men who are married to each other are better than the sexuality of a promiscuous but single gay man. For her, earlier feminisms view sexuality as negative and champion a conservative version of sexuality. For this reason, Rubin calls for an analytic separation of sexuality and gender, arguing that people who are oppressed by sexuality are not dominated in the same ways that those who are subjugated by gender are. That is, a lesbian is not just oppressed as a woman, but is dominated because of her sexuality.

Moving from an assumption that heteronormativity can be taken for granted to a perspective that pays attention to sexual diversity, these feminisms connect sexuality to processes of power. Invariably, these ways of understanding the world of sexuality differ from the earlier sexologists insofar as they can no longer merely describe how sexuality exists in our lives, but the context of control in which it is located must be emphasized.

Troubling the Sex/Gender Divide: Queer Theory

Alongside these feminist investigations, there emerged a new but not always clearly-defined field in the 1970s: Lesbian and Gay Studies, which focused on revealing the often-hidden lives of lesbians and gay men. Just like the arguments of earlier feminists being based on the identity categories of 'women' and 'men,' scholars in this field based their analyses on identities such as 'lesbian' and 'gay man.' Still, as the AIDS epidemic continued and dissatisfaction with the fixed identities of feminism and lesbian/gay studies, another field of theory emerged to examine sexuality from a different perspective. Coined 'queer theory' in 1990 by Teresa de Lauretis, it largely defined itself against feminism and previous lesbian and gay studies with its emphasis on fluid identities. For queer theorists, desire and identities are unstable and socially constructed.

Take the identity of a 'homosexual.' In queer theory, someone whose identity is that of a 'homosexual' is not based on some inherent sexual orientation. Rather, the term 'homosexual' carries with it certain assumptions that serve to mould the very identity that it is meant to describe. 'Homosexual' usually refers to a person who is attracted to those of the same sex. However, this identity negates the possibility for deviation for those who classify themselves as homosexual. For example, if you are a homosexual man, you usually define yourself as a man who is sexually attracted to men. What happens, though, if you find yourself attracted to women? Are you no longer a homosexual? In such a case, this man now must navigate his identity. Is he really a homosexual? Or is he bisexual? Or is he really heterosexual? These terms, then, limit what identities are available for this person. Consequently, the term 'homosexual' does not describe the identity of the person, but it creates the identity.

Through the social construction of identity, the focus on what it means to be sexual changes. Queer theorists tend to focus less on the identities of sexual persons *per se*, and more on how these identities are constituted through various acts. Thus, the focus is on how desire is created. Desire does not function along a binary that is implicit in many conceptions of sexuality. In other words, desire is not just about heterosexuality/homo-sexuality; desire is the subject of our wants. Capturing that there are many ways of being sexual, this idea of desire allows queer theorists to examine a plethora of different forms of sexuality without the risk of assessing any of them as 'right' or 'wrong.' They can value difference in such a way as to avoid evaluating such difference. As a consequence, queer theorists see sexuality as in flux, diverse, and complicated. Certainly, they took the feminist concerns with power to heart, but challenged the idea of identity as something that is static and single.

GOVERNING SEXUALITIES

As we mentioned earlier, sexuality is governed through both legislation and legal decisions. For instance, in some countries, the 'gay panic defence' can be used as a legal defence for murder. This strategy claims that violence can be used to defend oneself against unsolicited sexual advances by someone of the same sex. Based on this logic, one can claim that the advance inspired such feelings of panic that even extreme violence is justified in response. In this way, 'gay panic' is a psychological disorder that explains away violence as a product of temporary insanity. Such a defence is legal in Australia, under the label of 'homosexual advance defence.' Emerging out of the early 1990s, this defence was privileged through cases in the Australian High Court, enshrining it in jurisprudence. However, although the name of it is different, this form of defence is not unique to Australia, but has been used in the U.S., New Zealand, and even Canada (in the famous case of *Gary Gilroy* in 1994); indeed Shawn Woodward unsuccessfully attempted a similar rationale in 2010 to justify his 2009 assault on Ritchie Downey in a gay pub in Vancouver.

The body of laws governing sexuality also includes a collection of ones that make same-sex sexual relations illegal. This type of legislation has recently been thrust into the light with a proposed law in Uganda, proposed on 14 October 2009. Generally referred to as the *Anti-Homosexuality Bill* of 2009, the legislation not only proposes to make same-sex relations illegal, punishable by a life-sentence to prison, but certain types of other sexuality—which the bill refers to as 'aggravated homosexuality,' includes same-sex relations with someone who is a minor, is HIV-positive, disabled, or considered a 'serial offender'—would be subject to the death penalty. In fact, it would be illegal for those aware of such activities to not inform the government. This bill, while shocking in its level of sanction, may not be surprising in a global context within which only ten countries have legalized same-sex marriage (see Table 9.2).[8]

Within the context of these examples, it is apparent that sexuality is a political matter that seems important especially to politicians. However, not only lawmakers have been taking a hand in governing sexuality; doctors and scientists have also taken an interest.

Table 9.2 Year Same-Sex Marriage Legalized by Nation

Country	Year
Netherlands	2001
Belgium	2003
Spain	2005
Canada	2005
South Africa	2006
Norway	2009
Sweden	2009
Portugal	2010
Iceland	2010
Argentina	2010

Medical Discourses and Sexual Governance

One central way that sexuality is controlled is by constructing some populations as 'normal' and others as 'abnormal.' The sexology studies we mentioned earlier are good examples of how this process of 'normalization' works. Sexologists such as Krafft-Ebing and Ellis effectively invented the idea of sexual abnormality. Of course, to accomplish this task, they had to privilege one type of sexuality—usually heterosexuality—as normal. Establishing 'norms' is often a cultural process, however, when this process of normalization is supported by medical authorities, it has more power. That is, with the authority with which medical officials are given, when they engage in normalization, it affects a great many people.

A particularly significant example of normalization take place in and through **medical discourses**, which are ways of thinking/knowing that are institutionalized in the medical field; these represent and construct homosexuality in very particular ways. Rather than defining it as equivalent to other forms of sexuality, such as heterosexuality, medical officials have defined it as abnormal. In order to demonstrate how this has worked, it is necessary to briefly discuss one of the key sites within which this constitution of homosexuality has taken place: *The Diagnostic and Statistical Manual of Mental Disorders* (DSM)

The DSM is published by the American Psychiatric Association, and serves as a codification of criteria for deciding what constitutes a 'mental disorder.' In its first edition, in 1952, homosexuality was defined as a sexual deviation. Such a label defines it as something other than heterosexuality, which is normal. This designation remained unchanged for the 1968 publication of the next edition, the DSM-II. With the classification of homosexuality as a mental illness, in Canada, various practices were used to 'treat' homosexuality, including electroshock therapy, lobotomies, and aversion therapies.

However, in 1973, the Board of Trustees of the American Psychiatric Association (APA) decided to change the manual so that it no longer referred to homosexuality. Instead, they used the terminology of 'sexual orientation disturbance.' With the DSM-III in 1980, the issue of homosexuality was again examined. However, this time the debate was over a new variety of mental illness: ego-dystonic homosexuality. This 'disorder' is when a patient has sexual desires that are at odds with her/his self-image as being a heterosexual; that is, someone diagnosed with ego-dystonic homosexuality has a contradiction between the object of her or his desire and her or his sexual identity. Such a diagnosis continued to define homosexuality in terms of a medical model that posited that it was deviant from the normal. In other words, rarely was this assessment made for those who self-identified as homosexual, but were attracted to those of the opposite sex. In 1986, when the DSM-III was revised, this category of disorder was eliminated. Instead, the only reference to homosexuality in terms of a 'disorder' was under the category of 'Sexual Disorders Not Otherwise Specified,' which referred to "persistent and marked distress about one's sexual orientation".[9]

Another arena in which the DSM allows sexuality to be governed is in the area of gender identity. There are many people who are born in the body of one sex who identify as a different gender. This fact of life for many transgendered individuals has been captured in the DSM as a 'Gender Identity Disorder.' Like the category of homosexual in earlier DSM editions, the DSM-III defined 'Gender Identity Disorder' as a form of mental 'disorder.' This practice continued in the next edition. In fact, this edition formalized four different criteria for those with this so-called condition. Through these medical discourses, the experiences and lives of transgendered people are defined as 'disorders.'

While these medical discourses around Gender Identity Disorder may seem somewhat academic, they directly relate to the ways the nation-state uses such ideas to govern sexualities—especially those of people who identify as **transgendered** or transsexual. In Canada, for example, to legally change one's sex from the one assigned at birth, the government requires that a transsexual person must have a certificate from a practicing doctor, explaining that the individual wishing to change the birth certificate has undergone Sex Reassignment Surgery (SRS). In order to engage in everyday life activities, one requires a birth certificate that matches the sex that one currently presents to others. Without such consistent documentation trans folk face potential discrimination; that is, she or he may not get access to important documents, such as those dealing with health care, insurance, marriage, employment, or banking; they cannot even drive a car, since a driver's licence is required. Ironically, a person cannot have SRS unless they have been diagnosed with Gender Identity Disorder, which requires extensive medical evaluation and intervention, which is increasingly difficult to access. Some provinces, such as Alberta, have removed SRS from the list of medical procedures that are covered by health care. In short, both the Canadian government and the provinces use these medical discourses to regulate those who wish to change their bodies and to maintain control over who accesses these necessary medical procedures.

Moral Panics: Regulating Homosexualities

Another way that sexuality can be connected to governance is through **moral panics**, or an intense feeling of anxiety that the social order is under attack, often because a group is perceived to be a threat. This anxiety is often at the level of the nation-state, as the result of an issue that seems to undermine the existing social order. Sometimes the panic can be related to health issues that produce apprehension among citizens, such as the H1N1 epidemic of 2009. Others can be associated with moral threats to the country. Specifically, this latter form arises when a particular group is seen to challenge the nation.

Sexuality is sometimes associated with characteristics that are understood as opposing the nation. For example, in Japan, there have been some moral panics around women choosing either to postpone or elude marriage, which has resulted in anxiety over care for the elderly and a strain on the nation's resources.[10] Another example of moral panic that has emerged is over types of sexuality that have been constructed as 'deviant.' In the early to mid-19th century United States, there was a panic over **pedophilia** in which male sexuality was constructed as violent.[11]

In the United States, a moral panic in the 1950s occurred about the 'Red Scare.' Under the guise of Americanism, Senator Joseph McCarthy stated that he knew of several—sometimes as many as 205—names of communists who had infiltrated the government of the United States. Consequently, he ordered several investigations to examine how such 'Reds' had come to positions of power. Although the entire nation was fascinated and horrified by these accusations, there was another less-well known side to this moral panic that also occurred. Termed the **Lavender Scare** by David Johnson, this phenomenon saw accusations that paralleled McCarthy's comments.[12] Originally, in 1950 Undersecretary John Peurifoy told the Senate that ninety-one people had been discharged from the State Department because they were homosexual. Members of Congress demanded to know these people's identities. Soon, this call for names turned into a call for determining whether more of these 'homosexuals' existed in the government. Senator Kenneth Wherry of Nebraska claimed that there were 3750 homosexuals in government positions. The primary worry, it seemed, was that homosexuals could be blackmailed by a foreign power to release sensitive documents.

The reason for this susceptibility to blackmail is, as mentioned earlier, homosexuality was understood as a form of mental illness. In other words, all lesbians and gays were seen to have the potential of being spies, a political claim that was supported by medical discourses. Eventually, thousands of people were dismissed from the government with estimates of 5000 people losing their jobs.

Media representations of the Lavender Scare played a major role in how sexual orientation was understood in the wake of McCarthyism. For example, the media discussed issues around homosexuality under the guise of 'sexual perversion.' And discuss it they did. Print and television sources emphasized and exaggerated 'sex crimes,' often accentuating them more than violent crimes. Within this context, the Lavender Scare, a moral panic *par excellence*, served to further construct homosexuality as something to be feared and carefully monitored.

The AIDS/HIV epidemic provides another stark example of how moral panics can be created. As the AIDS epidemic captured national attention, fear was rampant and a particular caricature of AIDS emerged. It was a 'homosexual disease,' known as Gay-Related Immune Deficiency (or GRID). Later, medical officials decided to change the name to Acquired Immune Deficiency Syndrome (or AIDS) to more accurately capture the nature of the disease; after all, it was not unique to the gay population. However, even with a change in name, it was still understood as a 'homosexual disease.' For example, it is presently illegal for gay men to donate blood in Canada, because of a fear of the transmission of AIDS.

Like the Lavender Scare, the AIDS epidemic presented a moral panic that provided a call for the control of sexuality. Both of these events saw people identified with particular sexualities fired and barred from employment. However, the AIDS crisis called for greater control of those in the homosexual community, specifically that of gay men. Not only could they not donate blood, but they faced a variety of forms of discrimination and violence. Consequently, this example also demonstrates how some medical discourses can be used to create moral panics that govern sexuality. See Have You Heard? 9.1.

This case study raises some important questions: Why was the colonial nation-state so invested in controlling sexuality?

While controlling sexuality can be seen in medical discourses and moral panics, it can also be seen in the role that sexuality has in the political and legal lives of the nation-state. We provided some examples of the ways that political and legal systems govern sexuality in the beginning of this section. For example, many countries, such as Australia, have officially sanctioned some acts of violence because of homophobia. Also, same-sex relations are illegal in many nations. Why?

Controlling Sexuality in Political and Legal Systems

· ·

In 1871, British legislators in colonial India passed The Eunuch Act, which called for a registration of all men thought to be eunuchs. The reason for such a call for registration is that eunuchs were thought to be involved in illegal activities. Who were these eunuchs, such that they were thought to be so criminal that a law had to be created just for them?

For the British in India, eunuchs as a legal category were not simply men without penises. Instead, they were a social group who were thought to consist of impotent men who prostituted themselves; while neither impotence nor prostitution were of themselves necessarily illegal, prostitution potentially might involve anal intercourse, which was declared to be illegal in colonial India in 1860. In addition, eunuchs were thought to kidnap and castrate young boys. While the evidence for the existence of such a group who engaged in these practices is lacking, they existed in the British colonial imaginations as very real creatures. Consequently, the British created laws, designed to govern these people.

However, a practical question quickly arose: how does one recognize a eunuch? If the British thought that this group of people must be controlled because of their criminal activities (whether this group actually were involved in such conduct or not is irrelevant to the imagination of the colonial British), then they had to find a way to find them. Impotence, after all, can be quite difficult to detect. However, there was a quick and easy way for this to be detected. In the British imagination, impotent men could be quickly discovered because they wore women's clothes. Consequently, any man wearing women's clothes was thought to be guilty of being a eunuch and engaging in illegal activities (i.e., anal intercourse) and were therefore registered and controlled. In fact, during the creation of this piece of legislation, some British bureaucrats sought to make the owning of women's clothes by eunuchs to be against the law!

The explanation lies in the residue of colonialism, which, although it is officially over in many countries, still shapes how sexualities are controlled through legal and judicial systems, especially through the continued existence of laws created in the colonial context. For example anti-sodomy legislation has continued to exist in the Penal Codes of formerly colonized countries. In Fiji and India, both Commonwealth countries, **sodomy** was

Table 9.3   Legality of Homosexuality by Continent

		Legality of Homosexuality							
	Numbers of Countries	Males				Females			
		Illegal		Legal		Illegal		Legal	
Continent	Considered	Numbers	Percentage	Numbers	Percentage	Numbers	Percentage	Numbers	Percentage
Africa	50	38	76%	13	26%	24	48%	26	52%
North America	3	0	0%	3	100%	0	0%	3	100%
South America	43	10	23%	33	76%	5	12%	38	88%
Asia	43	25	58%	17	32%	13	30%	30	70%
Europe	58	0	0%	58	100%	0	0%	58	100%
Oceania	25	12	48%	13	52%	2	8%	23	92%
Total	222	85	38%	137	62%	44	20%	178	80%

Sources: Raw data acquired from Infoism, "About LGBT Rights by Country or Territory," 2006, <http://infoisim.net/wiki/LGBT_rights_by_country_or_territory>, accessed 1 May 2010; and Daniel Ottosson, "Legal Survey on the Countries in the World Having Legal Prohibitions on Sexual Activities between Consenting Adults in Private," 2006, <http://ilga.org/Statehomophobiia/LBGcriminallaws-Daniel_Ottosson.pdf>, accessed 9 November 2009.

criminalized in their Penal Codes established under British rule. In Fiji, where the Criminal Code was drafted in relation to the British Colonial Office Code, Article 176 outlawed homosexuality. In India, the Indian Penal Code of 1860 included section 377, which dealt with sodomy. It was not until the 20th century that both of these (and numerous other) legislations against sodomy were dismissed, with Fiji dismissing these laws in 2005 and India in 2009. However, it is clear that some, if not much, of the legislation against same-sex sexuality is a by-product of colonialism. In fact, in Table 9.3, one of the reasons that so many non-European nations criminalized homosexual intercourse is because of their colonial legacy; the irony, of course, is that these remnants of colonial law were imposed by the very European nations that have now decried such laws as undesirable.

CRITICAL THINKING OUTSIDE THE BOX 9.2

Why do you think that so many more countries criminalize male homosexuality than female homosexuality? Can this relate to the process of colonialism?

The process of colonialism is also important in understanding the challenges confronting sexual minorities elsewhere in the world. Leaders of formerly colonized nations often legitimate their leadership through espousing a particular conception of sexuality. As Jacqui Alexander famously argued, in an international context of economic competition and political instability, national leaders vie for authority.[13] However, the form of political governance that has become synonymous with legitimate leadership is one that privileges 'moral rectitude.' Such a sense of morality necessitates that the only people who are fit to lead are individuals who embody a specific form of morality, one that privileges only heteronormative sexuality.

Even though the origins of this type of legitimate nation-state (i.e., colonialism) are largely gone, the role of morality has been incorporated into global capitalism. Instead of valuing a particular type of morality *per se*, nations in the global context must compete with other countries. Consequently, only those citizens who contribute to the nation's productivity are valued. Since individuals who do not procreate are not considered productive, they are not considered important. As a result, groups who are considered 'sexual deviants' (i.e., those who do not engage in reproductive intercourse, such as prostitutes, unwed mothers, gays, and lesbians) are blamed for many of the social ills.

In addition, the nation-state has typically exhibited a concern with the reproduction of its citizens. As mentioned earlier, the Canadian government normally will only grant a change to the sex listed on the birth certificate if the person is provided with a diagnosis as having a Gender Identity Disorder. In addition, the government of Alberta has effectively guaranteed the povertization of anyone wishing to have a SRS, by no longer covering this procedure under health care. This control of the physical sex of its citizens is not unique to Canada. Until 1998, Australians who wished to have operations to change their sex had to go overseas. In fact, laws existed that made such sex reassignment surgeries illegal with the stated purpose of controlling the reproductive capabilities of its citizens.[14]

Elsewhere, in India, a transgender population, often called *hijra*, were systematically denied rights of citizenship. Even though they received the right to vote in 1936, it was not as women—their preferred identity—but as men. They did not receive the right to vote as women until 1994.[15] And, it was not until 2000 that the first *hijra*, Shabnam Mausi, was elected as a member of the legislative assembly.[16] This population was denied citizenship rights largely because of their qualities as transgendered—that is, non-reproductive—citizens. (In fact, this is the group that the Eunuch Act from Have You Heard? 9.1 was targeting!)

Colonial nation-states, such as Canada, were bequeathed a number of concepts that remained active long after the empire passed on. Contemporary nation-states also remain deeply interested in maintaining their legitimacy and their (re)productivity of its citizens. Within these contexts, the nation's control of sexuality can be better understood. Certainly, these explanations are just the metaphorical 'tip of the iceberg.' Nonetheless, this approach provides a beginning point to understand that both in colonialism and global capitalism, the state has been concerned with the sexuality and sex of its citizens.

Sex Laws in Canada: Governing Difference

Given the preceding discussion of the role of the nation-state in the control of sexuality, we want to ask an important question: what is the role of the Canadian government in controlling sexuality? Are we more accepting of sexual diversity than other places? Do laws promote tolerance and acceptance or assimilation? To examine these questions, we will focus on how laws that control sexuality have changed over the years, beginning in the 19th century. The record shows that despite its 'cool' image and adoption of same-sex marriage, Canada remains more ambivalent about sexual diversity than many may think. See Table 9.4.

In 19th-century Canada, the state controlled sexuality through laws prohibiting sexual relations between two people of the same sex. Based on the laws of England, sodomy—or anal intercourse—was punishable in Canada by death as early as 1833.[17] This prohibition was continued in 1859, at which time it was illegal for same-sex sexual relations, even if the act were consensual; then, too, the penalty was death. Capital punishment for sodomy was abolished in 1869, at which time the death penalty remained the punishment for crimes of rape, murder, and treason. In 1892, the *Canadian Criminal Code* institutionalized this statute, legislating that only sexual acts that involved males were deemed illegal, although still no longer punishable by death. Of course, in this code, the language did not explicitly criminalize homosexuality, but instead governed "gross indecency"; that is, through the guise of defining something as ambiguous as gross indecency, male/male sexual relations were criminalized. In fact, lesbian sexual relations were not defined as illegal until the mid-20th century.

The criminalization of male same-sex sexual relations continued to define the legality of male homosexuality well into the 20th century. In section 148 of the 1955 version of the *Criminal Code*, for instance, it states:

> Every male person who assaults another person with intent to commit buggery [anal intercourse] or who indecently assaults another male person is guilty of an indictable offence and is liable to imprisonment for ten years and to be whipped.[18]

Indeed, not only was it illegal for men to engage in male/male sexual activity, but, in 1953, the Canadian *Immigration Act* was altered so that suspected homosexuals could not immigrate to Canada. During this period, Canada had successfully controlled same-sex sexuality from penetrating and existing within its borders.

Table 9.4   Timeline of Canadian Laws Relating to Sexuality

Legislation	Date
Sodomy no longer punishable by the death penalty	1869
Canadian *Criminal Code* makes 'gross indecency' illegal	1892
Canadian *Immigration Act* restricts immigration of homosexuals	1953
Klippert declared a 'dangerous offender'	1965
Homosexuality effectively decriminalized	1969
Quebec changes *Human Rights Code* to disallow discrimination based on 'sexual orientation'	1977
Canadian *Immigration Act* now allows homosexuals to immigrate	
Ontario changes *Human Rights Code* to disallow discrimination based on 'sexual orientation'	1986
Manitoba changes *Human Rights Code* to disallow discrimination based on 'sexual orientation'	1987
Yukon changes *Human Rights Code* to disallow discrimination based on 'sexual orientation'	
Nova Scotia changes *Human Rights Code* to disallow discrimination based on 'sexual orientation'	1991
New Brunswick changes *Human Rights Code* to disallow discrimination based on 'sexual orientation'	1992
Ban against homosexuals from serving in Armed Forces lifted	
British Columbia changes *Human Rights Code* to disallow discrimination based on 'sexual orientation'	
Saskatchewan changes *Human Rights Code* to disallow discrimination based on 'sexual orientation'	1993
Homosexuals can apply for refugee status based on their 'sexual orientation'	1994
Newfoundland changes *Human Rights Code* to disallow discrimination based on 'sexual orientation'	1995
Human Rights Act changed to include prohibiting discrimination based on 'sexual orientation'	1996
Prince Edward Island changes *Human Rights Code* to disallow discrimination based on 'sexual orientation'	1998
Alberta changes *Human Rights Code* to disallow discrimination based on 'sexual orientation'	
Nunavut changes *Human Rights Code* to disallow discrimination based on 'sexual orientation'	1999
Bill C-23 passed, granting rights to benefits for same-sex couples	2000
Northwest Territories changes *Human Rights Code* to disallow discrimination based on 'sexual orientation'	2002
Bill C-250 passed, making it illegal to propagate hate based on sexual orientation	2004
Bill C-38 passed, legalizing same-sex marriage	2005

This cultural frame was challenged through the famous *Everett Klippert* case in 1965. After Klippert admitted to having sex with men, psychiatrists determined that he would not stop his practice of such sexual behaviour. Consequently, the Canadian legal system declared Klippert to be a 'dangerous offender,' and sentenced him to life in prison; the Supreme Court of Canada upheld this sentence. Partially because of the outcry against the Klippert sentence, in 1969, the *Criminal Code* was amended. The amendment, called

Bill C-150 (also known as the **Omnibus Bill)**, was based on the argument that these legalities violated individual privacy rights. "The state has no business in the bedrooms of the nation," stated then Justice Minister Pierre Elliot Trudeau. The Omnibus Bill also repealed the law criminalizing 'buggery' in private. As a consequence of these changes, Klippert was released in 1971. Later, in 1977, the Canadian Parliament amended the Canadian *Immigration Act*, removing the prohibition regarding homosexuals immigrating to Canada.

As the timeline shows (see Table 9.4), the movement towards accepting lesbian and gay rights intensified in the 1980s, but only in the 1990s and 2000s did laws governing homosexuality change. In 1992, after a ruling from the Canadian Supreme Court, the federal government lifted the ban that disallowed homosexuals from enlisting in the Canadian Armed Forces. In 1994, the Supreme Court decided that it is allowable for refugees to Canada to apply based on their sexuality. While in 1996 the federal Canadian *Human Rights Act* was amended to include sexual orientation, some provinces still lagged behind. In 1998, however, the Supreme Court of Canada's decision in the *Vriend v. Alberta* case 'read into' Alberta and PEI human rights charters a prohibition of discrimination based on sexual orientation.

This trend continued into the 21st century. In 2000, Bill C-23 amended the *Employment Insurance Act* so that benefits could be provided to same-sex couples. However, this *Act* was explicit in that it did not change the definition of marriage; rather, it only altered required qualifications of those who could officially receive benefits. Nevertheless this change granted rights to same-sex couples that were previously denied them, such as the right to spousal benefits and old-age security. In 2004, despite much debate, the term 'sexual orientation' was included in the section of the *Criminal Code*, which dealt with hate crimes. Through this *amendment*, the promotion of hatred based on sexual orientation became a crime.

Same-Sex Marriage in Canada

From the above, it seems that Canada was and is moving to greater tolerance of sexual diversity, especially in terms of laws that govern sexuality. Indeed, Canada's progressive reputation is based on the legalization of same-sex marriage instead of the acknowledgment of **civil unions**, a route that other countries have pursued instead. On 28 June 2005, the House of Commons passed Bill C-38—also known as the *Civil Marriage Act*—by a vote of 158 to 133. On 19 July 2005, the Canadian Senate approved this Bill with a vote of 47 to 21. Through this legislative process, the definition of marriage was changed to the "lawful union of two persons to the exclusion of all others," which made no differentiation between heterosexual and homosexual couples.[19] In achieving this milestone, Canada became the fourth country to legalize same-sex marriage (see Table 9.2).

Reasons for Wanting to Get Married

Legalizing same-sex marriage represented a major breakthrough for lesbian and gay rights. As the Ontario Court of Appeal stated in its ruling on same-sex marriage: "Marriage is, without dispute one of the most significant forms of personal relationship. For centuries, marriage has been a basic element of social organization in societies around the world. Through the institution of marriage, individuals can publicly express their love and commitment to each other." [20] With the proclamation of Bill C-38, same-sex couples could have their longstanding commitments recognized as equal to those of heterosexuals. After years of being unable to have input into life-altering decisions affecting long-time companions and being unable to inherit common property, same-sex couples could enjoy the same rights as opposite-sex partners. For many in the Lesbian, Gay, Bi-sexual, Transgendered, Two-Spirited, Intersexed, and Queer (**LGBTTIQ**) community, the possibility of marriage meant that queers could finally have a seat at the nation's table.

Why Not Marriage?

It may be surprising but not all in the LGBTTIQ community saw same-sex marriage the same way. Echoing the approach of gay liberationists and many feminists, some observers felt that since the normative ideal of family is a heterosexual one, the granting of same-sex marriage is not the triumph that many think it to be. That is, the historical legacy of the institution of family is one based on the union between a man and a woman. Critics argued that the inclusion of same-sex couples in the legal construction of marriage, then, encourages those in the LGBTTIQ community to be assimilated in an institution designed to support compulsory heterosexuality. In other words, heterosexuals were not required to alter their idea of marriage to accommodate the different kinds of relationships sometimes found in the LGBTTIQ community, but the opposite was true. Without such accommodations, some have argued, sexual difference is erased and sexual diversity is reduced to a single form of union that is defined historically as heterosexual.

Consequently, assimilation takes place through two ways. The first is that the primacy of the family as a social unit is not challenged. Even though many critiques—feminist and otherwise—of the family exist that challenge its central role in our lives, by including same-sex couples in the institution of family, these criticisms are virtually silenced. As a result, a conservative concept of the family is not challenged. Second, including the union of same-sex couples in the definition of marriages negates other forms of union as legitimate. For example, if you recall, C-38 states that marriage is a "lawful union of two persons to the exclusion of all others." This excludes non-monogamous relationships from the legal understanding of marriage. In fact, polygamy is still illegal in Canada. In this legislative framework, those from the LGBTTIQ community must conform to normative standards in order to marry legally. In this way, they are assimilated into the institutions of Canada, rather than encouraged to practice their own sexual diversity.

Second, by focusing on rights, the same-sex marriage issue moves the concern for equality in the institution of marriage to the larger realm of civil liberties. This movement puts it into conflict with several other civil rights. For example, according to C-38, the new definition of marriage allows religious officials to legally refuse to carry out same-sex marriages, if performing the marriage violates their religious beliefs. With this situation, the right to practice one's own religion comes into conflict with the right to marry a person of the same sex. Moreover, by making it possible for those of a particular religion to decline to marry same-sex couples, this law places one right—the right to religious belief—over that of same-sex couples to marry. Such an **economy of rights** does not provide the equality that C-38 claims.

The ambivalence about same-sex marriage may be reflected in the statistics related to same-sex marriage in Canada. According to the 2006 Census, roughly 16 percent of Canada's 45 300 same-sex couples had decided to get married while 83 percent still chose to live in common-law relationships. Same-sex marriages are not just in the major centres. As Figure 9.2 shows, just about half of all same-sex couples (50.3 percent) live outside of Vancouver (10.8 percent), Montreal (18.2 percent), or Toronto where 21.7 percent of same-sex couples live.[21] In 2010, about 18 percent of all same-sex couples are married. Gay men tend to marry more frequently than lesbians.

Recent Challenges to Sexual Diversity

Same-sex marriage is only one of several examples that illustrate how the LGBTTIQ community can be assimilated into an economy of rights. Recently in Alberta, the Conservative provincial government proposed and passed Bill 44, *The Human Rights,*

Figure 9.2   Breakdown of Same-Sex Marriage by Major Centre

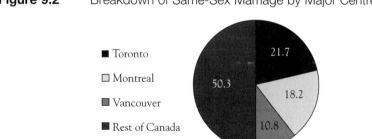

- ■ Toronto
- □ Montreal
- ■ Vancouver
- ■ Rest of Canada

Source: Statistics Canada census data 2008.

Citizenship, and Multiculturalism Amendment Act, 2009. This legislation mandated that all teachers in primary and secondary institutions inform parents if they plan to instruct students on, among other things, issues relating to sexuality. If the parents request that their children not be exposed to this educational content, the Bill continues, the teacher must permit the student to leave for the duration of the lesson. This concession was designed partly to accommodate the religious beliefs of parents who did not want sexuality to be taught in the schools. This Bill, many have argued, suppresses the teaching of diversity in the classroom, not to mention silences teachers, who must now keep non-heterosexual relationships out of the schools. In addition, this law subjugates knowledge of sexual diversity to the right to religious belief. In this way, this law serves to erase sexual difference while subordinating sexuality to other rights.

Furthermore, in Canada, the medicalization of homosexuality continues to play a role in constructing homosexuality as abnormal. For example, the Canadian Blood Services, a not-for-profit organization that is operated in conjunction with provincial governments,[22] has stated that no man who has had sex with another man since 1977 can give blood. Reminiscent of the previous discussions of moral panics, this policy is based on the concern over AIDS and the potential of 'polluting' the blood bank. Such regulations, then, depict certain types of sexual activities as based on risk. Thinking back to the earlier discussion of normalization, these national guidelines designate certain types of individuals—in this case, men who have sex with men—as abnormal and others as normal.

Canada has seen a transformation in attitudes towards sexuality in the past 150 years. While many have understood this change to be representative of greater tolerance, if not acceptance of sexual diversity, we have argued that growing tolerance and acceptance is not the only way to understand these changes over time. In fact, despite the changes we've outlined, "heterosexuality" continues to be the dominant framework that serves to assimilate sexual diversity, and place it in an economy of rights. Rather than simply demonstrating moral progress, Canada's history of the regulating sexuality reveals how nation-states can and do use the very concept of sexual orientation to facilitate control over its citizens.

RESISTING DOMINANT WAYS OF CONSTRUCTING SEXUALITY: GAY AND LESBIAN COMMUNITIES

The rainbow flags on Davie Street, Church Street, and Rue St. Catherine proudly line the main streets of Canada's largest 'gay villages.' In these bustling urban spaces, there are gay-owned bars, restaurants, bookstores, community groups, gyms, and hair salons. In Toronto, PRIDE-FM Radio designs its programming to target the LGBTTIQ community.

On the west coast, building on Vancouver's long history of homophile activism, the shops and bars on Davie Street form the core of the West End's gay community. Meanwhile, Montreal has built on its reputation as a fun-loving city to market itself as a gay destination spot. Providing a positive space where lesbian, gay, bisexual, and transgendered lives are affirmed, these visible sites of queer identity serve to both celebrate sexual diversity and resist the practices of Canada's mainstream heterosexual culture. Of course, these villages have not always existed and their emergence was not an easy or predictable development. Rather, these places have been shaped by the history of creating and regulating sexuality as we've discussed above.

Homosexuality and the Closet

Once the sexologists had successfully positioned male homosexuality as an aberration, people needed to distinguish male homosociality and the non-sexual friendships it promoted from male homosexual relationships. The problem, however, was telling the difference between a strong male friendship and a homosexual love affair was not easy; homosocial desire—the wish to have same-sex friendships—could easily be confused with homosexual desire. The fear that male-male relationships might be mistaken for homosexual love gives rise to **male homosexual panic**, which functions to create a clear division between straight and gay men, one that some think can be enforced through violence if required. Similar to domestic violence, **gay bashing** is the means by which the homosocial/homosexual boundary is maintained. Indeed, as we noted earlier, homosexual panic has been recognized as a legitimate defence in cases when a heterosexual man has attacked a gay man. Male homosexual panic also underlies the common practice among adolescent boys who use the word "fag" to regulate each others' masculinity.[23]

Given that homosexuality could be punished in a variety of ways, many homosexuals hid their sexual identity from public view. Just as one's closet can contain many private and secret possessions, the homosexual **closet** was a way that lesbians and gays could maintain a public identity as a heterosexual bachelor or spinster while hiding their same-sex desires. Sociologists emphasize that the closet is both the product of the laws and legal cases that make homosexuality illegal and of the social attitudes, beliefs, and practices that make it difficult if not dangerous for sexual minorities to express themselves openly. The closet was a place of safety, but, ironically, it also lead homosexual men and women to create ways to identify themselves to other same-sex people so that they could meet. In this way, the closet also laid the groundwork for the visible gay communities that exist today. In the 1970s as the **gay liberation** movement gathered force, increasing importance was placed on the need for lesbians, gays, and bisexuals to 'come out' of the closet and declare their sexual orientation so that heterosexuals could see that sexual minorities were everywhere. Coming out became an important feature in establishing lesbian and gay

---

CRITICAL THINKING OUTSIDE THE BOX 9.3

Why would some lesbians and gays resist "coming out"? Should everyone have to "come out" regardless of their sexual orientation?

---

communities in the 1970s onwards since they provided a space where resistance could be organized and political action taken.

Communities based on same-sex desire are not an exclusively 20th century innovation. Much has been written, for example, about the 18th-century **Mollyhouses** of England where men cross-dressed and some engaged in same-sex relations. In Canada, there is also a history that predates contemporary queer communities. For example, in Toronto, Alexander Wood's farm became known as "Molly Wood's Bush," and is now the site of Toronto's gay village. Montreal boasts North America's first gay establishment, Moise Tellier's apple and cake shop set up in 1869.

The industrialization of North American economies also contributed to the possibility for lesbian and gay communities to emerge. Burgeoning urban spaces allowed individuals to live and work independent of their families, which in turn opened opportunities to identify themselves primarily through their erotic attraction to the same sex.[24] By the early 20th century, same-sex communities were becoming well-established in large North American cities such as New York City. Women attracted to other women were able to meet in women's colleges and other same-sex establishments. Interestingly, during this time the term 'fairies' was used to differentiate men who tended to be more flamboyant and effeminate from "queers," who tended towards more masculine presentation but still had sex with other men.[25]

World War II proved to be a decisive moment for gays and lesbians in North America. The war effort conscripted many young men and women who might have otherwise remained isolated in their rural communities. With the war, however, these men and women were gathered up and placed in sex-segregated environments where they could meet and interact with others like themselves. In the post-war period, despite the moral, legal, and political strictures against homosexuality, many of these people stayed in large urban centres where it was easier to maintain connections that resisted the oppressiveness of the closet. For example, Aerlyn Weisman and Lynne Fernie's 1994 documentary *Forbidden Love* shows how lesbians in the 1950s managed to create lives for themselves despite the lurid depictions of lesbian sexuality prevalent in Canada at the time.

A pivotal moment in understanding the challenges to compulsory heterosexuality occurred in the wee hours of the morning on 28 June 1969 when New York City police staged a raid on the Stonewall Bar in Greenwich Village in Manhattan. Popular history notes that the drag queens who were present resisted the arrests and gave rise to a series of riots. Although there had been growing unease about the oppression that gay men in particular had been experiencing, **Stonewall** became a coalescing moment that inspired gay liberation, which drew on experiences from the American civil rights movement as well as the women's movement. Similar to radical feminism, gay liberation sought to resist compulsory heterosexuality and its strictures and asserted the importance of sexual desire in social relations. Gay liberation pointed to the gay bathhouses and other practices in gay culture that challenged heterosexuality's claim to be the best way to organize emotional and social relationships.

Gay Communities in Toronto, Montreal, and Vancouver

Although Canadian lesbians and gay men had developed spaces where they lived together prior to the 1970s, the post-Stonewall era gave rise to more visible forms of community in the major metropolitan cities of Toronto, Vancouver, and Montreal. In Toronto, parts of Yonge Street and the Church-Wellesley area formed a hub for lesbian and gay communities as did the newly urbanized space of Davey and Denman Streets in Vancouver's West End.[26] In Montreal, parts of Rue St. Catherine became the focal point. Still, despite the passage of the Omnibus Bill, which made homosexual sex a private matter, politicians and police in the 1970s continued to make life difficult for sexual minorities across Canada. In Toronto, police continued to raid gay bathhouses and pressure gay bookstores and publications such as the *Body Politic*. In Montreal, in anticipation of the 1976 Olympics, Mayor Drapeau initiated a morality campaign that culminated in the largest mass arrest since the October Crisis and the proclamation of the *War Measures Act*. Vancouver also saw police continue to pressure gay establishments. The 1980s and 1990s saw increased visibility accorded to gay and lesbian communities as efforts intensified for equal rights and activists confronted politicians about their inaction on HIV/AIDS.

Lesbian Communities

Lesbians in Canada have a different but parallel history to that of Canadian gay men. Like the history of women, lesbian history has been less visible and more difficult to document. The growth of the women's movement in Canada provided new spaces for lesbians to meet and organize. In Vancouver and Toronto, lesbian activists organized both alongside and separately from women's organizations that worked towards establishing gender equality. Other lesbians became involved with gay men pushing for equal rights for sexual orientation. These alliances were sometimes difficult since gay men's issues around sex did not always align with those of women, especially around the question of pornography. Some lesbian women chose to organize separate lesbian communities. However, the proclamation of the *Charter of Rights and Freedoms* in 1981 led to a partial rapprochement between gays and lesbians as both groups started to use legal challenges to press for equal rights.[27] The national lesbian and gay rights organization, EGALE (Equality for Gays and Lesbians Everywhere), emerged out of this new alliance. Lesbians continue to work both in the women's movement as well as in organizations such as EGALE to press for women's equality.

Challenging the Sex-Gender System Again: Transgendered and Intersexed People

As gay and lesbian people have become integrated into mainstream Canadian life, issues affecting transgendered people have come to the foreground. Transgendered is a still-new term used to denote individuals whose sense of core gender identity does not cohere with the gender to which they have been assigned. "Transgender" refers to a range of identities including:

- those who may present themselves as being of a gender even while feeling a part of another;

- those who present themselves as the opposite gender to which they were born and to which they feel they actually belong;

- **pre-operative transsexuals** who have undertaken hormonal treatment to cohere to traits of the opposite gender; and

- **post-operative transsexuals** who have undertaken various surgeries to align their gender identity with bodily appearance.

Trans individuals can be either M->F trans women or F->M trans men. In both cases, some individuals undergo procedures including hormonal treatments, phalloplasty, breast implantation and/or mastectomies to bring their sex characteristics into alignment with their gender identity. Trans folk face challenges on many fronts from the everyday decision about which washroom to use, to being accepted within straight as well as gay and lesbian communities.

Transgendered people also challenge both our assumptions about the congruence of sex and gender and our notions about sexual orientation. For example, when some individuals transition to their new sex/gender assignment, their orientation may remain the same. This means, for example, that a man who transitions to become a woman may also find herself identifying as a lesbian or as a heterosexual woman. Similar outcomes are evident in female→ male transitions where a trans man may find himself attracted to women, or, alternatively, still attracted to men.

Intersexed people—formerly referred to as hermaphrodites—have also come to the forefront as they talk about how their experience of sex and gender is not perfectly aligned. Intersexed people are those who present atypical sexual characteristics that do not match either those of male or female. There are variations on intersex that make it hard to identify the condition since the parameters are largely based on norms about gender and sex. Individuals may also be intersexed on the chromosomal level such that they appear to conform to a specific gender even if outwardly they appear to be of a different gender. Statistics about intersexed people differ but some conservatively estimate that one in every 2000 people is intersexed. When a child is born intersexed, the practice is often still to decide which gender the child should be and to perform sex reassignment surgery to assign a physical gender to the baby.

Intersex people remind us just how much of sex is about what humans decide. After all, at what point does a smaller penis start to be a clitoris or what hormonal levels are required to be taken to be male or female? Some argue that gender assignment is necessary to allow the child to grow up 'normally' as a boy or girl. As the Intersexed Society of North America (ISNA) notes on its website, "Nature doesn't decide where the category of 'male' ends and the category of 'intersex' begins, or where the category of 'intersex' ends and the category of 'female' begins." If anything, intersexuality highlights precisely how normalizing our binary conceptions of sex and gender really are. Cultural norms often dictate when a boy's penis is so small that it has to become a clitoris. Humans decide whether a person with XXY chromosomes or androgen insensitivity will count as intersex.

Celebrating Sexual Diversity

Across Canada each summer, the LGBTTIQ community stages Pride events, which celebrate sexual and gender diversity in Canadian cities. Pride events also draw attention to continuing forms of discrimination in the world. Today, Toronto's Pride Parade is an annual spectacle that attracts huge crowds to Yonge Street. But the scale of today's events belie its roots in the first Gay Pride Picnic held at Hanlan's Point on Toronto Island in August 1971 with a goal of raising money for various political actions. Pride celebrations were intermittent in Toronto throughout the 1970s. In the wake of the 1981 Toronto bathhouse raids, however, the ensuing protests led to an organized gay pride parade. Over the 1980s and the early 1990s, the **Gay Pride Parade** was as much a celebration as protest as AIDS activists joined with those demanding equal rights. Similar patterns are evident in Montreal, which today has positioned itself as a gay destination spot, highlighted by its hosting the first OUT Games in 2008. As in Toronto, Montreal "Gai-lon-la" emerged in the 1980s as gays and lesbians pressed for equality even though Quebec was the first province to acknowledge sexual orientation in its *Bill of Rights*.

As Pride celebrations have become more spectacular, they have brought more mainstream attention to the event. This increased attention has highlighted the tensions within and between the diverse groups that are often evident in Pride events. For example, the question of lesbians' relationship to Pride has often been debated. One solution has been to stage separate marches for women. In 1979, Vancouver staged a Dyke March, a practice which has grown into its own celebration of women and lesbian culture. The dyke marches are for women only and men are encouraged to support the marchers from the side. Following the dyke march example, recently trans folk have begun organizing their own separate march to celebrate their pride and provide more visibility to trans issues.

CONCLUSION

Sexuality is not necessarily a personal issue. How we understand sexuality influences how we experience it. These understandings are embedded in cultural frames that serve to provide a degree of commonality to the experiences of many people. The comparatively recent emergence of Enlightenment science and medicine has fundamentally altered how we understand our own sexual identities. Indeed, sexuality is necessarily a political issue, one that brings the experience of sexuality as a personal matter into conflict and conformity with political interests of not only the social world, but of the nation-state. Consequently, in Canada, there is rhetoric of social change that often stands in opposition to the assimilative laws and practices that the nation-state institutionalizes. Yet, in spite of this political governance, sexuality has become a source of celebration and pride that allows for resistance to the governing practices of the political sphere. In the end, Canada has become more diverse. However, the diversity is not always in the form that one would expect. It is not in the 'tolerant' same-sex marriage laws, nor in the inclusion of 'sexual orientation' in all provincial and national human rights codes. Instead, diversity is in the streets, the communities, and the bedrooms of Canada.

CHAPTER SUMMARY

This chapter has examined how sexuality has been understood in Canada, through tracking the notion of sexuality itself. To accomplish this goal, we have looked at what the concept means today, and how the notion developed in the 19th and 20th centuries. In examining the ways that scholars have studied sexuality, we provide an overview of the idea through the lens of sexology, feminisms, and queer theory. In addition, we explored how sexuality becomes a tool of governance and control. Specifically, we provided an overview of how sexuality has been criminalized and legislated over time. To this end, we provided a discussion of the Canadian context in relation to its changing legislation around sexuality, illuminating the complicated ways that sexuality is understood, controlled, and monitored in Canada. Moreover, we have examined how sexual communities—including gays, lesbians, bisexuals, and transgendered people—have resisted these attempts to control sexuality, highlighting the ways in which people have genuine agency.

KEY TERMS

civil unions, p. 263

closet, p. 267

'coming out,' p. 267

compulsory heteronormativity, p. 251

cultural frames, p. 243

economy of rights, p. 265

Enlightenment, p. 246

gay bashing, p. 267

gay gene, p. 245

gay liberation, p. 267

Gay Pride Parade, p. 271

gays, p. 243

heterosexism, p. 251

heterosexuality, p. 244

homophobia, p. 245

homosexuality, p. 244

identity, p. 245

intersexed, p. 271

Lavender Scare, p. 256

lesbian continuum, p. 251

lesbians, p. 243

LGBTTIQ, p. 264

liberal feminism, p. 250

male homosexual panic, p. 267

medical discourses, p. 254

Mollyhouses, p. 268

moral panic, p. 256

nature/nurture, p. 244

normalization, p. 247

Omnibus Bill, p. 263

pedophilia, p. 256

post-operative transsexual, p. 270

pre-operative transsexual, p. 270

radical feminism, p. 251

sexology, p. 247

sexual identity, p. 244

sexual inversion, p. 247

sexual orientation, p. 244

Socialist/Marxist feminism, p. 251

sodomy, p. 258

Stonewall, p. 269

transgender, p. 255

DISCUSSION QUESTIONS

1. Rubin argues that sexualities ranked based on their deviation from reproductivity and respectability. According to Rubin, sexual relations between two gay men married to each other are better than the sexuality of a promiscuous but single gay man. What other forms of sexual desire are ranked below the "charmed circle" of respectability and reproduction? How does heterosexism and heteronormativity shape our thinking about what is 'permissible' sexual activity?

2. Think about a time when you have experienced sexual attraction to someone of a sex whom you typically wouldn't find attractive. Which perspective better captures your experiences: Kinsey's spectrum, feminist theory, or queer theory? How do these frameworks overlap in your experience?

3. Other than ones discussed in the chapter, what ways is sexuality controlled and monitored by the Canadian nation-state? What is the consequence of such governance?

4. Discuss both the lesbian continuum and male homosociality. Why do boys and young men shy away from physical expressions of affection? How does fear of being called a fag or dyke work to maintain the gay/straight divide and to maintain heteronormative identities?

5. Transgendered folks challenge the binary of male and female. Given this challenge, how are sexual identities based on this binary (i.e., straight, lesbian, gay) affected?

6. Imagine that you encounter a same-sex couple who wishes to adopt a child. From the different perspectives of nature and nurture, what are reasons for and against such adoption, as opposed to reasons for and against conception?

7. Discuss how Gay Pride Parades can be seen as both signs of resisting dominant ideas about sexuality and also celebrating identities. Connect these ideas to fears about assimilation and/or desire for sexual liberation?

NOTES

1. Statistics Canada. "Police Reported Hate Crimes 2007," *The Daily*, <www.statcan.gc.ca/daily-quotidien/090513/t090513c2-eng.htm>, accessed 29 May 2010.
2. Dan Allman, M *is for Mutual, A is for Acts: Male Sex Workers and AIDS in Canada* (Ottawa: Health Canada, 1999).
3. Michel Foucault, *History of Sexuality: An Introduction, Volume One* (1978, New York: Vintage Books, 1990), p. 43.
4. Jennifer Terry, "Anxious Slippages between 'Us' and 'Them': A Brief History of the Scientific Search for Homosexual Bodies," in Jennifer Terry and Jacqueline Urla, eds., *Deviant Bodies: Critical Perspectives on Difference in Science and Popular Culture* (Bloomington: Indiana University Press, 1995), pp. 129–169.
5. Nikki Sullivan, *A Critical Introduction to Queer Theory* (New York: New York University Press, 2003).
6. Mona Nag, "Sexual Behaviour in India with Risk of HIV/AIDS Transmission," *Health Transition Review* 5 (1995): 293–305.
7. Terry, p. 157.
8. In February 2010, the Australian senate overwhelmingly voted to reject a bill for same-sex marriage. However, it is expected that Nepal will join this group in 2010–2011.
9. James Krajeski, "Homosexuality and the Mental Health Professions: A Contemporary History," in Robert P. Cabaj and Terry S. Stein, eds., *Textbook of Homosexuality and Mental Health*, (Washington: American Psychiatric Press, 1996), p. 26.

10. Margaret Lock, "Perfecting Society: Reproductive Technologies, Genetic Testing, and the Planned Family in Japan," in Margaret Lock and Patricia A. Kaufert, ed, *Pragmatic Women in Body Politics* (Cambridge: Cambridge University Press, 1998).

11. Erna Olafson, David L. Corwin, and Roland C. Summit, "Modern History of Child Sexual Abuse Awareness: Cycles of discovery and suppression," *Child Abuse and Neglect*, 17 (1993): 7–24.

12. David L. Johnson, *The Lavender Scare: The Persecution of Gays and Lesbians in the Federal Government* (Chicago: University of Chicago Press, 2004).

13. Jacqui Alexander, "Not Just (Any) Body can be a Citizen: The Politics of Law, Sexuality and Postcoloniality in Trinidad and Tobago and the Bahamas," *Feminist Review* 48 (1994): 5–23.

14. Vera Mackie, "The Trans-sexual Citizen: Queering Sameness and Difference," *Australian Feminist Studies*, 16 (2001): 185–192.

15. Kira Hall, "Go Suck Your Husband's Sugarcane! Hijras and the Use of Sexual Insult," in Anna Livia and Kira Hall, ed., *Queerly Phrased: Language, Gender and Sexuality* (New York: Oxford University Press, 1997).

16. Gayatri Reddy, "'Men' Who would be Kings: Celibacy, Emasculation, and the Re-production of Hijras in Contemporary Indian Politics—Gender Identity, Social Stigma, and Political Corruption," *Social Research* 70, no. 1 (Spring 2003): 163–200.

17. William Renwick Riddell, "Criminal Courts and Law in Early (Upper) Canada," *Journal of the American Institute of Criminal Law and Criminology* 9, no. 2 (August 1918), 173–186.

18. *Criminal Code and Selected Statutes, 1955* (Ottawa: The Queen's Printer, 1955), p. 47.

19. Parliament of Canada, "Bill C-38: The Civil Marriage Act," 2005, <www2.parl.gc.ca/HousePublications/Publication.aspx?Docid=3293341&file=4>, accessed 26 May 2010.

20. "Ontario Court of Appeal—*Halpern et al. v. Attorney General of Canada et al.*" 10 June 2003, Guide to Ontario Court site, available <www.ontariocourts.on.ca/decisions/2003/june/halpernC39172.htm>, accessed 20 May 2010.

21. Statistics Canada. "Gay Pride . . . by the Numbers." <www42.statcan.ca/smr08/smr08_118-eng.htm>, accessed 29 May 2010.

22. The Provincial Minister of Health in each province is "responsible for the overall expenditure of public funds by Canadian Blood Services in delivering the blood program and for selecting a Board of Directors" (Canadian Blood Services).

23. C. J. Pascoe, *Dude, You're a Fag: Masculinity and Sexuality in High School* (Berkeley: University of California Press, 2007), pp. 53–54.

24. John D'Emilio, "Capitalism and Gay Identity" in Ann Snitow, Christine Stansell, and Sharan Thompson, eds, *Powers of Desire: The Politics of Sexuality* (New York: Monthly Review Press, 1983), p. 470.

25. George Chauncey, *Gay New York: Gender, Urban Culture and the Making of the Gay Male World, 1890–1940* (New York: Basic Books, 1994).

26. Bekki Ross "Sex and (Evacuation from) the City," Paper at Engendering Social Justice Conference. University of British Columbia, <www.wmst.ubc.ca/b_ross.html>, accessed 29 May 2010.

27. Miriam Smith, *Lesbian and Gay Rights in Canada: Social Movements and Equality-Seeking, 1971–1995* (Toronto: University of Toronto Press, 1999), p. 31.

CHAPTER 10

Diversity in Canadian Families: Traditional Values and Beyond

Geoff Ondercin-Bourne

There is no golden age of family life to long for, no past pattern that, if we only had the moral will to return to, would guarantee us happiness and security. Family life is always bound up with the economic, demographic, and cultural predicaments of specific times and places.

—Arlene Skolnick, *Embattled Paradise*

Family: *from the Latin,* familia, *"the slaves of a household"*

—*Random House Dictionary of the English Language*

Objections

Objectives
. . . .

After reading this chapter, you should be able to

- define family in a way that accounts for the many variations of families in Canada today

- critically assess the underlying assumptions of the "traditional family"

- compare several theoretical approaches used to understand the evolution of families and relations among family members

- describe recent changes in Canadian families

- link the changes in familial structures and relationships to broader changes in society

INTRODUCTION

The family, we are told, is an institution in crisis. News headlines announce, "New Mega-trends Reflect Family Decline."[1] Social service agencies such as Children's Aid with support from the courts restrict the use of corporal punishment by traditional parents. So-called "special interest groups" lobby governments on behalf of nontraditional families such as single parents or gays and lesbians. In June 2005, the federal government passed Bill C-38, which acknowledged the constitutionality of same-sex marriage. As the conservative lobby group, Focus Canada, laments, "With all the attacks now aimed at the natural family, is it any wonder that the majority of Canadians feel that 'the state of the family is a national crisis?'"[2]

If the family is now "under siege," then presumably there was a golden age when the traditional family thrived. This golden age was represented on television in the 1950s and early 1960s by such programs as *Leave It to Beaver*, *Father Knows Best*, and *Ozzie and Harriet*. Arlene Skolnick opened her book on the family with the tongue-in-cheek title "Who Killed Ozzie and Harriet?" This title suggests the apparent deterioration of modern family life, a "Paradise Lost," if you will. More recent television shows such as *Brothers and Sisters*, *Little Mosque on the Prairie*, and *Modern Family*, have provided more up-to-date versions of family life that nonetheless retain many of the traditional values associated with that same "golden age."

As the title of this book implies, society can best be understood through its diversity. In this diversity the very notion of the family is misleading at best. Families are evolving, as they always have, in response to social, political, and economic change. Consequently, to answer Skolnick's tongue-in-cheek question, no one killed Ozzie and Harriet, because in fact they never existed. The traditional family is an idea or belief, not a fact.

In this chapter we will (1) provide some definitions of families and outline the difficulties of doing so, (2) explain some theoretical approaches to the study of families, making

---

CRITICAL THINKING OUTSIDE THE BOX 10.1

In today's multi-channel universe, you can still see many of the TV shows your parents (and grandparents!) watched. Compare the family life portrayed in some of those shows with that portrayed in your favourite, current family TV show. How have family relationships on TV changed since the early days of television? In what ways have they remained the same?

---

a key distinction between what we describe as unification theories and liberation theories, and (3) look at how families in Canada have changed, as well as the challenges facing Canadian families in the 21st century.

DEFINING FAMILY

Traditional Definitions

Definitions of family have generally been based on the inclusion or exclusion of individuals from the group; either you are in, or you are out. An example is George Murdock's definition, quoted in many sociological studies of family: "a social group characterized by common residence, economic cooperation, and reproduction. It includes adults of both sexes, at least two of whom maintain a socially approved sexual relationship, and one or more children, owned or adopted, of the cohabitating adults."[3] A more recent definition, by Rose Laub Coser, is clearly influenced by Murdock: "[The family] finds its origin in marriage; it consists of husband, wife, and children born in their wedlock, though other relatives may find their place close to this nuclear group, and the group is united by moral, legal, economic, religious and social rights and obligations."[4]

The traditional definitions highlight the importance of the biological function of families. Families that consist of a mother, a father, and their children are called **nuclear families**. However, does such a definition adequately describe the modern family? For example, can there be families that are not based on producing children?

Some critics see many limitations with the traditional concept of the nuclear family. For example, by defining family in biological terms, we seem to legitimize the notion of family as a "natural" unit. The implication here is that any relationship or grouping that falls outside this exclusive definition is necessarily "unnatural," whether or not it is generally accepted in society as a family. Among those excluded are childfree couples, same-sex couples with or without children, single-parent families, commuting families, and remarried families.

Finally, let's look at the definition used in Canada's census, which, although more inclusive than the traditional definitions, is still heavily influenced by them. According to Statistics Canada, "census families include married couples and common-law couples with or without never-married children living at home, as well as lone-parent families."[5] However, as we shall see, even this definition omits many living arrangements that are considered "families" in today's society.

Two further issues raise questions about traditional definitions of family. For one, cultural differences are not factored into them. To what extent, for example, do North American Aboriginal families meet the criteria of the nuclear family? Does the structure of families immigrating from all over the world resemble that in the definitions of Murdock and Coser?

If we accept a definition of family based on the nuclear family, we may be marginalizing the impact of the **extended family** in many cultures, including our own. An extended family comprises two or more nuclear families joined together through blood ties. The classic example of an extended family is a husband and wife, their unmarried children, their married children, and the spouses and children of their married children. By focusing solely on the nuclear components that make up an extended family, the analysis ignores the unique character of that particular set of relationships. On the basis of these examples, it is hard to imagine a realistic "one size fits all cultures" definition of family.

The second issue is the changing nature of family. How applicable are the definitions of nuclear family to the families of the past? Consider the assumption of parents and children living under one roof. In Canada, this has not always been the case for everyone. For example, in the middle of the 18th century, many children in New France, some as young as five or six, were forced to work as live-in household servants. Were these children no longer part of a nuclear family?

The point is that uniform, fixed definitions of family are incomplete, and even misleading. Increasingly, the family is regarded as "a social construct."[6] Consequently, the mutability of the structure of family must be an important component of its definition. Later in this chapter, we will discuss the ways in which the structure of the Canadian family has adapted to its changing socioeconomic environment.

The Dimensions of Family Life: An Inclusive Approach

If the traditional definitions of family are incomplete, how do we at least determine some key characteristics of "family"? Margrit Eichler attempted to answer this question by developing a series of concepts she referred to as "internal dimensions."[7] We will focus here on five of these: the procreative dimension, the socialization dimension, the residential dimension, the economic dimension, and the emotional dimension. Have You Heard? 10.1 describes some of the main elements of each.

This list is by no means complete, but even the five dimensions included here do provide a framework for analyzing the diversity of Canadian families. When we compare Eichler's dimensional approach with the traditional definitions offered by Murdock, Coser, and even Canada's census, we see an important distinction: Eichler viewed families as a set of relationships, whereas Murdock and Coser defined them as a fixed set of characters. Eichler's perspective allows us to look at "the family" as a dynamic institution that can account for a wide range of configurations. We will therefore use a dimensional analysis to understand Canadian families and the changes they have undergone, particularly since the 1950s.

Next, we will examine some theoretical perspectives that sociologists have used to study families. These theories enable us to determine how families affect, and are affected by, other social institutions and social relationships.

HAVE YOU HEARD? 10.1

Five Internal Dimensions of the Family

. . . .

Procreative Dimension
- Does the couple have children?
- If so, are they from the current relationship or a previous one?

Socialization Dimension
- Are both parents, one parent, or neither parent involved in childrearing?

Residential Dimension
- Do all family members live under the same roof?
- Does one family member live in a separate dwelling only?
- Does one family member have an additional separate dwelling?

Economic Dimension
- Is one family member solely responsible financially for the other members?
- Do two or more family members share the financial responsibility for other members?
- Are family members financially responsible for themselves?

Emotional Dimension
- Is the positive involvement of family members mutual or one-sided?
- Is there a lack of involvement from family members?
- Is there mutual negative involvement?

Source: Margrit Eichler, *Families in Canada Today* (Toronto: Gage, 1983). Reproduced with permission of the author.

THEORETICAL PERSPECTIVES ON UNDERSTANDING DIVERSITY IN FAMILIES

Why do we consider theory? Why not just "look at the facts" and forget about theoretical questions and debates? The answer is that theories are useful models that help us make sense of the complexities of the real world. As Emily Nett explained: "To omit theory would be to reduce knowledge about families to a series of simple statistics or journalistic accounts at one extreme, and a compendium of value judgements, like a sermon, at the other. . . . Theory relates concepts and provides a basis for asking questions, finding answers, or doing both."[8]

Having acknowledged the importance of theory, we are faced with a dilemma. Given the limitations of space, how do we cover the many theorists who have written about families? In fact, we cannot. As a result, we have selected some of the theories that have appeared consistently in the literature on the family.

In this chapter, we divide theories of family into two groups, based on the analysis by David Cheal, a family sociologist:[9] (1) unification theories emphasize the universality of family structures and the benefits of family over its costs, (2) liberation theories emphasize both the diversity of families and the limitations that families place on individual members, as well as the strategies used to overcome these constraints. The debate between unification theorists and liberation theorists is central to our discussion about the nature of family.

Unification Theories

Following World War II, sociological analysis in the United States and Canada, including analysis of the family, was dominated by several schools of thought that were all variations of the unification approach. Although some of these theories had appeared earlier in the 20th century, it was during the prosperous decades of the postwar boom that they enjoyed immense popularity.

Unification theories of the family hold the view that the family is an adaptive unit mediating between the individual and society; the family meets the needs of individuals for personal growth, development, and physical and emotional integrity. To the extent that the family meets an individual's social needs, it is seen as "functional." See Have You Heard? 10.2.

Since the 1960s, however, competing schools of thought have put forward alternative perspectives on family life that have generated a lively debate on the family and its role in modern society. We will describe in detail two of the predominant sociological perspectives within the unification school—structural–functionalism and general systems theory—and offer brief summaries of two other perspectives that have been used by unification theorists.

Structural–Functionalism

Talcott Parsons, G.P. Murdock, W.F. Ogburn, W. Goode, and B. Schlesinger are well-known and influential structural–functionalists who wrote about families. **Structural–functionalism** argues that the family is an important institution that maintains social stability. Family members have many and diverse normatively prescribed activities that become integrated into a dynamic system called family. That is to say, family members

---

HAVE YOU HEARD? 10.2

Two Other Approaches to Unification Theory

. . . .

Symbolic Interactionism
Interactionist theorists define the family as "a unity of interacting person-alities" and believe that through the interactions of its members, a family develops a conception of itself. Proponents of this approach include E. Burgess, C. Cooley, G. Mead, and S. Stryker. Social psychologists have used this approach in small-group laboratories to study parent–child and husband–wife interactions.

Family Life Course Perspective
According to life-course theorists, most families pass through a series of four stages: (1) a childless couple, (2) a couple with children, (3) **empty nesters**, when the children leave home, (4) a widow or widower. T. Hareven, G. Elder, and P. Uhlenberg are key proponents of this theory.

---

behave according to the prescribed family norms of the society in which they live. Talcott Parsons, the sociologist most closely associated with this theory, saw the family as performing three particular functions that contribute to social harmony and integration: reproduction, socialization of new members, and emotional support.

As society changes, institutions, including the family, adapt to new social realities. For example, before industrialization and urbanization, families played a central role in educating their own children. They performed as a "unit of production" as well as a "unit of consumption." These families grew much of their own food, produced some of the implements used in their daily lives, and in some cases built their own houses. With all these responsibilities, extended families were important for a family's well-being.

As industries grew and people moved off the land to the cities, families became essentially units of consumption only. Institutions such as schools began to take over some of the social functions of families. A highly mobile family unit meets industrial capitalism's need for a flexible workforce. Therefore, according to Parsons, the smaller nuclear family was ideal. The extended family declined in importance in favour of the more independent nuclear family. Fewer familial commitments, argued Parsons, meant that workers were less preoccupied with concerns of family members and more with productivity. Thus, the breakdown of the extended family, in structural–functional theory, served the needs and interests of the modern capitalist economy. The family adapted. The isolated **conjugal family**, which superseded the extended family, was based on marriage, and it included a "breadwinner," usually the father, a homemaker, usually the mother, and the children conceived from that marriage. In the view of the structural–functionalists, this family type became the norm. It was, to use their terminology, "functional."

If such a familial arrangement is seen as functional, however, then those arrangements that do not conform to this model, or attempt to alter it, must, by definition, be dysfunctional. Structural–functionalists have not dealt with conflict and change, nor have they considered the dynamic nature of interpersonal relations. Change is seen as disruptive, and individual opposition to social pressure as "deviance." But, regardless of the criticisms that have been levelled at it, structural–functionalism has played a major role in determining how we conceive of families in our society.

General Systems Theory

General systems theory, also referred to simply as systems theory, analyzes the family as a total system that has an impact on all its members. This theory became popular in the 1960s, and although some ideas associated with it have been severely criticized since the 1970s, it is still being used in psychiatry, psychology, and family therapy. Of the many sociologists who have made important contributions to family studies using systems theory, the most influential is Reuben Hill.[10] According to Hill four qualities make it possible to study the family as a system:

1. Family members occupy various interdependent positions, that is, a change in the behaviour of one member leads to a change in the behaviour of other members.
2. The family is a relatively closed, boundary-maintaining unit.
3. The family is an equilibrium-seeking and adaptive organization.
4. The family is a task-performing unit that meets both the requirements of external agencies in the society and the internal needs and demands of its members.

Qualities 3 and 4 illustrate some of the similarities between structural–functionalism and systems theory. With reference to the first quality, Maureen Baker explained the emphasis of systems theory on recurring behaviour that is triggered by similar and interdependent conditions or responses. Baker gave the example of the cyclical nature of family violence, pointing out that children who grow up in a violent home environment are more likely to be abusive when they are parents.[11]

With respect to the second quality, systems theorists do not universally accept the idea that a family is relatively closed, although there is agreement that it is a "boundary-maintaining unit." In a study by Montgomery and Fewer, it was argued that families differ along a continuum of "relative openness" and "relative closure" that acknowledges some diversity in family behaviour. A family's relative openness "refers to the degree to which a mindful system is receptive to information."[12] For systems theorists, then, the boundaries that families maintain are in most cases permeable.

Perhaps the most controversial belief of systems theorists is their rejection of the idea of "causes of behaviour." As Montgomery and Fewer explained: "In systems theory, there is no cause, since behaviour is interactional and processual and has no discernible beginning."[13] Rather than cause, systems theory looks at behaviour in terms of "fit." Causal explanations of behaviour are viewed as inadequate because of three assumptions they make: (1) there is only one possible response to a given action, (2) the receiver of a particular action is incapable of generating alternative responses, and (3) the receiver has no impact on the person who commits the action. This line of reasoning ignores other factors that have an impact on behaviour. The following example will illustrate this deficiency.

If Driver A is cut off by an aggressive and inconsiderate Driver B, Driver A might respond by giving Driver B "the finger," to use the vernacular. However, according to systems theory, Driver A has other options. He or she could simply ignore Driver B. (If they are driving on a freeway in Los Angeles, Driver A might pull out a gun and shoot Driver B, as has actually happened on occasion.) Driver A's response, however, is not caused simply by Driver B's action. The choice made by Driver A might be based on his or her own background and personality. Furthermore, Driver B's action might be prompted by something that Driver A has done, driving too slowly, for example. Behaviour is too complex to be attributed to a single cause.

As already mentioned, systems theory is applied regularly in family therapy, as well as in psychiatry and psychology. But sociologists from other schools of thought have criticized this approach. For example, systems theory's approach to spousal abuse, as illustrated by Montgomery and Fewer, suggests that the abused are at least partly to blame for their own abuse, because there is no "cause" that can be attributed solely to the abuser. The "circular pattern" of behaviour identified with systems theory means that "a problem within a family is not attributed to one individual as its instigator, but rather the problem is seen as being sustained by a continuous, circular interaction process among all family members."[14] Consequently, the victim must accept some of the blame, which draws attention away from the abuser. As you can imagine, this analysis has drawn considerable fire from researchers and frontline workers dealing with the problem of abuse, usually that of women by men. We will refer to this problem when we discuss liberation theories.

Liberation Theories

Liberation theories of family emerged in the 1960s and 1970s as people became increasingly skeptical of perceived "traditional" family roles. This growing skepticism of the traditional family was part of the general demand for changes in many social institutions and values, changes that invariably meant more freedom from the restrictions of traditional norms and values.

Traditional family patterns are inherently restrictive for some family members, as liberationist theorists point out. If the family is functional, it is only to the extent that it helps maintain unequal relationships that are based on the power of some individuals, or classes of individuals, over others. Liberation theorists, therefore, question the assumption that the family merely adapts to social change in a way that meets the personal needs of individual members.

Another important distinction between the unification and liberation approaches is that sociologists of the latter school do not limit their analyses to the identification of inequalities in the family. Instead, they extend their theories to consider alternative strategies to overcome those inequalities, up to and including the establishment of new relationships. Diversity, then, becomes the norm in the study of family, which makes dimensional theories, such as the one used by Eichler, useful tools for the analysis of families. We will describe two approaches that dominate liberation theories: conflict theory and feminist theory.

Conflict Theory

Conflict theory had its beginnings in the writings of Karl Marx and Friedrich Engels. During the 1960s, Marxist and neo-Marxist analyses were increasingly used by sociologists to explain relations within families as well as the family's role in capitalist society. Many feminist theorists have been influenced by conflict theory, although as the discussion of feminism will show, Marxists and feminists differ in some respects on the reasons for the subordination of women in families and in society as a whole. More recent theorists associated with conflict theory include D. Smith, W. Seccombe, and E. Zaretsky.

According to Marx and Engels, the character of social institutions and relationships, including the family, are determined by the economic system, or **mode of production**. As a result, families have evolved throughout history to serve the economic needs of each historical period. These historical periods have been characterized by a class struggle between oppressors and oppressed, including that between slave owners and slaves, feudal lords and serfs, and capitalists and workers. Now let us illustrate the impact of the mode of production and class struggle on the family.

If we examine the evolution of the family from prehistoric times, two major transformations stand out. First is the gradual change from natural tribal societies where group marriages were the norm, and the entire community was considered a family, to an increasingly monogamous (single-partner) marital arrangement that led to a smaller, more independent family structure. Second is the rise of **patriarchal** cultures and the subsequent decline and virtual disappearance of **matriarchy** as the social and religious norm. On the basis of the literature and the archaeological evidence, this fundamental shift is thought to have begun at approximately 2400 B.C.E. as a result of invasion and conquest.

In Roman times family had an entirely different connotation. Friedrich Engels explains that the Latin word *famulus* means "household slave," and the plural *familia*, refers to "the totality of slaves belonging to one individual."[15] Under the Romans, the family developed into an institution where the male had absolute power over the rest of the family. Such an arrangement allowed him to ensure that his inheritance was bequeathed according to his wishes, which were stated in his will.

Obviously, families have come a long way since the days of "swords and sandals." Nevertheless, to appreciate the etymological roots of the word "family," consider that from Roman times until this century, a father's inheritance invariably went to his sons. If not slavery, then modern family relations have at least clung to a clearly defined hierarchy. Only in the latter part of the 20th century was this custom successfully challenged in some societies.

On the basis of these two changes, from large natural families to small independent families, and from matriarchal to patriarchal families, Engels reached the conclusion that monogamy was the first family form based "not on natural but economic conditions, namely on the victory of private property over original, naturally developed common ownership."[16] He also concluded that monogamy led to antagonism between men and women.

The antagonism in capitalist society can be illustrated by examining the dual role that the family plays in the service of industry. On the one hand, the family consumes the outcome of production, which is consumer goods, and on the other, it produces the workers employed by the industries that produce the goods. The patriarchal character of families results from the division of labour between men and women. As already discussed, women play a larger role in meeting the domestic needs of their families, a role for which they are not paid, and one that often compromises their wage-earning capacity. Although there is evidence that women are playing a more significant role in the workplace, as we shall see later in this chapter, in domestic affairs women are still the main providers. Conflict theorists argue that this creates a relationship of dependence and is the basis of the antagonism between male and female within the family.

Ironically, there is a similarity between conflict theory and the structural–functionalism of Talcott Parsons. It was Parsons, after all, who decreed that the nuclear family was best suited to industrial capitalism. Marxists would not disagree; particular family structures are tailored to meet the needs of the mode of production. However, the crucial difference between Parsons and conflict theorists is that whereas the former sees the ties between family and the economy as beneficial and positive, the latter see them as oppressive and conflictive.

Engels argued that the victory of workers over the ruling, or capitalist, class will lead to the elimination of other forms of oppression. Hence, with the disappearance of private property, the oppressive character of monogamy will also disappear, and a new monogamy, one based on mutual respect and equality, will emerge. This will result in a fundamentally different kind of family.

Sociologists from the feminist school who also identify the subordination of women with the present social order have utilized conflict theory. However, as we will see in the next section, some feminists see Marxist theory as incomplete because, although it demonstrates the inequality between male and female partners, it ignores the female's role as mother; the focus here is on "production," rather than on "reproduction." Consequently, there is a series of issues related to reproduction, the intervention of governments, for example, that conflict theory does not take into account. These differences have led to a feminist–Marxist dialogue that has clarified some important issues for both sides.

Feminist Theory

Feminist theory of the family differs from all other approaches, including conflict theory, because it uses gender, rather than the individual, the family unit, or class as the most important factor in analyzing families. For feminists, gender is not a concept to be taken for granted. Despite the biological differences between men and women, gender is regarded as a "complex social construction with multiple dimensions that bear on the dynamics of families and other institutions."[17] Gender shapes our individual identities, which are played out in school and work, as well as in the family.

Gender is essentially about "power" as it determines what is expected of males and females. These expectations reinforce a patriarchal hierarchy of relations that are based

---

CRITICAL THINKING OUTSIDE THE BOX 10.2

What kinds of stress do modern families endure as a result of economic hardship? To what extent do these stressors affect family stability? If these stressors were eliminated, how do you think familial structures and relationships might differ from their present forms? Think of the kinds of conflicts that might be reduced. Are there some tensions you would expect to persist even in a world where basic economic needs were met?

---

on the domination and oppression of women by men and that play an important role in shaping "family norms." The family, in return, is the primary organizational institution for gender relations. It is "the place where the sex/gender division of labour, the regulation of sexuality, and the social construction and reproduction of gender are all rooted."[18]

To understand the concept of family, feminists argue that we must focus on aspects of familial relationships that in many ways challenge the idea of "harmony" associated with traditional family life. Feminist theorists draw four conclusions from their analysis of these relationships:

1. Families are "arenas" in which individuals struggle to pursue different social and economic interests.

2. Families are founded on relationships in which men dominate; hence, they are patriarchal systems.

3. Families are systems where women generally accept their subordinate position, resulting in the **ideological legitimation** of inequality.

4. The definition of families as unified groups promotes **familism**, an ideology that presupposes "traditional" family norms and values.

The first two conclusions are consistent with the views of conflict theorists, who also view families in terms of competing interests and power relationships. As stated earlier, according to Engels, the antagonism between male and female led to the first class oppression—that of men over women. Class conflict, then, can take on a patriarchal form. The second two conclusions raise an important distinction that merits further discussion, namely the distinction between the **ideology of the family** and the family as it exists in modern society. Here is how the sociologist Meg Luxton explains the distinction:

> To understand "the family" we have to differentiate between ideology and the actual ways in which people interact, co-reside, have sexual relations, have babies, marry, divorce, raise children, and so on. In other words, "the family" exists in two quite different forms: as "familism," a widespread and deeply embedded ideology about how people ought to live; and as economic and social groups which in fact organize domestic and personal life.[19]

We have already discussed theoretical approaches that focus on how families "ought" to be structured. The patriarchal basis of the nuclear family dictates a "natural" structure where men dominate women and children and where men have an independent identity outside the family. However, by emphasizing the complementary functions performed by men and women in the family, we keep the power of men over women hidden or "obscured."

The ideology of family extends beyond the family itself to define women's "proper place" in the economy. Because motherhood is seen as women's primary vocation, their labour outside the home is assumed to be of secondary value to that of men, who traditionally have had the role of earning enough money to provide for their entire family. Furthermore, women are seen as most qualified for occupations that resemble their roles as wife and mother. "Suitable" careers for women include caring for and teaching the young, nursing, clerical and service work, as well as producing and selling food and clothing. As a result, familism has reinforced the economic exploitation of all women.

Another important element of familism is the belief that the family shelters us from an increasingly impersonal world. The harmony that characterizes nuclear families contributes to a more stable society. If we deviate from this model, we risk undermining social stability. Feminists, on the other hand, argue that such harmony is in many cases an illusion maintained by ignoring the gender and age basis of family violence. Traditional theorists sometimes view family violence "as a series of individual assaults or else a pathology of 'family systems.' These views ignore a crucial fact . . . violence runs along the lines of power, with adult men and women abusing children, and men abusing women, much more than the reverse."[20]

In response to their oppressive environment, feminists such as Marlene Mackie urge women to take action. First, women must examine more carefully the social basis of their roles in reproduction, parenting, and the gender division of labour. Next, they must reject the ideology that underlies the traditional model of family and begin to examine how familial relationships can be a source of conflict and violence, rather than of harmony. In the end, feminists believe, women will recognize that "family" is not experienced the same way by all family members and that its hierarchical divisions can produce conflict.[21] Such an examination enables women to create a more satisfying life for themselves, both inside and outside their families.

Feminists have also demonstrated an awareness of some of their own shortcomings by carefully examining some of their own biases. For example, the multicultural character of our society has led many feminists to be more conscious of their own white, middle-class assumptions. In addition, the demands of gays and lesbians to have their family experiences recognized and accepted has forced feminists to broaden their analysis of the social norms that determine the reproductive and childrearing choices permitted in society.

Such analysis leads to the conclusion that family patterns and structures are subject to social rules and constraints, not just to biological ones. Consequently, for feminists, as for liberation theorists in general, it is the diversity of families that enables individuals to engage in meaningful and fulfilling relationships.

We have described some of the most commonly used theoretical approaches to the study of families. Each theory provides at least a partial picture of the structure of families, the roles played by their members, and how they are related to society as a whole. We have also attempted to account for diversity in families from the various theoretical approaches. Next, we will examine how families in Canada have changed and the extent to which these changes reflect a growing diversity in what we call "families."

THE CHANGING PATTERN OF CANADIAN FAMILIES

Depending on your point of view, families are doing one of two things: they are either evolving or deteriorating. For those whose image of family is based on two parents—one male and one female, married, with 2.2 children, the changes in the last several decades indicate the deterioration of what they regard as the traditional family. On the other hand, for those with a more inclusive perspective on family, the current changes are evidence that the family is a dynamic institution that has known change throughout history and that will continue to evolve regardless of what is considered a traditional family at any given point in time.

We will now identify some of the key changes that have taken place in contemporary family life, using a dimensional framework. Then we will present a brief summary of our conclusions.

Procreative Dimension

Childbirth: Not So Soon, Not So Many

Several important transformations have occurred in families that are related to procreation. One of the most dramatic is the decline in the birth rate since the 1950s. To say "They don't make them like they used to" is no overstatement when we examine the changes illustrated in Table 10.1. As you can see, the birth rate peaked in the middle of the 20th century and then declined by approximately 53 percent by the beginning of the 21st century. The most recent data shows that the rate dropped another 1.5 percent in 2002 from

---

CRITICAL THINKING OUTSIDE THE BOX 10.3

The Government of Quebec offers cash incentives to entice Quebec families to have more children. Given concerns over Canada's declining birth rate and looming labour shortage, do you believe that governments should use incentives, cash or otherwise, to encourage larger families? Discuss the pros and cons of such policies.

Table 10.1 Canadian Births per 1000, 1901–2001 (population and growth components, 1901–2001 Censuses, thousands)

Period	Census Population at End of Period	Total Population Growth[i]	Births	Deaths	Immigration	Emigration
1901–1911	7 207	1836	1925	900	1550	740
1911–1921	8 788	1581	2340	1070	1400	1089
1921–1931	10 377	1589	2415	1055	1200	970
1931–1941	11 507	1130	2294	1072	149	241
1941–1951[ii]	13 648	2141	3186	1214	548	379
1951–1956	16 081	2433	2106	633	783	185
1956–1961	18 238	2157	2362	687	760	278
1961–1966	20 015	1777	2249	731	539	280
1966–1971	21 568	1553	1856	766	890	427
1971–1976	23 450	1488	1760	824	1053	358
1976–1981	24 820	1371	1820	843	771	278
1981–1986	26 101	1281	1872	885	678	278
1986–1991	28 031	1930	1933	946	1164	213
1991–1996	29 611	1580	1936	1024	1118	338
1996–2001	31 021	1410	1705	1089	1217	376

[i]Total population growth is the change in population numbers between two censuses.

[ii]Beginning in 1951, Newfoundland is included.

Source: "Births per 1000, 1901–2001," adapted from the Statistics Canada website <www40.statcan.ca/l01/cst01/demo03.htm>.

the previous year, which was the 11th decline in the past 12 years.[22] Thus, the downward trend in Canada's birth rate continues into this decade.

One contributing factor to the lower birth rate is that women are choosing to have their children later in life. Table 10.2 shows that for women in their 30s, the birth rate has steadily increased since the late 1960s; whereas for women in their 20s, the general trend has been downward (see table). According to the 2006 Census, this upward trend in the average age of women giving birth has continued with women in the 20–24 range experiencing a further decline from 64.1 in 1997 to 51.1 births per 1000, while those women in the 35–39 range experienced a dramatic increase from 32.5 to 44.9 births per 1000.[23]

Table 10.2   Age-Specific Birth Rates (per 1000 women), 1961–1997[i]

Year	Age Group			
	20–24	25–29	30–34	35–39
1967	161.4	152.6	91.8	50.9
1977	102.9	125.5	65.4	20.2
1987	76.1	116.7	73.2	23.2
1997	64.1	103.9	84.4	32.5

[i]Newfoundland included only in 1997.

Source: Adapted from Statistics Canada, *Births and Deaths* 84-210-XIB 1995000, Released May 1997; *Selected Birth and Fertility Statistics, Canada, 1921-1990* 82-553-XPB 1990001 1921 to 1989, Released March 15, 1993.

Because of these changes, families in Canada are becoming smaller, on average, than they have ever been, and the age gap between parents and their children is growing as families put off having children until later in life. Future studies may provide insights into the impact of this evolving family structure on relationships within families.

Childless and Childfree Couples

So far in this section, our focus has been on families with children. However, some families either choose not to have children or are unable to have them. In addition, there are families whose children have grown up and left home, the so-called empty nesters.

Among childless and childfree couples, the number of empty nesters tends to fluctuate the most. During good economic times, their number rises as the result of children becoming financially independent enough to leave home and in many instances start a family of their own. The departure of children is often seen as positive by the parents who gain a measure of freedom and independence for themselves once the responsibilities of childrearing are completed. However, during periods of economic uncertainty, some children either delay leaving home or return after encountering financial difficulty. In these cases, the "empty nest" becomes the "cluttered nest." Consequently, as we learned from conflict theory, economic conditions play an important role in shaping the structure of families.

Increasing economic pressures on families, along with changing attitudes regarding the role of women in society, and changing attitudes, specifically, toward the overall impact of having children, have led some couples to decide not to have children at all. There is even a website called *childfree.net*, which is dedicated to families who choose not to have children. As stated on the website's home page, "We choose to call ourselves "childfree" rather than "childless," because we feel the term "childless" implies that we're missing something we want—and we aren't. We consider ourselves childFREE—free of the loss of personal freedom, money, time and energy that having children requires."[24]

Further arguments from childfree couples are discussed by Annie Kingston in *Maclean's* magazine. She quotes a New York lawyer who views having children as a calling. Her 'case for the defence'? "I didn't want to make such a major lifestyle change just because it was something society expected of me," she says. "Children should be something people have because they really want them."[25]

On balance, childless and childfree couples make up a growing percentage of families in Canada. According to the 2001 Census,

> As of May 15, 2001, married or common-law couples with children aged 24 and under living at home represented only 44% of all families in Canada. In 1991, they accounted for 49% of all families, and in 1981 they represented more than one-half (55%). At the same time, couples who had no children living at home accounted for 41% of all families in 2001, up from 38% in 1991 and 34% in 1981.[26]

More recent statistics from the 2006 Census show that since 2001, the proportion of childless common-law couples grew by 20.9 percent, while that of married couples increased by 9.5 percent.[27] Marital bliss, it seems, can be either maintained after the kids are gone, or achieved without kids at all. Therefore, the family structure in Canada continues to change.

Socialization Dimension

The socialization dimension focuses on who in families is responsible for parenting. With a majority of women working outside the home nowadays, stereotyped attitudes toward raising children have changed. Traditional role differentiation, which cast men in the role of "breadwinner" and women in the role of "nurturer," has gradually been replaced by a recognition that both parents have a role to play both in the financial stability of families and in the nurturing of their young. However, this rethinking of male–female roles has not been accepted universally, or to the same degree, so that the process of change has been uneven.

On average, although men are playing a much more significant role in childrearing than they ever have before, in many families women are still spending more time than men as the family caregivers. In addition, despite men's increasing involvement in household chores, women devote more hours per day to **domestic labour** than their spouses do, whether they—the women or the men—work outside the home. Next, we will address the issue of childrearing itself and then the division of other forms of domestic labour.

Balancing Family Responsibilities with the Rest of Our Lives

Statistics Canada reported that in families with two working parents, women spend much more time on childcare than men do. Table 10.3 compares the daily time allocation of married women and men with and without children. One thing is for sure: children take their toll on men and women alike. Having children results in spending more time on unpaid work for both parents, and less time for sleep, free time, and paid work.

However, as the table shows, that impact is not distributed evenly between mothers and fathers. Women spend more than an hour and a half more on unpaid work than their partners, and that extra time appears to be at the expense of other areas of their lives. It is therefore clear that, despite the progress that has been made to date, equality between the sexes where family responsibilities are concerned is far from a reality. To further illustrate this point, only 20 percent of respondents to a national survey disagreed with the statement "When children are young, a mother's place is in the home."[28]

Women's time allocation of unpaid labour naturally has an impact on the time they have to earn a living. In fact, the gap between women and men in the time devoted to unpaid labour is almost identical to that devoted to paid labour. That is, women work roughly one and a half hours less per day outside the home than their partners, 5.5 hours versus 6.9 for men. Statistics from the 2006 Census show that the gap between women's paid and unpaid work versus that of men has not changed much in the last decade. Men worked 6.3 hours outside the home, while women worked 4.4 hours. As for unpaid labour, men worked 2.5 hours, compared to 4.3 hours for women.[29]

Another important conclusion is that women in childless families still do more unpaid labour per day than their spouses do. Thus, having no childcare responsibilities

Table 10.3 Time Allocation of People Aged 25–44 Employed Full-Time, 1998 (hours per day)

	Married Women Without Children	Married Men Without Children	Married Women with Children	Married Men with Children
Unpaid work	3.2	2.3	4.9	3.3
Paid work	6.2	7.1	5.5	6.9
Sleep	8.0	7.8	7.8	7.5
Free time	4.3	4.9	3.6	4.2

Source: Adapted from Statistics Canada, *Women in Canada: A Gender-based Statistical Report* 89-503-XWE 1998001 2000, Released September 14, 2000.

does not necessarily equalize the workload at home. Thus, while men are doing more domestic chores than they did in earlier times, families still rely on the unpaid contribution of women's time more than that of their male counterparts.

Gender roles have been transformed by changing economic conditions that have made two-income families the norm and by social values that have forced women and men to rethink their roles in day-to-day family life. Another factor that has an important impact on socialization within families is where family members actually live. In particular, the rise in the number of single-parent families and families formed from previous marriages has reshaped the way family members, particularly children, are socialized.

Residential Dimension

For unification theorists, the nuclear family, with parents and children living under one roof, is assumed to be the norm and is considered one of the foundations of a stable, functional society. However, families can be characterized by an increasing diversity of living arrangements. This diversity is the result of two factors. First, a higher divorce rate has led to a larger number of lone-parent families and families in which children spend time at the residences of both parents. Apart from divorce, the choice of single women to have children without getting married first has also contributed to the higher number of lone-parent families.

The Impact of Divorce

The liberalization of divorce laws through the 1968 *Divorce Act* and the revised *Divorce Act* of 1985 has had an enormous impact on the divorce rate in Canada. In 1968 there were 11 343 divorces, or 54.8 per 100 000 people. By 1987 it had peaked at 96 200, or 362.3 per 100 000. Since then it has fluctuated, peaking again in 1992 at 79 034 and dipping to 67 408 in 1997.[30] Regardless of the recent fluctuations, the increase between 1968 and 1997 was enormous—almost 600 percent! However, by 2005 the rate had climbed slightly to 71 269 or 220.7 per 100 000.[31]

Of course, as the divorce rate climbed, so did the number of lone-parent families. As shown in Table 10.4, lone parents made up 18.5 percent of the total number of families with children in 1996, in contrast with 9.0 percent in 1961. However, that dipped to 15.7 percent between 1996 and 2001, and increased slightly to 15.9 percent in 2006, so it remains to be seen if this decline since the 1990s is a minor hiccup or a more permanent reversal of a four-decade trend.[32]

Of the total number of lone-parent families, more than four-fifths are headed by women, and this rate has not changed much since 1961. Statistics from 2001 show a further increase of 12.7 percent in female lone-parent families, while the figure for males was even greater, at 27.8 percent. The pattern of mostly female lone-parent families is reinforced by court custody decisions, whereby in 73.6 percent of the cases the children were

Table 10.4   Single-Parent Families, 1961–1996

	Families Headed by Women		Families Headed by Men		
	000s	As % of All Families with Children	000s	As % of All Families with Children	Women as % of Single Parents
1961	272.2	9.0	75.2	2.5	78.4
1966	300.4	9.0	71.5	2.2	80.8
1971	378.1	10.4	100.7	2.8	79.0
1976	464.3	11.6	95.0	2.4	83.0
1981	589.8	13.7	124.2	2.9	82.6
1986	701.9	15.5	151.7	3.3	82.2
1991	786.4	16.4	168.2	3.5	82.4
1996	945.2	18.5	192.3	3.8	83.1

Source: Adapted from Statistics Canada, *Families: Number, Type and Structure (Data Products: Nation Series: 1991 Census of Population)* 93-312-XPB 1991000 1991, Released July 6, 1992.

awarded to the mother and in 11.8 percent to the father. In the remaining 14.3 percent of the cases, the decision was in favour of joint custody.[33] However, between 2001 and 2006, "the number of lone-father families increased more than twice as fast as the number of lone-mother families. One explanation for the faster gain among lone-parent families headed by men is that fewer mothers are granted sole custody following a divorce."[34]

What effect do these figures have on the residential dimension of family life and the overall quality of that life? Carolyne Gorlick contrasted the traditional, or unification view of divorce with its reverse, what we are calling the liberation perspective. To the unification theorist, divorce is a deviant phenomenon, "characterized by stages of denial, mourning, anger, and readjustment."[35] Therapeutic and casework analyses, according to Gorlick, see divorce as a crisis, rather than as a necessary part of an adjustment period.

Those who disagree with the traditional family perspective argue that separation from a marriage that is not working can contribute to the individual's personal growth in a way that was not possible during the marriage. First, it can create opportunities for widening the circle of family ties through remarriage and through new friendships that become possible in a different residential setting. Second, for family members leaving a non-supportive family environment, divorce is a means of liberation from fear, anxiety, and physical and emotional abuse. Finally, the opportunities for family renewal are not necessarily dependent on remarriage. Lone custodial parents enjoy a measure of independence to make choices for themselves and their children that would not be possible otherwise. Particularly for parents fleeing domestic abuse, this is an important part of their liberation.

Gorlick pointed out that neither the unification nor the liberation perspective provides a complete picture of divorce and its impact on families. Separation initially creates stress for all family members, especially children, who often cannot understand the complexities of divorce. With time, however, divorce can be seen as the beginning of a new life and a new family, not merely as the end of an old one. Diversity in residential patterns then has a positive impact on family growth and renewal.

In addition to divorced women, there are those who choose to have children without getting married. The number of women in this category rose from 11.0 percent in 1981 to 24.2 percent in 1996.[36] These women made a conscious decision that the traditional family structure is not the most suitable for them or their children. As women's incomes increase, having children without being married becomes a more economically viable option. That, in part, may explain the findings in a recent study by Susan Crompton: in a survey of mature women, aged 29–54, 52 percent believed that having children was very important, even though they had no desire to marry.[37] Consequently, the lone-parent family is becoming a more common family structure for many reasons.

Economic Dimension

Women in the Workforce

The most dramatic economic transformation in family life is the sharp increase in the number of two-income families. Duxbury and Higgins reported that in 1961, of all two-parent families in Canada, only 20 percent were dual-income.[38] By comparison, the latest census shows that that figure is now 62 percent, a more than threefold increase in the number of women in the workforce.[39]

We have already discussed the impact of women working outside the home on the division of parental responsibilities in the areas of childrearing and domestic labour. The traditional "breadwinning" and "nurturing" roles are not adequate to characterize Canadian families in the early 21st century. This is a direct result of changes in the economy and the makeup of the workforce. For example, because the financial stability of families has become increasingly dependent on having two incomes, families have had to adjust to (1) both parents balancing both family and occupational responsibilities, (2) the growing need for external childcare, and (3) the emotional stress of job loss for both parents. In addition, lone parents are faced with the task of raising a family on only one income, as well as meeting childrearing and occupational responsibilities without the emotional and physical support of a spouse.

As families have become more dependent on two incomes, they have also become more dependent on external childcare, which has, in itself, added to the expense of

CRITICAL THINKING OUTSIDE THE BOX 10.4

Some people believe that if families would make do with less, one parent could afford to stay home with the children. As a result the "traditional family" would be preserved. Do you believe the current cost of living makes this option feasible, or has the dual-income family become a necessity?

family life. To demonstrate, in 1987, two-parent families with preschool children spent 4.4 percent of their income on childcare, a sizeable sum. However, lone-parent families with preschool children fared much worse, spending 11.8 percent of their income on childcare.[40] The cost of childcare is just one of the pressures facing today's families in Canada. Next, we will focus on the broader issue of the financial pressures that are brought to bear on families.

Unemployment and Poverty in Canadian Families

One way that parents have adapted their jobs to their family responsibilities is by working part time. However, in keeping with what we learned about the socialization dimension, women have been most often the ones to do the adjusting. According to Statistics Canada, 29.1 percent of women in two-parent families choose to work part time because of the needs of the family, compared with 4.2 percent of men. For lone female parents, this figure drops to 20 percent because these women do not have a spouse with whom to share childrearing responsibilities.[41]

An obvious problem that affects a family's financial stability is unemployment. This is serious for all families, but the numbers indicate that it is particularly devastating for single-parent families. Statistics also indicate that considerably more female lone parents face unemployment than male lone parents. In 1992, for example, the unemployment rate for women who were single parents was more than double that of women in two-parent families, 19.2 percent versus 9.8 percent. That same year the figures for men were 13.9 percent and 8.3 percent, respectively.

Although the unemployment crisis of the 1990s improved by the end of the decade, poverty has persisted and the gap between rich and poor has increased. To measure the rate of poverty, the Canadian government uses a "low-income cutoff" according to which any family that spends more than 58.5 percent of its income on food, shelter, and clothing is considered poor. By this standard, the percentage of Canadian families living in poverty has grown significantly in the past decade. The sociologist Alfred Hunter reported that "according to the current criterion, 14 percent (or 3 800 000) of Canadians were poor in 1991, up from 11.8 percent in 1986 and 12 percent in 1981."[42] By 2000 the figure had improved slightly to 12.6 percent.[43] However, given that government cuts to spending on welfare and other social services during the 1990s remain largely in place, many Canadian families continue to struggle with poverty.

Which family types are most vulnerable to financial stress? Table 10.5 gives a breakdown of the percentages of low-income families by category, including those in elderly families, two-parent families, and female single-parent families. As you will see, female single-parent families are far more at risk of falling into the low-income category than other family types. Also, Table 10.5 illustrates that the percentage of members of low-income families had actually begun to decline in the mid-2000s. However, we have no

Table 10.5   Persons in Low Income After Tax

	2003	2004	2005	2006	2007
			prevalence[i] in %		
Persons in economic families	8.7	8.2	7.5	7.3	6.0
Males	8.1	7.7	7.1	6.9	5.7
Females	9.2	8.8	7.9	7.8	6.3
Persons 65 years of age and over	2.2	1.7[E]	1.2[E]	1.4[E]	1.1[E]
Males	2.0[E]	1.7[E]	1.1[E]	1.1[E]	1.2[E]
Females	2.3[E]	1.6[E]	1.3[E]	1.7[E]	1.1[E]
Persons under 18 years of age	12.5	12.9	11.7	11.3	9.4
In two-parent families	7.9	8.4	7.8	7.7	6.5
In female lone-parent families	41.4	40.4	33.4	32.3	26.6
In all other economic families	14.3[E]	14.9[E]	14.5	11.0[E]	9.5[E]
Persons 18 to 64 years of age	8.1	7.4	6.9	6.8	5.5
Males	7.1	6.3	6.0	6.1	4.9
Females	9.0	8.4	7.7	7.5	6.2

[E] Use with caution.

[i] Prevalence of low income shows the proportion of people living below the low income cutoffs within a given group. It is expressed as a percentage.

Source: Adapted from *Statistics Canada* http://www40.statcan.gc.ca/l01/cst01/famil19a-eng.htm *and the CANSIM database* http://cansim2.statcan.gc.ca 202-0802, accessed June 1, 2010.

statistics yet on the impact of the recession, which began in 2008. With the job losses that occurred since then, it's not unreasonable to expect that the percentage of low income families has risen in the last three years.

Emotional Dimension

Any discussion of the emotional dimension of family relations inevitably leads to the issue of domestic violence. We will briefly describe the kinds of abuse that are most common and how the high incidence of domestic violence affects our perception of the family.

Violence Against Female Partners

In 2006, 38 000 reports of spousal violence were filed in police departments across Canada, four-fifths of which involved violent crimes committed against women. Of these reports, 61 percent were for common assault, 14 percent were for major assault (involving a weapon and/or causing bodily harm), 11 percent were for uttering death threats, and 8 percent were for stalking. Where men were the victims, almost one-quarter of the reports were for major assault.[44]

Table 10.6 identifies the perpetrators of violence against family members, including spouses, parents, children, and siblings.

If we look at the most serious crime, homicide, we find that between 1993 and 2002, roughly two-thirds of female victims of solved homicides were killed by either their spouses or their ex-spouses, in contrast to 24 percent of male victims.[45] This ratio remained unchanged in 2008, when 45 women were murdered by their spouses versus 17 men.[46] Sadly, spousal abuse of all types is a well-documented fact of life in Canada today.

Although violence against women has been traced back as far as ancient Greece and Rome, it has not always been seen as a problem. Marion Lynn and Eimear O'Neill quote from *The Rules of Marriage*, from the 15th century, on what were considered at the time the merits of wife assault: "When you see your wife commit an offence, don't rush at her with insults and violent blows. Scold her sharply, bully and terrify her. And if this still doesn't work . . . take a stick and beat her soundly, for it is better to punish the body and correct the soul. . . . Readily beat her not in rage but out of charity . . . for [her] soul so that the beating will rebound to your merit and her good."[47]

This tolerance of wife assault was still common in 19th-century Britain, where a husband was permitted to strike his wife with any instrument no wider in diameter than his thumb. Thus, although today wife assault is illegal, for most of recorded history it has been accepted in patriarchal societies as a consequence of a man's authority over his wife and his children. (Remember the Latin origins of the word *family*, as quoted at the beginning of this chapter.)

Table 10.6 Number of Violent Crimes by Sex of Victim and Relationship to Accused, Reported to a Subset of Police Services, 2007

Relationship of Accused to Victim	Total		Sex of Victim			
			Female		Male	
	Number	Percent	Number	Percent	Number	Percent
Total victims of violent crime	335,676	100	167,994	100	167,682	100
Total family	75,779	23	54,186	32	21,593	13
Total spouse	40,165	12	33,227	20	6,938	4
Current spouse[i]	28,637	9	23,726	14	4,911	3
Ex-spouse[ii]	11,528	3	9,501	6	2,027	1
Total other family	35,614	11	20,959	12	14,655	9
Parent[iii]	11,064	3	6,412	4	4,652	3
Child[iii]	6,640	2	4,282	3	2,358	1
Sibling[iv]	8,317	2	4,782	3	3,535	2
Extended family[v]	9,593	3	5,483	3	4,110	2
Total friends/acquaintances	125,918	38	66,412	40	59,506	35
Boyfriend/girlfriend	19,851	6	16,333	10	3,518	2
Ex-boyfriend/girlfriend	11,886	4	9,817	6	2,069	1
Close friend	11,143	3	5,534	3	5,609	3
Casual acquaintance	64,858	19	27,754	17	37,104	22
Business relationship	12,534	4	4,767	3	7,767	5
Criminal relationship	1,863	1	399	0	1,464	1
Authority figure	3,783	1	1,808	1	1,975	1
Stranger	77,250	23	22,888	14	54,362	32
Unknown[vi]	56,729	17	24,508	15	32,221	19

[i] Includes legally married and common-law partners.

[ii] Includes separated and divorced partners.

[iii] Includes some cases where age or the relationship to the accused may have been miscoded.

[iv] Includes natural, step, half, foster, or adopted brother or sister.

[v] Includes others related to the victim either by blood or marriage, e.g., aunts, uncles, cousins and in-laws.

[vi] Includes cases where the relationship between the victim and the accused is unknown.

Notes: Percentages may not total 100 percent due to rounding. Excludes incidents where the sex and/or age of the victim was unknown. Data are not nationally representative. The Incident-based Uniform Crime Reporting Survey collected data from 153 police services representing approximately 94 percent of the population of Canada in 2007. Hamilton Police Service is excluded from the analysis due to data quality of the relationship variable. Current spouse and ex-spouse categories include victims aged 15 to 98. Violent crime includes violations causing death, attempted murder, sexual assaults, assaults, robbery, criminal harassment, uttering threats and other violations involving violence or the threat of violence.

Source: Adapted from Statistics Canada, *Family Violence in Canada: A Statistical Profile* 85-224-XWE 2009000 2009, Released October 15, 2009.

CRITICAL THINKING OUTSIDE THE BOX 10.5

In 2010, Aruna Papp, M.Ed., M.A., a social worker in the area of domestic violence released a report called *Culturally-Driven Violence Against Women: A Growing Problem in Canada's Immigrant Communities*:[48]

"Honour killings" are carried out in order to "cleanse" the family name and restore the family honour. Unlike normative western domestic violence, typically perpetrated by one intimate partner on another, honour violence is perpetrated within the context of the extended family: against girls and women by male relatives—such as fathers, fathers-in-law, brothers, brothers-in-law, husbands, and occasionally sons—often with the complicity of older females.

Do you believe that there is a link between some kinds of family violence and either culture or religion? Can you find evidence elsewhere in this text to support your opinion?

Women are not the only victims of domestic violence. Children, too, bear the emotional scars of the dark side of family life. Violent assaults against children and youths committed by family members accounts for roughly 30 percent of the total number of these assaults, which include both physical and sexual abuse.[49] What the statistics show is that some children have at least as much to fear from their families as they do from strangers.

Effect of Violence on Family Relations

The high incidence of domestic violence runs counter to the traditional view of the family as a refuge from a cold, heartless world. It cuts across class lines, although it tends to be more visible among lower-income groups because people in these groups have more frequent interaction with relevant government departments, such as social services.

Feminist theorists have been at the forefront of research into the causes and outcomes of domestic violence. The subjects of their studies, be they women or children, are seen not only as victims, but also as "survivors." The pain suffered by victims is acknowledged, but so too is their capacity to overcome their circumstances through their adaptive capacities and strengths. Thus, the end of one negative family structure can lead to the emergence of a new positive one, although, of course, this does not happen without its own sacrifice and struggle. The emotional dimension, as Eichler concluded, "runs the gamut from the most tender, emotionally satisfying, positive involvements to the most frightening, abusive physically and mentally harmful relationships."[50] The diversity in these relationships must be the basis for further analysis of families.

SAME-SEX MARRIAGE: THE CONTINUING EVOLUTION OF CANADIAN FAMILIES

On 20 July 2005, Bill C-38, Canada's **same-sex marriage** law received royal assent. This bill, while legalizing marriage between gays and lesbians, also guarantees the right of religious groups to refuse to perform marriages that go against their beliefs. Gays and lesbians, as well as their supporters celebrated what amounts to the latest redefinition of family in Canada. As of July 2010, there are approximately a dozen countries that recognize gay marriage, the latest being Portugal, Iceland, and Argentina.

This legal redefinition of marriage and, consequently, the family came after much heated and emotional debate. "Traditional family" proponents lobbied against the passing of C-38. One such group, United Families Canada, argued in a petition to the government that "[L]egalizing same sex marriage in Canada would undermine traditional marriage in our society, thereby undermining support for families as well . . ." and that ". . . same-sex marriage will hurt Canada, disenfranchise our children of their right to a parent of both genders, and drastically weaken the family."[51]

On the other side of the debate, organizations such as Equality for Gays and Lesbians Everywhere (EGALE) defend same-sex marriage as a human rights issue, as you can see from the following press release that came out after the passage of C-38: "In a generation, Canadians will look back on a time when lesbian and gay people were denied full citizenship, just as we look back on the days when women or Aboriginal people could not vote or times when Canadian citizens were interned because of ethnic origin."[52]

CRITICAL THINKING OUTSIDE THE BOX 10.6

In this chapter we have analyzed the family using five "dimensions." Can you think of any other "dimensions" that might be added to those we have discussed? How would your additional dimensions enhance our understanding of families? What forms of diversity would they demonstrate?

In the last census, 7465 same-sex couples identified themselves as being married, out of a total of 45 345 couples who simply identified themselves as same-sex couples.[53]

From the perspective of diversity, the broadening of the definition of marriage to include same-sex couples merely reaffirms that the structure of families in Canada continues to change as it always has. The intensity of the debate demonstrates that controversy, as always, is no stranger to the issue of defining "family" in our society.

CHAPTER SUMMARY

We began this chapter by referring to what some describe as a crisis in the family as a social institution. What we have attempted to show is that changes to the modern family do not necessarily constitute a crisis. Although the traditional ideology of the family has come under attack, families themselves are doing what they have always done. They are responding to political and economic changes in society by changing themselves, becoming more diverse as they adapt to their new circumstances.

We began by attempting to reach a meaningful definition of the term *family*—one applicable to the wide variation in the structure of Canadian families. As the process by which the definition is developed is as important as the definition itself, the introductory section of the chapter also examined how we arrive at our definition. In attempting to reach a suitable definition, we discovered that the notion of the "traditional family" is incomplete at best, as it is unable to transcend the constraints of popular middle-class culture.

Next, we looked at how families have been studied from several theoretical perspectives, which are broadly divided into two categories: unification and liberation theories. Each approach has its own rationale for the nature of relations among family members and of family structure. No one approach gives a complete picture of family life or reasons for changes that have taken place in Canadian families, but some approaches are better equipped than others to explain the diversity of modern families.

Change has always been an essential characteristic of families. Consequently, we should not be surprised that what is referred to as the "traditional family" has always been more of an abstract idea than a reality. The statistics provided in this chapter have clearly demonstrated the kinds of changes that have taken place in Canadian families, particularly since the 1950s. They reveal a social institution that is evolving, as it always has, in response to other changes in our environment, be they social, political, or economic.

Finally, we addressed the redefinition of families, including the addition of same-sex marriages as a recognized, if not universally accepted fact in Canada. Now, as always, understanding the diversity of family life is essential if we are to address the stresses and challenges facing Canadian families.

KEY TERMS

conflict theory, p. 286

conjugal family, p. 284

domestic labour, p. 294

empty nesters, p. 283

extended family, p. 280

familia, p. 287

familism, p. 289

feminist theory, p. 288

general systems theory, p. 284

ideological legitimation, p. 289

ideology of the family, p. 289

liberation theories, p. 286

matriarchy, p. 287

mode of production, p. 286

nuclear families, p. 279

patriarchal, p. 287

same-sex marriage, p. 304

structural–functionalism, p. 282

unification theories, p. 282

DISCUSSION QUESTIONS

1. Conduct two interviews, one with someone you know who is from what the text defines as a traditional family, and someone from a nontraditional family. What similarities and differences can you identify in their familial relationships? To what extent do the concepts from this chapter apply to either family?

2. Review the content of Bill C-38. Then, conduct research on some of the groups who have argued for and against the recognition of same-sex marriage. Evaluate the basis of each side of the debate. Why do you think the government finally chose to legalize same-sex marriage?

3. Canadian families are based on patriarchal (male-dominant) authority. What would life be like in a family based on matriarchal (female-dominant) authority? Would it differ significantly from the current patriarchal structure? If so, how? If not, why not?

4. Which of Eichler's dimensions do you think has the greatest impact on family relationships? Explain your answer.

5. Do you agree that "traditional" family patterns of authority can create antagonistic relationships of dependence in families? Why or why not?

6. You are married and have a child. Both you and your partner work full time. Plan a schedule for a week that ensures that the domestic chores are divided equally.

NOTES

1. "New Mega-Trends Reflect Family Decline," *Today's Family News*, 7 January 2005, available FamilyFacts.ca <www.fotf.ca/familyfacts/tfn/2005/010705.html>, accessed 8 April 2006.
2. Dr. Darrel Reid, "Crisis or Opportunity? Eleven Practical Steps for Strengthening the Family," *Commentaries*, November 1999, available FamilyFacts.ca <www.fotf.ca/familyfacts/commentaries/110199.html>, accessed 8 April 2006.
3. George P. Murdock, *Social Structure* (New York: Macmillan, 1949), p. 1.
4. Rose Laub Coser, *The Family: Its Structure and Functions*, 2nd ed. (New York: St. Martin's Press, 1974), p. xvi.
5. Statistics Canada, *A Portrait of Families in Canada* (Ottawa: Vanier Institute, 1994), p. 7.
6. Brigitte Kitchen, "Family Policy," in Maureen Baker, ed., *Families: Changing Trends in Canada*, 2nd ed. (Toronto: McGraw-Hill Ryerson, 1990), p. 313.
7. Margrit Eichler, *Families in Canada Today* (Toronto: Gage, 1983), p. 8.
8. Emily Nett, *Canadian Families* (Vancouver: Butterworths, 1993), p. 24.
9. David Cheal, *Family and the State of Theory* (Toronto: University of Toronto Press, 1993), p. 4.
10. Reuben Hill, "Modern Systems Theory and the Family: A Confrontation," *Social Science Information* 10 (1971) (5): 12.
11. Baker, "Theories, Methods, and Concerns," p. 13.
12. Jason Montgomery and Willard Fewer, *Family Systems and Beyond* (New York: Human Sciences Press, 1988), p. 118.
13. Montgomery and Fewer, p. 21.
14. David Cheal, "Theoretical Perspectives," in G. Ramu, ed., *Marriage and the Family Today*, 2nd ed. (Scarborough: Prentice-Hall, 1991), p. 22.
15. Friedrich Engels, "The Origin of the Family, Private Property and the State," in Robert Tucker, ed., *The Marx-Engels Reader*, 2nd ed. (New York: W.W. Norton, 1978), p. 737.
16. Engels, p. 739.
17. Barrie Thorne, "Feminism and the Family," in Barrie Thorne and Marilyn Yalom, eds., *Rethinking the Family* (Boston: Northeastern University Press, 1992), p. 12.
18. Marlene Mackie, "Gender in the Family," in Nancy Mandell and Ann Duffy, eds., *Canadian Families* (Toronto: Harcourt Brace, 1990), p. 50.
19. Meg Luxton, "Thinking About the Future," in Karen Anderson et al., eds., *Family Matters: Sociology and Contemporary Canadian Families* (Toronto: Methuen, 1987), p. 238.
20. Thorne, p. 147.
21. Mackie, p. 50.
22. Statistics Canada, Health Statistics Division, "Birth Rate at All-Time Low," *Infomat: The Week in Review*, 27 April 2004, available <www.statcan.ca/english/freepub/11-002-XIE/2004/04/11804/11804_02p.htm>, accessed 8 April 2006.
23. Statistics Canada, "Live Births by Geography—Crude Birth Rate, Age-specific and Fertility Rates," available <www.statcan.gc.ca/pub/84f0210x/2006000/ 5201680-eng.htm>, accessed 9 July 2010.
24. Childfree.net, "Who are We?" available <www.childfree.net/index.html>, accessed 15 July 2010.

25. Anne Kingston, "The Case Against having Kids," Mcleans.ca, available <www2.macleans. ca/2009/07/24/no-kids-no-grief/>, accessed 15 July 2010.

26. Statistics Canada, "Profile of Canadian Families and Households: Diversification Continues," *The Daily*, October 22, 2002, available <www12.statcan.ca/english/census01/products/ analytic/companion/fam/contents.cfm>, accessed 8 April 2006.

27. Tenille Bonoguore, "Married, with Children? No Thanks," *The Globe and Mail*, 12 September 2007.

28. Rick J. Ponting, *Canadian Gender-Role Attitudes* (Unpublished Manuscript, University of Calgary, 1986).

29. Statistics Canada, "Average Time per Day Spent on Paid and Unpaid Work Activities, Men, Women and Total, 1986 and 2005," available <www.statcan.gc.ca/pub/89-630-x/2008001/ c-g/10705/5200920-eng.htm>, accessed 15 July 2010.

30. Statistics Canada, *Women in Canada 2000*, Catalogue No. 89-503-XPE, p. 43.

31. Dr. Anne-Marie Ambert, "Divorce: Facts, Causes and Consequences," *Contemporary Family Trends* (Ottawa, Ontario: The Vanier Institute of the Family, 2005).

32. Statistics Canada, "The Proportion of Lone-parent Families has been Increasing Since 1966," available <www12.statcan.ca/census-recensement/2006/as-sa/97-553/figures/c2-eng. cfm>, accessed 8 July 2010.

33. Statistics Canada, "Lone-Parent Families as a Proportion of All Census Families Living in Private Households, Canada, Provinces, Territories, Health Regions and Peer Groups, 2001," 26 November 2003, <www.statcan.gc.ca/english/freepub/82-221-XIE/01103/tables/ html/49_01.htm>, accessed 8 April 2006.

34. Statistics Canada, "Families, Households and Housing," available <www41.statcan. gc.ca/2008/40000/ceb40000_000-eng.htm>, accessed 16 July 2010.

35. Carolyn Gorlick, "Divorce: Options Available, Constraints Forced, Pathways Taken," in Nancy Mandell and Ann Duffy, eds., *Canadian Families* (Toronto: Harcourt Brace, 1990), p. 212.

36. Statistics Canada, *Women in Canada 2000*, p. 43.

37. Susan Crompton, "Always the Bridesmaid: People Who Don't Expect to Marry," *Canadian Social Trends*, Summer 2005, available <www.statcan.ca/english/studies/11-008/feature/ 11-008-XIE20050017961.pdf>, accessed 8 April 2006.

38. Linda Duxbury and Christopher Higgins, "Families in the Economy," in Maureen Baker, ed., *Canada's Changing Families: Challenges to Public Policy* (Ottawa: Vanier Institute, 1994), p. 29.

39. Roger Sauvé, *Profiling Canada's Families III* (Ottawa: The Vanier Institute of the Family, 2004), available <www.vifamily.ca/library/profiling3/sample2.html>, accessed 8 April 2006.

40. Statistics Canada, *A Portrait of Families in Canada*, Catalogue No. 89-523E, 1993, p. 27.

41. Ibid., p. 29.

42. Alfred Hunter, "Social Inequality," in Robert Hagedorn, ed., *Sociology* (Toronto: Harcourt Brace, 1994), p. 275.

43. Statistics Canada, "Income of Canadian Families," *Analysis Series*, Catalogue No. 96F0030XIE2001014, 13 May 2003 <www12.statcan.ca/english/census01/products/ analytic/companion/inc/contents.cfm>, accessed 8 April 2006.

44. Statistics Canada, "Family Violence: Spousal Violence in Canada," *The Daily*, 9 October 2008, available <www.statcan.gc.ca/daily-quotidien/081009/dq081009b-eng.htm>, accessed 16 July 2010.

45. Maire Gannon, "Family Violence in Canada: A Statistical Profile," Statistics Canada, Catalogue No. 85-224-XIE, 2004, p. 35.

46. Statistics Canada, "Homicide in Canada," *The Daily*, 28 October 2009, available <www.statcan.gc.ca/daily-quotidien/091028/dq091028a-eng.htm>, accessed 16 July 2010.

47. Marion Lynn and Eimear O'Neill, "Families, Power, and Violence," in Nancy Mandell and Ann Duffy, eds., *Canadian Families* (Toronto: Harcourt Brace, 1990), p. 285.

48. Aruna Papp, "Culturally-Driven Violence Against Women: A Growing Problem in Canada's Immigrant Communities," *Frontier Centre for Public Policy*, available <www.fcpp.org/publication.php/3352>, accessed 19 July 2010.

49. Statistics Canada, "Table 3.4: Child and Youth Victims of Physical and Sexual Assault Committed by Family or Non-family Members by Level of Injury, Reported to a Subset of Police Services, 2007", available <www.statcan.gc.ca/pub/85-224-x/2009000/t019-eng.htm>, accessed 16 July 2010.

50. Eichler, p. 13.

51. Canadian Citizens to Defend Marriage, Defend Marriage, 2003 <www.defendmarriage.ca>.

52. Canadians for Equal Marriage, "House of Commons Adopts Equal Marriage Bill by Decisive Margin," press release, 28 June 2005, available <www.egale.ca/index.asp?lang=E&menu=20&item=1160>, accessed 8 April 2006.

53. Brodie Fenlon, "Do Same-Sex-Marriage Numbers Reflect Reality?" *The Globe and Mail*, 13 September 2007, available <http://v1.theglobeandmail.com/servlet/story/LAC.20070913.CENSUSSEX13/TPStory/SIRI+AGRELL>, accessed 8 July 2010.

PART THREE

THE TREATMENT AND PERCEPTION
OF DIVERSITY

Part III examines how diversity is treated in the media and is perceived in literature. Continuing with the house analogy, if Part I is the foundation and structure and Part II the ever-changing interior, then Part III is how people view the house—that is, how they assess it, value it, and treat it.

Chapter 11 looks at how the media portray diversity. It begins with a definition and overview of the history of mass media. The primary purpose of this chapter is to help the reader to understand the impact of mass media, especially the U.S. mass media, on the world in general and on diversity in Canada in particular. The addition of Theodor Adorno's model of media behaviour helps dispel the myth of an objective and independent media pursuing the truth.

New Chapter 12, "Literature: The Voice of Diversity," explains how diverse voices in Canadian literature impacts our ever-changing ideas of who we are. By better understanding who we are, we are much more likely to admit, accept, and allow diversity.

CHAPTER 11

The Medium Diversifies the Message: How Media Portray Diversity

Grant Havers

The media are the avant-garde of our society.
—Marshall McLuhan

In each lived moment of our waking and sleeping, we are technological civilization.
—George Grant

Objectives

After reading this chapter, you should be able to

- explain the meaning and uses of "mass media"

- explain the four major stages in the history of mass media

- understand the rise of the global village

- understand the influence of television on attitudes toward diversity

- understand the impact of American media on the world

INTRODUCTION: MEDIA AND DIVERSITY

Media have had enormous influence on human culture and are as old as civilization. They disclose a great deal about the cultures that employ them and the rich diversity within and among human cultures. How do mass media portray diversity?

Since the beginning of the electronic age, many observers have wondered whether mass media can encourage awareness of cultural diversity or, in fact, hinder such awareness. Mass media present the possibility of bringing the world together in peace and tolerance, because of their power to beam the news of the entire world in the living rooms of each family in every nation. However, this achievement does not only guarantee greater awareness of diversity but also presents diversity through distorted lenses. Whatever the implications, there is no question that representation of diversity by the media has an enormous impact on how we all see diversity.

DEFINING MEDIA AND "MASS" MEDIA

Perhaps it is easier to understand the meaning of "medium" than of "mass medium." A medium (*media* is the plural form) is a technique of communication. Language is the oldest medium of all. However, a **mass medium** is more than the means by which people speak and write to each other. If we understand the world as a "mass" of people, the term "mass media" suggests that media have enormous impact on the entire world. Two elements are important here.

First, mass media usually have "mass" audiences. All cultures in history have used various media (see Table 11.1), but these have not always been "mass" media. A "mass" medium is available to most people and cultures. It connects different parts of the entire world together.

Second, mass media vary in purpose. They may be sources of entertainment, such as television; information, such as newspapers; communication, such as telephones; or a combination of all three, such as computers. But they must always be available to a wide audience.

Throughout this chapter considerable discussion will be devoted to how successful mass media have been in educating the world about its diversity. One useful rule of thumb to remember is that every medium has an impact on its environment. Mass media, as Marshall McLuhan pointed out, are not simply tools that perform simple functions of informing or assisting human beings. A medium is more than a useful artifact; it affects human behaviour itself. To quote McLuhan's famous saying, "The medium is the massage"[1] (see Have You Heard? 11.1). This claim can be interpreted in numerous ways, but only one will be offered here: every medium shapes the content of what it is conveying.

Table 11.1   Which Civilizations Use(d) Which Media

Civilization	Main Medium Used
Sumerian	Pictographs, stone (3500 B.C.E.)
Egyptian	Papyrus, hieroglyphics (3000 B.C.E.)
Indian	Script (2400 B.C.E.)
Greek	Parchment, stone (700 B.C.E.)
Roman	Papyrus, parchment, stone (50 C.E.)
Chinese	Paper, script (105 C.E.)
Mayan	Script (50 C.E.)
Aztec	Script (1400 C.E.)
English	Paper (1200 C.E.)

Note: The dates here suggest approximately when the civilizations developed these media or made use of them. C.E. means "Common Era" and indicates the same time frame as *A.D.* refers to. *B.C.E.* means "Before the Common Era" and indicates the same time frame as B.C.

This means that books, newspapers, radio, and television all can influence (or massage) the message that is delivered to its audience. As any consumer knows, how advertising portrays the product is usually more important than the product itself. Given this fact, it is centrally important to understand how mass media have shaped and influenced the meaning of diversity, for good or ill.

HAVE YOU HEARD? 11.1

The "Prophet," Marshall McLuhan (1911–1980)

....

More than anyone else in this century, Marshall McLuhan understood the mass media. Born in Edmonton in 1911, he attended university in England in the 1930s, when he first studied the media. McLuhan became famous in the 1960s with his publications on the printing press, television, advertising, and technological change. *The Gutenberg Galaxy* and *Understanding Media* made him into a celebrity. It is ironic that by the time of his death in 1980, McLuhan himself had become a media phenomenon, appearing on the cover of major magazines, being asked for advice by politicians, and being hailed by many as a "prophet" for the television age.

A BRIEF HISTORY OF MEDIA AND MASS MEDIA

As already mentioned, throughout history civilizations of diverse origins have used media. People have always communicated with each other. "Mass media," however, have not always existed; that is, they have not always been available to large numbers of people. For example, writing was not always a mass medium; until the 15th century only elite groups in societies could write. By studying the history of media, we can begin to understand how media eventually became mass media.

The history of media can be divided into four stages (see Table 11.2), each of which marks a revolutionary turning point: (1) the oral stage, (2) the rise of the alphabet and writing, (3) the printing press, and (4) the electronic age, in which we now live.

The Oral Stage

The first stage was based on the condition of **orality**. Before the development of writing, the earliest human beings communicated almost entirely orally. Although human civilization has existed for perhaps 6000 years, the earliest writing appears to be not much more than 5000 years old. Until 3500 B.C.E. most people relied on the oral medium. It is estimated that the vast majority of languages spoken in human history have never been written down; little more than a hundred of them have a literature.[2] Human beings spoke words, sang poems, and gestured, but they did not write. Because they lacked any means of written communication, these oral cultures relied heavily on the constant memorization of their most cherished epics and folklore. It is important not to dismiss an oral culture as "primitive" on the basis of its lack of writing. Indeed, oral cultures were extremely sophisticated in their use of memory, which was their sole way of recording stories. Ancient Greek, African, Middle Eastern, and Aboriginal storytellers resorted to the oral transmission of their cultures' tales. This process required poets of each generation to pass down stories to the next through the spoken word.

The Rise of the Alphabet and Writing

The second stage began to emerge when oral cultures initiated the long transition toward written language. Around 3500 B.C.E. the Sumerians in Mesopotamia (modern-day Iraq) developed the **pictograph**, which consisted of pictures representing words or utterances. Other peoples, such as the Babylonians and Assyrians of the Middle East, also developed elaborate systems of pictographs. Around 3000 B.C.E. the ancient Egyptians developed their own system of pictographs, known as **hieroglyphics**.

By 1500 B.C.E. the second period of media had taken hold in the Middle East, which greatly accelerated the transition to written language: the alphabet had been invented. Human beings could now communicate using a system of signs that had letters, rather than symbols as in the case of pictographs.[3] This invention also enabled people around

Table 11.2 Important Dates in the History of Mass Media

3500 B.C.E.	Sumerians develop pictographs.
3000 B.C.E.	Egyptians develop hieroglyphics, papyrus.
2000 B.C.E.	Hebrew begins to develop.
1500 B.C.E.	Phoenicians invent an alphabet.
105 C.E.	Chinese invent paper.
1455	Gutenberg invents the first printing press using moveable type.
1478	First printed ad appears.
1702	First English daily newspaper appears.
1741	First magazines appear in America.
1844	First telegraph line operates.
1873	Newspapers appear in the Middle East.
1876	Telephone is invented.
1877	Phonograph is invented.
1887	Gramophone is developed.
1895	Marconi develops the radio.
1896	First public motion picture shown in America.
1947	First TV news programs appear.
1979	Walkman is introduced.
1982	CD player emerges.
1985	Personal computer is established.
1990	Virtual reality becomes popular.
1998	Universities, industry, and government begin planning for Internet2.
2000	Napster file sharing upsets music industry.
2000	The Love Bug virus infects 45 million computers worldwide.
2006	MySpace becomes most popular social networking site in June; Facebook is created three months later.
2007	iPhones are released for sale.
2008	Computer worm "Conficker" infects up to 15 million Microsoft server systems.

the world to communicate with each other. Once it was discovered that materials such as papyrus could be employed to transmit the written word across great distances, various cultures became known to each other. The alphabet cannot be called a mass medium at this time, for until the invention of the printing press writing was still inaccessible to the vast majority of people.

Gradually, other cultures adopted the alphabet. The Phoenicians, a seafaring people of the Middle East, invented their alphabet about 1500 B.C.E. This reflected their desire to be able to trade goods using a flexible alphabet and enabled them to become independent of the dominant Egyptian culture of the time.[4] Eventually, the Greeks, in the 8th century B.C.E., took over the Semitic alphabet, which had twenty-two letters, and adapted it to their needs. One of the adaptations made by the Greeks was the introduction of vowels to the alphabet.[5]

As long as the alphabet remained the dominant medium, various ancient empires used it and expanded on it. Other cultures simply stuck to pictographs or combinations of symbols known as **script**. Whatever the type of medium used by a particular civilization, it reveals much about the priorities of that civilization. The Canadian historian Harold Innis shed light on these priorities by distinguishing "**time-oriented**" **media** from "**space-oriented**" **media**. Empires, such as Greece, that used durable media such as **parchment** (dried sheep- or goatskin) put great importance on the preservation of time, the recording of their history on materials that would last. Other empires that used papyrus, such as Egypt and Rome, and paper, such as China, viewed the conquest of space (or linkages to the outside world) as central. As a result, they cultivated media that could be transported across vast distances.[6] Because media such as stone and clay are impractical for transportation, it is clear that the empires that used papyrus, which is a very transportable medium, were most successful in acquiring knowledge about the rest of the world.

McLuhan introduced the idea that all technologies are "extensions" of human beings. Media "extend" a part of the human body by allowing that part to do something that it could not do by itself. For instance, print media—such as books and newspapers—are extensions of the eyes: they permit the eyes to see people, events, and cultures around the world that ordinary vision could not do by itself. Similarly, a computer extends the brain: the memory of the computer retains vast amounts of information that the brain cannot hold. The kinds of extensions a culture uses reveal which parts of the body that culture considers most important (see Table 11.3). That certain cultures adopted an alphabet suggests that the eye was very important to them, for the alphabet extends vision.

Although not all nations developed an alphabet (e.g., China did not), the alphabet became the dominant medium of western Europe, Russian Asia, India, and sections of the Far East (see Table 11.4). It has been said that every alphabet in the world is based on the Semitic alphabet.[7] The effects of the alphabet on the world increased with the third stage in the history of media.

The Printing Press

The third stage of history of media began in 1455, when Johannes Gutenberg (1390–1468), in Germany, invented the printing press with moveable metal type. This ushered

Table 11.3   Technology: The Extensions of Humanity

Technology	Part of Body It Extends
Club, hammer	Fist
Clothing	Skin
Knife	Teeth
Glasses, telescope, camera	Eyes
Writing, books, newspapers	Eyes
Refrigerator	Stomach
Wheel	Legs
Automobile	Legs
Radio	Ears
Television	Eyes, ears
Computers	Brain
Virtual reality	Whole body

Table 11.4   Some Major Alphabets of the World

Alphabet	Origin
Hebrew	Middle East
Ugaritic	Middle East
Greek	Mediterranean
Roman	Mediterranean
Cyrillic	Eastern Europe
Arabic	Middle East
Tamil	Southern India
Malayalam	Southwest India
Korean	Korea, East Asia

in a wave of social change that continues to shake the world today. (Before this time, the Chinese had developed a printing technique for wooden type.) Before the printing press with moveable metal type, reading in the Western world was restricted mostly to the learned scribes and elites of the ancient and medieval worlds. Gutenberg's invention made it possible for millions to become literate, because it enabled the mass production of inexpensive books. Thus, the alphabet became a mass medium. Indeed, the age of mass media had arrived. The printing press had two major effects on the meaning of diversity.

First, it made people greatly aware of their diversity. Now it was possible to produce literature on a mass scale for a mass audience. The various peoples of western Europe became more aware of how different their cultures and languages were. The common, everyday languages or **vernaculars** of particular geographical areas could now be published using the printing press. Everyday French, German, and English people could now read the languages that they spoke. Nationalism, or love of one's nation, could not have developed without the printing press.[8] It made it possible for the various European peoples to read in their own languages. It also enabled them to develop languages that were truly "national," or common to all regions of a particular nation. Martin Luther translated the Bible into ordinary German by 1534. The different **dialects** (different versions of one standard language) of the various regions of Germany became one German language, because the printing press could put out books teaching different Germans how to conform to one national, printed language. Soon after 1455 cultural influences that had largely been restricted to Europe spread across the world.

Second, the press encouraged homogeneity or mass sameness. Once the printing press was used as the way of standardizing the language of a culture, everyone had to learn the same language. There was no longer room for individuals to create their own vernaculars—all had to conform to one language now. There was no such thing as "bad grammar," until the printing press made it possible to force one "good" grammar on everyone.[9] Indeed, Gutenberg's creation made compulsory education possible. Thanks to the printing press, everyone could now become literate, because everyone could be educated in the same language.

Thus, the print media of the alphabet and the printing press opened up the distinctive possibilities of diversity and homogeneity. This two-headed and contradictory process accelerated even further with the emergence of electronic media in the 19th century.

The Electronic Stage

The fourth stage, the electronic stage, began in 1844 when Samuel Finley Breese Morse's **telegraph**, a device that transmitted messages via electric wire, was installed between Baltimore and Washington, DC (see Table 11.5). Morse's first message on the telegraph was "What hath God wrought?"[10] It is not clear what Morse meant by this statement, but he may have been expressing surprise at the fact that his new invention had created a world whose diverse peoples could now communicate with each other almost immediately. The age of instantaneous communication through mass media had arrived.

Table 11.5 Who Invented It?

Invention	Approximate Year	Who Got the Credit	
Printing press[i]	1455	J. Gutenberg	Germany
Telegraph	1844	S.F.B. Morse	United States
Telephone	1876	A.G. Bell	United States
Phonograph	1877	T. Edison	United States
Gramophone	1887	Emile Berliner	France
Radio[ii]	1895	G. Marconi	Italy
Movies	1895	Lumière brothers	France

[i]This was the first printing press with moveable metal type; the Chinese had invented presses with *wooden* type almost 700 years before Gutenberg.

[ii]There is no single inventor of the radio: credit must also be given to Heinrich Hertz (1857–94), a German scientist; Reginald Aubrey Fessenden (1866–1932), a Canadian, who experimented with radio transmission of voices in the early 1900s; and Lee de Forest (1873–1961), an American, who patented the vacuum tube in 1907.

Before the telegraph, messages and newspapers were transmitted as quickly as human beings could carry them—or move them—by horse. Now the telegraph could communicate messages across great distances in a relatively short time. The telegraph was the first of many inventions that were to be able to accomplish this feat: the telephone, radio, television, and computer followed in the 20th century. All of these encouraged the instantaneous transmission of messages from one part of the globe to another, allowing everyone everywhere to be involved in everyone else's business. Thus emerged the **global village**. This achievement was entirely the result of the discovery of electricity. This village produced **tribalism** among the human species, a contradictory feeling that manifests both feelings of interconnectedness (due to global technology) and insecurity over the survival of one's identity in the new global village.[11]

Tribalism seems to foster awareness of diversity in an unprecedented manner. Thanks to electronic media, people around the world can now communicate with people in all the other parts, and they can do so instantaneously and effortlessly. For "space-oriented" cultures bent on developing linkages with the outer world, electronic media are a blessing, not a curse. But the question remains: Does this leap forward in communication translate into greater tolerance of diversity, or is the global village intolerant as well?

IS THE GLOBAL VILLAGE GOOD FOR DIVERSITY?

Television and Diversity

Media affect our behaviour. They are not only tools that perform the functions of communication and information; media "massage" their audiences: they can affect people's behaviour without people even being aware of this influence. Observers are increasingly putting media under the spotlight in case these media ignore, insult, stereotype, and misrepresent minorities of all kinds. As Michael Parenti observed, "The major distortions are repeatable and systemic—the product not only of deliberate manipulation but of the ideological and economic conditions under which the media operate."[12]

To answer the question "Is the global village good for diversity?" let us consider the effects of television, the dominant mass medium of our time and the technology credited as the most successful in expanding the global village. It is easy to observe why television is so successful, for it is one of the most widely available media of all time. Unlike print, television does not require the ability to read for it to be understood: no one requires special education to comprehend the messages of television. Long before they pick up a book to read, three-year-olds, for example, want the toys advertised on television.[13] In the global village, which consists of so many different cultures, how is life affected by the media? Four factors address this question.

First, television has encouraged many diverse communities and cultures to become aware of each other and themselves. Because television provides millions of people with access to a wider world, one of the effects has been to force many cultures to recognize their own isolation in the world. The feeling is that their failure to appear on the nightly news is a reflection of their lack of importance. Although television has encouraged a feeling of isolation, it has also encouraged minorities and marginalized groups to demand an end to this isolation. Now that television can overcome the distances within the world, previously isolated groups want to be involved in the world's affairs. Access to the world's information has encouraged this new demand. Indeed, it is significant that many political movements of minorities did not emerge until the television age.[14] Politics has been redefined in the media age (see Have You Heard? 11.2).

Second, television has made it more difficult for the world to ignore the concerns and needs of these movements, especially when they have constantly appeared on the nightly news since, say, the 1960s. The plight of the poor around the world, for example, is increasingly difficult to ignore in the age of television exposure. The Live Aid concert organized by various musicians to fight starvation in Ethiopia in the mid-1980s is an example of how mass media exposure can make a huge difference to the success of a cause or movement—it succeeded in raising millions of dollars.

Third, television often distorts the meaning of diversity to suit its own aims and purposes.[15] Whereas it is true that television responded to the political movements of

---

HAVE YOU HEARD? 11.2

The Politics of Mass Media

. . . .

Mass media have influenced political movements for as long as politicians have existed. The printing press made possible the mass publication of pamphlets and newspapers, which are widely used by politicians.

Television debates can also make and break a politician's career. Stephen Harper's performance on the television debates during the 2006 Canadian election helped his Conservative Party win a minority government. His performance in similar debates during the 2004 federal election campaign contributed to the defeat of his party. The medium does matter. In 1960, when John F. Kennedy debated with Richard Nixon for the U.S. presidency, those who watched the debate saw Kennedy, with his cool charm, as the winner. Those who listened to the debate on radio thought Nixon won. Evidently, television won over radio that year, because Kennedy defeated Nixon in the election by a narrow margin.

---

the 1960s with unprecedented exposure, this coverage had less to do with informing its audience than with providing entertainment. For example, at first glance it would appear that the media coverage of the various African-American and Vietnam protest movements in the 1960s represented an informative response to newsworthy events. It was hoped that this coverage would dramatize the plight of the African-American poor in the ghettoes of the United States, as well as the concerns of the antiwar protesters. What happened instead, according to some observers, was that the media decided to focus on those members of the movements who could provide the most entertainment or "news value." Typically, the media focused on leaders who packed the biggest dramatic punch, entertained the audiences, and looked physically attractive. Those leaders who lacked a dynamic visual image were ignored in the media coverage, even if they were important to their movements.[16] This was a sobering lesson about television coverage, and it raised a disturbing question: Does television inform about the diversity of the global village, or does it simply entertain?

Fourth, the nature of television is that it favours entertaining, fast-moving imagery that grabs the attention of audiences. For this reason, many political movements around the world choose television as the medium best able to get across their message.

CRITICAL THINKING OUTSIDE THE BOX 11.1

Do TV Shows Encourage Critical Thinking?

How often do TV shows feature documentaries on the concentration of corporate ownership in the media?

Entertainment is far more important as an objective to the producers of television than is providing copious detail on a subject. For this reason, television cannot inform as well as books or newspapers can. Yet television does not simply entertain. It can also misrepresent the reality of diversity. Although in recent years television networks have become more attentive to the need to reflect the minority population of North American society, their attempts have often been misleading.

The same holds true for Canadian media. In the history of television in Canada, there have been very few shows documenting or describing the lives of minority and Aboriginal communities. Canadian television, especially the CBC, has produced some fine documentaries on this subject, but very few visible minority and Aboriginal actors appear on mainstream dramas, comedies, and the like. *The Rez, North of 60*, and the Aboriginal Peoples Television Network (APTV) are attempts to remedy this. To make matters worse, visible minorities and Aboriginal Peoples are often unfairly portrayed on the news as militant, violent, or unreasonable (see Have You Heard? 11.3). This misrepresentation on television only serves to stereotype the Aboriginal and ethnic communities. It also results in coverage that is sorely lacking in information about the lives of these communities. However, the media now employ women, as well as members of Canada's ethnic and Aboriginal communities, as journalists and broadcasters (see Have You Heard? 11.4).

CRITICAL THINKING OUTSIDE THE BOX 11.2

Diversity and the News

How often do the media portray visible minorities as villains? How often do the media portray them as heroes?

HAVE YOU HEARD? 11.3

Indigenous Peoples and the Media

· ·

Until recently, Indigenous peoples in Canada were represented either unfairly or incompletely by the mass media. They suffered stereotypes that depicted them as criminally oriented, alcoholic, or lazy. Or their stories and histories simply were not seen or heard in the media. In the past fifteen years, because of an increased awareness of the Aboriginal contribution to Canada's history, TV shows have included some Aboriginal actors, and the Aboriginal Peoples Television Network was founded in the early 1990s. News programs still occasionally portray Indigenous peoples as violent and prone to conflict when airing stories about land claims and treaty negotiations. The 2006 Native "occupation" of a Caledonia, Ontario partially finished subdivision is the latest example.

HAVE YOU HEARD? 11.4

Journalists and the Canadian Supreme Court

· ·

The accuracy of court judgments is sometimes lost in the world of journalism, dominated as it is by time constraints (finding and tracking sources), deadlines, and collegial, and editorial expectations. Yet, accurately or not, journalists always have the "last word."

More generally, the courts and media have the power to set the parameters of debate, acceptance, and taste. In their own way each has the ability to inflict penalties on those who violate these norms.

Source: Florian Sauvageau, David Schneiderman, and Davis Taras, *The Last Word: Media Coverage of the Supreme Court of Canada* (Toronto: UBC Press, 2006). This text meticulously traces the media coverage of four cases that captured the attention of all Canadians: *Delwin Vriend* (gay rights); the *Quebec Secession Reference* (the right to leave Canada); *Donald Marshall, Jr.* (Aboriginal rights); and *John Robin Sharpe* (child pornography).

In recent years, there has been a decline of racism in the media. This is especially true of issues in the fields of law enforcement and the treatment of minority groups.

One way the media disseminates coverage based on stereotypes is through their narrative on criminals and victims.[17] Minority crimes are sometimes analyzed as systemic ones, whereby entire groups are implicated and lumped together with the perpetrators. White lawbreakers, on the other hand, are sometimes individualized. This means their behaviour is reduced to some sort of individual shortcoming thereby separating them from their group. In short, when white people commit crimes their acts are random and individualized and are not symptomatic of all white people.[18] One example of this type of narrative and reporting is the two high-profile crimes of the 1990s: the murder trial of Paul Bernardo and Karla Homolka and the Just Desserts shooting of 1994.

The Just Desserts reporting was extensive and high-profile. The media negatively implicated an entire group, Jamaican-Canadians,[19] and subsequently, Canadian immigration and deportations policies.[20] Their crimes are sometimes portrayed as the product of black culture and lifestyle; individual acts lead to the indictment of entire groups/cultures.[21] This is especially acute when the victims are white. Five months after this shooting, a man shot and killed two people at the Whip Burger Menu nightclub in Toronto's west end. The shooting disappeared from the media agenda within a couple of days.[22] Both the victims and shooter were black. Again, in March 1998, Christine Ricketts was canvassing door-to-door for the *Toronto Star*. The mother of two was strangled and found in the stairwell of a high-rise apartment. The *Toronto Star* paid serious attention, since she was in their employ, while it was a "yawner" for the rest of the media.[23] Ms. Ricketts was black and the strangler was white and just released from prison three months earlier where he served time for violently assaulting a prostitute.[24]

The reporting on the Bernardo and Homolka trial was more intensive and emotional than the Just Desserts reporting. Yet these crimes were reduced to the actions of two individuals. The actions of both were explained by individual sicknesses and deficiencies[25] or individual mental illness.[26] No one asked: "What's wrong with blue-eyed, blond-haired men of Italian descent?"[27] Regardless of how horrific and sickening the crime, the white "race" card was never played.[28] Similarly, no one equated the behaviour of Homolka with that of all blonde-haired white women.

Since the fall of the Soviet Union in 1989, the terrorist attacks of 11 September 2001, and the second American invasion of Iraq in 2003, the group that has most often been demonized by the media are people of Middle East descent, especially Muslims. This is especially the case with racial profiling (see Chapter 4). Muslims are continually portrayed as terrorists, violence-prone, technologically backward, incapable of understanding democracy, having a disdain for the idea of freedom, and hardcore fundamentalists. A six-month study of five major Canadian newspapers found that Muslims were routinely portrayed as barbaric fanatics.[29] Western media also often misrepresent Christians, and particularly conservative Christians, as dangerous radicals on the Far Right who seek to oppress all peoples that fail to share their faith or worldview. In practical terms, this bias has led in part to the prosecution of both Christians and conservatives in Europe under the anti-hate speech laws of that continent.[30]

> This consistent adherence to the stereotyping of major faith communities is made all the more likely by the collective behaviour of journalists. Individually, the phenomenon of **pack journalism** also plays a role. Reporters feed off one another, move in unison, and rush to be the first to receive accolades for "breaking" the story.[31]

A larger picture is provided by University of Windsor professor, James Winter, who uses the term **media think** to describe the way media owners, managers, and workers think, see, and represent the world around us.[32] In fact, he argues that the "bias framework" provided by the media is "discernible and consistent" and reflects "their class, gender, race and corporate ties."[33] The media do not just represent corporate interests, they are corporate interests. Major newspapers, magazines, radio stations, and television stations are owned by corporate conglomerates. This is especially true of American television stations. For example, ABC is a wholly owned subsidiary of Time Warner, which owns, among others, Warner Brothers and MGM movie studios, CNN Radio, thirty magazines (including *Time*, *People*, and *Sports Illustrated*), book publishing companies, Internet companies (AOL), and cable television. Another example is NBC. During the early 1990s NBC never mentioned the fact that corporate giant General Electric was the target of a worldwide boycott that culminated with an Academy Award for the 28-minute documentary *General Electric: Deadly Deception*, which chronicled this very fact.[34] NBC is wholly owned by General Electric.

The most recent and visible example of media think and pack journalism is the Jessica Lynch "rescue" story of July 2003. The soldier had not been shot, tortured, or stabbed defending democracy in Iraq. Her injuries were a result of a truck accident during transport and the "heroic" rescue was in fact a benign visit by U.S. troops to pick her up at the hospital in the city of Nasiriyah without encountering any resistance.[35] Her "heroic" rescue was a wonderful example of Pentagon and media manipulation. The BBC referred to it as "one of the most stunning pieces of news management ever conceived."[36] Nonetheless, Jessica Lynch received a hero's welcome on her arrival home.

The Power of American Media

One related issue here is whether mass media can accurately reflect the ideas of all societal groups. Most of the mass media in the world are controlled by American corporations whose aim may include the marketing of a particular version of diversity for profit. The

United States has been accused of **television imperialism**, referring to the idea that it attempts to control other nations by using television as a means to dominate cultures.[37] In other words, it has been suggested that American media persuade people around the world to adopt American values by selling television shows and print media that portray American life, while paying little attention to life in other societies. How is this possible?

Theodor Adorno's influential work *The Culture Industry* (1972) provides a useful methodology that repudiates the idea of an objective, independent, and truth-seeking media operating in democratic society. Rather, the media are part of a complex process of "managing" public opinion in a way that favours dominant groups at the expense of those that are not. Adorno, a sociologist whose critiques of institutional power greatly affected the study of American media, contends that the media manufacture a "mass culture" that creates an artificial reality of news and entertainment; the upshot of this critical analysis is that the corporate media transmit information to the public that is overwhelmingly biased in favour of ruling elites, capitalism, and other private interests. Perhaps most damaging to a functioning liberal democracy is the fact that this **culture industry** diverts the mass voting population from understanding and critiquing the powers that control the media.

The culture industry functions successfully as long as the media screen out unfavourable elements from news stories so that the final message that reaches the public is one that supports the dominant interest. There are five interrelated ways in which this "industry" accomplishes this feat.[38]

The first way is to maintain the size, ownership, and profit-driven orientation of the culture industry. While media conglomerates are large, they are owned by a relatively few (see Have You Heard? 11.5). Media companies are expensive to run. Like any industry,

---

HAVE YOU HEARD? 11.5

CanWest Global

· ·

In 2000 the late Izzy Asper, owner of CanWest Global, purchased Southam newspapers and the *National Post* from former media mogul Conrad Black's Hollinger Corporation. Shortly thereafter, Asper sought to reverse Southam's longstanding claim of editorial independence. No local editorials were allowed to differ from those emanating from head office.

Source: Jeffery Klaehn, ed., *Filtering the News: Essays on Herman and Chomsky's Propaganda Model* (Montreal: Black Rose Books, 2005), p. 86.

the culture industry is owned and operated by a small number of people for the sake of profit. The cost of resources, technology, machinery, land, salaries, and buildings is enormous. This severely limits the number of people who can "set up shop." Consequently, making money is essential to survival. This is best achieved by supporting monied interests. Only the wealthy need apply.

The second way is advertising. Advertisers choose which media will survive when they choose where to spend their advertising dollars. The media will link a buying market (general public) to sellers (advertisers). This advertising distorts news, since the media are more accountable to advertisers that to the pursuit of the "truth." The virtue of rapacious consumerism is promoted above all. The culture industry is successful when consumers are taught that they "need" advertised products, after being exposed to an unending barrage of images that promote the latter. Consumer "needs" in fact are simply artificially contrived desires, due to the repetitive marketing of products.

A third way relates to the "false realism" of media news. It is extremely expensive to attempt to cover the world with reporters, journalists, radio transmitters, cameras, and satellites. A far cheaper alternative is to accept the constant stream of information and analysis from government, corporations, and other "experts." Therefore, the kind, favourable, and timid media treatment of these sources translates into a defense of the capitalist way of life, or at least a rejection of alternatives to this mode of existence.[39] The pursuit of the truth is the first casualty of this symbiotic relationship.

The fourth way involves the false image of serious conflict or diversity in the media. The culture industry, if it operates in a democracy, must give the impression that there is actually serious debate among differing political interests, in order to avoid the more accurate impression that the elites in control of media are in fact fairly homogeneous in their lifestyles and assumptions. In actual fact, a mass culture of consumption cannot tolerate any serious conflict between elites and masses. Despite its vested interest in appearing to be "objective" or open to all points of view, true ideological diversity is shunned.[40] For example, media networks in Canada and the United States, during the outbreak of the second Gulf War (2003), gave the impression that they were open to all perspectives on the war, both supportive and critical. Leftists who criticized the war were interviewed almost as often as neoconservatives (media allies of the Bush administration) who supported the war. Yet antiwar conservatives, who opposed wars of global democracy-building, received scant attention from the media on the grounds that a "true" conservative must support this foreign policy of aggressive nation-building. What little attention antiwar conservatives did receive was usually negative and dismissive from the established neoconservative press (e.g., Fox News).[41]

The fifth and final way in which the culture industry serves its interests is through the promotion of an ideological goal. Adorno contends that it is essential in a capitalist society to promote "resignation," among the voters, or an attitude of fatalistic acceptance to allegedly unchangeable realities and policies.[42] Since the fall of communism, the western corporate media have taught that capitalism is the wave of the future, and nothing can be done to resist this juggernaut of change. Terms like "globalization" are used to coerce the general population to accept lower wages, lower standards of living, the shredding of the social safety net, the curtailment of civil liberties, and the attack on national identity. The writings of Canadian leftist Linda McQuaig and American rightist Samuel Francis provide a common North American critique of the implications here. They both meticulously document how capitalist elites have used "globalization" (and often "multiculturalism") to rationalize the breakdown of national cultures and borders for the purpose of building a world economy in which all citizens are consumers and are bound only to the market while they are encouraged to abandon the ties of region, culture, or faith.[43]

Certainly the United States has a huge role in media markets far beyond its borders: in almost thirty nations, including Canada, U.S. companies control 70 percent of the market for films, and they control 35 percent of the cable television market in Canada.[44] Moreover, U.S. movie corporations are the largest in the world. Using Innis's terms, the United States is a "space-oriented" culture that is intent on broadening its cultural and economic access. This effort on the part of the United States has many effects.

Indeed, the perception among many nations is that U.S. movies and media as a whole are subtle forms of political propaganda, aimed at flattering and spreading the influence of the United States. Mass media often celebrate the values and benefits of their country of origin, and American media are no exception here. The American philosopher Allan Bloom, in his bestselling book *The Closing of the American Mind*, offers a useful ideological rationale to explain his nation's global role as the "universal nation." On the one hand, Americans typically believe in "equal access" to the literature and cultures of the world; America is particularly egalitarian in claiming the world's cultures as her own.[45] On the other hand, America uses her great cultural influence to shape the world, or to undertake an "educational project" to force her principles onto the rest of the world.[46] What Bloom is presenting here is the paradox that America's success lies in her openness to other cultures and her determination to reshape these cultures at the same time around the world. With the assistance of her mass media empire, America need not use military power to influence the world.

American media have at least two major effects on non-American nations. First, the flood of U.S. programming into other nations discourages the latter from creating their own programs that might better reflect their own national identities. Often the United States is accused of promoting **ethnocentrism**, a feeling of cultural superiority, through mass media. In short, it is believed that U.S. dominance over mass media has weakened attempts to strengthen ethnic diversity. The cultures of Latin America and the Middle East have constantly struggled to create programming alternatives that reflect their national identities.[47] Even nations such as France, which began this century dominating the film industry and the arts, have now fallen under the influence of U.S. media. It has reached the point where these nations are concerned about preserving their own culture and language. For this reason, both France and Canada have occasionally imposed tariffs to limit U.S. media imports.[48]

Second, some observers argue that the success of U.S. media throughout the world is difficult to challenge because these media can appear to convey and represent ethnic diversity so well. (Recall Allan Bloom's view that Americans typically claim other cultures as their own.) For example, the film directors, comedians, and dramatic actors featured in U.S. programming are increasingly coming from diverse ethnic backgrounds (e.g., Jewish, Italian, and African-American), reflecting the multicultural nature of U.S. society. These diverse elements may explain the broad appeal of American media to various parts of the world.[49] Big business recognizes that "diversity" is profitable, particularly when political action groups in government, media, and academia demand that show business act more "inclusively" of historically oppressed minorities who otherwise have been excluded from movies and TV shows. That staple of American popular culture, for example, known as the "western" in recent years has been reinvented as a narrative that glorifies the exploits of both Native and African-Americans in the settlement of the West.[50] This reinvention is almost a total reversal of past westerns; in contrast to the adulation of white settlers and cowboys in westerns from the 1950s and 1960s, it is more likely today that modern westerns will portray peoples of European descent as the villains. The attempts of western media to portray the West as historically ignoble and oppressive in part reflect a historic guilt over past injustices that, ironically, is unique to the West. In other words, western media, unlike the media of other civilizations, are most likely to critique their own cultural identity in order to raise the self-esteem of oppressed peoples that live in the West.[51]

The Language of the Global Village

Another problem related to the representation of diversity in media is the dominance of the English language, which hinders non-English cultures from developing their own networks: English is the "media language."[52] This condition is becoming apparent on the Internet, too. Even though the Net has been described as an electronic, computerized global village (see Have You Heard? 11.6), the dominant language or **lingua franca** (the language spoken by all cultures in a given area of business) on the Net is English. Despite the fact that almost half of Internet users live outside North America, most computers cannot translate non-English into English. Fortunately, a North American consortium

---

HAVE YOU HEARD? 11.6

Advertising and Consumerism

. . . .

The mass media have always targeted the consumer through advertising. With the advent of the Internet, this process has accelerated rapidly; every good and service imaginable can be purchased around the world.

Yet consumerism teaches only one value—the desire to obtain the newest commodities; the new is heralded over the old. Some media observers (such as David Rieff) claim that even multiculturalism is the "silent partner of capitalism," a policy that breaks down cultural homogeneity, including the identity of western civilizations, in order to transform all peoples into consumers. Will the hunger for new and improved goods displace the need to preserve distinctive cultures, traditions, and roots?

---

has now developed a universal translation code, known as Unicode, to allow computers on the Net to represent the letters and characters of virtually all languages.[53]

Unicode has been successful in international technology platforms, which should drive it into more environments. Unicode's continued success will rely on new computer operating systems, beginning with Microsoft NT, which are compatible with Unicode. The dream of developing a truly multilingual World Wide Web representative of all the world's languages is not yet a reality, but it is gradually moving towards that goal.

There is some additional reason to anticipate change in this area. To be sure, a white Anglo-Saxon establishment has controlled the airwaves in the past; in addition, the vast majority of the world's media corporations are in the United States. But this establishment may not always have a monopoly. Historically, ethnic communities in Canada and the United States who feel ignored by the mainstream Anglo-Saxon press have taken to developing their own. Since the early 20th century African-Americans and other minorities, with broad political support, have used the media to take dead aim at what they consider to be an oppressive WASP establishment.[54] In Canada, newspapers have been set up by Indian, Asian, Jamaican, and many other ethnic publishers to serve their own communities.

This trend toward greater ethnic participation in the industry continues. The rise of ethnic diversity in North America has led to the demand for hundreds of cable channel systems, divided by language and culture. For example, 107 languages are now spoken in Southern California, and the media industry has responded with videocassettes, disks, and computerized banking geared to the traditions and needs of these various ethnic groups. Canada's magazine *Maclean's* has recently introduced a special edition in Chinese. Women's television networks are gaining popularity in North America. Several television networks exist to serve the needs of distinctive ethnic communities, instead of placing network programming into the hands of only a few media companies.[55] Observers concerned about the "Americanization" of the world through mass media predict that nations as diverse as India, Egypt, Mexico, and Brazil will enjoy the benefits of the Anglo-American mass media while developing their own distinctive programming.[56] Since the 1960s, for example, India has ensured that an official radio network exists for each of its dozen most-spoken languages.

Surviving in the Global Village: Canada and Brazil

Canadians should take particular interest in those nations that have been able to maintain their ethnic identity against the onslaught of U.S. media. Canada has produced many influential thinkers on the subject of media technology and how it is a powerful support for American media.[57] Perhaps this is because Canada, more than any other nation, has been bombarded with U.S. programming ever since the rise of the media industry in the United States. The importation of American media into Canada has been seen by many Canadians as a threat to their identity. In a sense, this threat is serious: by 1900 Canadians read mostly American books, and the Canadian press was seen as modelled on American newspapers. Since the 1930s, the Canadian government has sometimes responded to this problem by creating agencies that favour Canadian broadcasting (such as the CBC) and by placing tariffs on U.S. magazines.

Still, many Canadians are skeptical about the success of these efforts. The Canadian conservative George Grant has argued that national identity cannot be reconciled with technological progress in the global village.[58] In 1995 these concerns again became pressing, when Disney successfully acquired exclusive rights to use the symbols of the Royal Canadian Mounted Police (those rights have now reverted to the Mounted Police Foundation). It is simply impossible to maintain one's distinctive ethnic identity in an

---

CRITICAL THINKING OUTSIDE THE BOX 11.3

Diversity and Education

How many of your textbooks discuss in detail the history and culture of ethnic communities in Canada?

---

age driven by technical advancement. In Canada, the Québécois want to maintain the language and culture of their French ancestors, and they also want to enjoy the benefits of U.S. technology and media. Some argue, however, that this effort is contradictory and doomed to failure, for the embrace of American technology and media might mean the disappearance of Québécois culture. Can a time-oriented culture survive in an age of space-oriented media?[59]

The problem of keeping traditional cultures alive is compounded by the fact that modern mass media, especially television, tend to be so "present oriented." Media tend to focus simply on the present, at the expense of the past.[60] "There is no memory on TV," as the saying goes. In an age of instantaneous information achievable through electronic media, it is understandable that consumers would not want to study the past or tradition. Why focus on what is antiquated when the new is changing all the time? But there remains a problem for those concerned with the survival of diversity. Because our technological age tends to value the "new" or the most technically sophisticated as the "best," and the "old" as the inferior and irrelevant, can a traditional culture survive?

This last question is particularly important to the study of diversity, for if cultures cannot survive in the media age, how can diversity? Some thinkers, such as McLuhan, have contended that the lack of a strong national identity is advantageous in a deeply technological age. Because the rate of change is so great, it is not wise to develop an inflexible nationalism. While McLuhan praised Canada for its lack of such a strong identity and its consequent ability to adapt to technological change, other critics are less sanguine about the influence of the media. Writing after World War II, the political philosopher Leo Strauss worried about the new "universal homogeneous state," a global regime that utilized technology so relentlessly that no individual or nation could escape from its reach, much less preserve any distinct identity.[61] The haunting question here is: What if cultures and communities want to maintain their differences? Can this be done in the age of the global village, where the media appear so committed to a rigidly ideological definition of diversity?

There is reason to hope for an optimistic response to these questions. Consider the example of Brazil. It has one of the largest television audiences in the world.[62] It also has wide access to U.S. programming. Yet there is no hard evidence to show that Brazilians are becoming "Americanized" because of this access. Indeed, despite the high level of violence in Brazilian society, there is no great demand for violent genres like the "slasher films," so popular in the United States. Indeed, according to one survey, Brazilians continue to admire the technological innovation represented by U.S. television, but they do not adopt the values of the United States.[63] Of course, Brazil has been able to enjoy these attitudes because its government is determined to maintain a high level of its culture's programming, to compete with the constant onrush of U.S. media.

CRITICAL THINKING OUTSIDE THE BOX 11.4

Canadian Content

Why do Canadian news stories show up so rarely on U.S. news programs?

As nations come to grips with the effects of television on their cultures, a new media revolution is already on its way. The emergence of virtual reality (computer-generated imagery that mimics reality) is said to herald this new era.[64] Can this new age of mass media create greater awareness of diversity? It will certainly accelerate the impact of the global village, for this age promises technologies that will link the world more instantaneously than ever before. The webcam and cellphone (along with other technologies that combine the computer and television to permit a user to see, hear, and communicate with another user from a distant part of the globe) have existed for decades now. The world is officially "wired." Whether this new interconnectedness through computers, the Internet, virtual reality, or cellphones will create greater tolerance of diversity is another question. The record of mass media on this subject is mixed: television advanced the global village's reach, but this form of technology has not always produced greater harmony or understanding among cultures.

CHAPTER SUMMARY

Human beings have always employed techniques of mass communication. The use of mass media ranges widely from communication to information to entertainment. Mass media also affect our behaviour. They shape the message and content of what is being communicated to millions of people, especially the message and content of diversity.

In each of the four stages in the history of media, great changes in human behaviour have taken place. The oral stage demanded that people use their memories to "record" events; the rise of the alphabet extended the power of the eye, as ordinary people began to see what they were saying for the first time; the printing press encouraged nationalism; and the advent of the electronic age created the global village.

Electronic media have had by far the greatest impact on defining diversity in the modern world. Perhaps the most important effect of electronic media was turning the world into a global village, in which, because of the speed of communication via electricity, people of all nations feel interconnected. Since the emergence of the telegraph, this effect has only been strengthened by other electronic media.

Television and the Internet, still the dominant media in the world today, continues to accelerate this feeling of global interconnectedness. Whether they can represent diverse cultures in an accurate manner is an open question, for the success of television lies in focusing on the new, the entertaining, and the profitable. The record is mixed. These media can make people more aware of other cultures, but its presentation of diversity can be misleading and superficial.

To complicate matters further, most of the media markets are controlled by U.S. corporations. This control has led to the dominance of the English language in these markets, as well as the sustained influence of U.S. programs around the world, including Canada. Many nations have taken steps to control the influx of U.S. programming to protect their national identities.

One thing is certain. Mass media have changed every aspect of our world forever (see Have You Heard? 11.7). There is no possibility of returning to an age when media technology was restricted to a privileged few and people—the "masses"—knew little about other cultures in distant lands. For those concerned with emphasizing diversity, the permanence of mass media is ultimately a good thing. After all, even if the media in the global village do not always foster peace among its members, they certainly encourage the need to be aware of the various people who live in this village.

HAVE YOU HEARD? 11.7

Media Facts: Did You Know?

. . . .

- Canadians watch on average 25 hours of television weekly.
- Some European TV networks start broadcasting in the afternoon.
- Africa has 2000 language dialects.
- The Chinese language has 40 000 characters.
- By age 20, the average North American has seen 800 000 commercials.
- There are 180 languages spoken in India.
- The average American has more TVs than bathrooms.
- Brazil has the fifth-largest TV audience in the world.
- The best market for American movies (outside the United States) is Japan.
- The average American 12-year-old has spent 13 000 hours in school and almost 20 000 hours watching TV.

KEY TERMS

culture industry, 328
dialects, p. 320
ethnocentrism, p. 330
global village, p. 321
hieroglyphics, p. 316
lingua franca, p. 331
mass medium, p. 314
media think p. 327
orality, p. 316
pack journalism, p. 327

parchment, p. 318
pictograph, p. 316
script, p. 318
space-oriented media, p. 318
telegraph, p. 320
television imperialism, p. 328
time-oriented media, p. 318
tribalism, p. 321
vernaculars, p. 320

DISCUSSION QUESTIONS

1. Discuss five examples of commercials that illustrate how the "medium is the massage."
2. Outline the characteristics of the "culture industry."
3. Is Canada being threatened by television imperialism? Compare the number of Canadian and U.S. TV shows on a typical programming day.
4. You have been asked to produce and direct a TV situation comedy that accurately portrays the multicultural makeup of our society. How do you do this?
5. The Canadian government has asked your advice on how to improve programming so that it reflects Canada's diversity but is also entertaining. What do you suggest?

NOTES

1. The title of Marshall McLuhan's book from which this quotation is taken is called *The Medium Is the Massage*, not "the message." McLuhan's point was that the form of the message (the medium) shapes (or massages) how the message is perceived. McLuhan's clever use of language is evident in his choice of wording here.
2. Walter Ong, *Orality and Literacy: The Technologizing of the Word* (New York: Routledge, 1988), p. 7.
3. See Harold Innis, *Empire and Communications* (Toronto: Press Procépic, 1986), p. 32.
4. Ibid., pp. 38–42.
5. Ong, p. 28.
6. Innis, p. 5.

7. Ong, p. 89.
8. Innis, p. 128. See also Marshall McLuhan, *The Gutenberg Galaxy: The Making of Typographic Man* (Toronto: University of Toronto Press, 1962), pp. 218–19.
9. McLuhan, *Gutenberg Galaxy*, p. 231.
10. Morse, quoted in Neil Postman, *The Disappearance of Childhood* (New York: Delacorte Press, 1982), p. 68.
11. See Marshall McLuhan, *Understanding Media: The Extensions of Man* (New York: New American Library, 1964), p. 156.
12. Michael Parenti, *Inventing Reality: The Politics of News Media* (New York: St. Martin's Press, 1993), p. 1.
13. Neil Postman, *The Disappearance of Childhood* (New York: Delacorte Press, 1982).
14. Joshua Meyrowitz, *No Sense of Place: The Impact of Electronic Media on Social Behaviour* (New York: Oxford University Press, 1985), p. 132.
15. See Augie Fleras and Jean Leonard Elliott, *Multiculturalism in Canada: The Challenge of Diversity* (Toronto: Nelson, 1992), pp. 233–48.
16. Todd Gitlin, *The Whole World is Watching: Mass Media in the Making and Unmaking of the New Left* (New York: Oxford University Press, 1980), pp. 152–53.
17. James Winter, *Media Think* (Montreal: Black Rose Books, 2002), p. 147.
18. Winter, p. 147.
19. Jeffery Klaehn, ed., *Filtering the News: Essays on Herman and Chomsky's Propaganda Model* (Montreal: Black Rose Books, 2005), p. 31.
20. Winter, p. 146.
21. Winter, p. 147 and Klaehn, p. 31.
22. Winter, p. 146.
23. Winter, p. 146.
24. Winter, p. 146.
25. Augie Fleras and Jean Lock Kunz, *Media and Minorities: Representing Diversity in Multicultural Canada* (Toronto: Thompson Educational Publishing, 2001), p. 31.
26. Winter, p. 146.
27. Fleras and Kunz, p. 31.
28. Fleras and Kunz, p. 31.
29. Fleras and Kunz, p. 29.
30. Grant Havers, "The EU's Hatred of 'Hate'," *Today's Zaman*, 1 September 2008. This article was published in an English-language daily in Turkey.
31. Parenti, p. 42.
32. Winter, p. xxvii.
33. Winter, p. xxvii.
34. Parenti, p. 36.
35. Klaehn, p. 41.
36. Klaehn, p. 36.
37. Fleras and Elliott, *Multiculturalism in Canada*, p. 238.
38. Theodor Adorno, *The Culture Industry: Selected Essays on Mass Culture*, edited and with an introduction by J. M. Bernstein (London & New York: Routledge, [1972] 2002).
39. Ibid., pp. 158–77.

40. Ibid., pp. 76–79.

41. Samuel T. Francis, *Shots Fired: Sam Francis on America's Culture War* (Vienna, Virginia: Fitzgerald Griffin Foundation, 2006), pp. 25–29.

42. Adorno, pp. 198–203.

43. See Linda McQuaig, *The Cult of Impotence: Selling the Myth of Powerlessness in the Global Economy* (Toronto: Penguin Books, 1998) and *All You Can Eat: Greed, Lust and the New Capitalism,* (Toronto: Penguin Books, 2001); Francis, *Shots Fired,* pp. 289–302.

44. Jeremy Tunstall, *The Media are American: Anglo-American Media in the World* (London: Constable, 1977), p. 182. See also Mary Vipond, *The Mass Media in Canada* (Toronto: Lorimer, 1989), p. 134.

45. Allan Bloom, *The Closing of the American Mind: How Higher Education has Failed Democracy and Impoverished the Souls of Today's Students* (New York: Simon & Schuster, 1987), p. 54; see also McLuhan, *Understanding Media,* p. 271.

46. Bloom, p. 153.

47. Shirley Biagi, *Media/Impact: An Introduction to Mass Media* (Belmont, CA: Wadsworth, 1994), p. 472; see also Vipond, pp. 24–25.

48. Biagi, *Media/Impact*; Vipond, *Mass Media in Canada.*

49. Bloom, *Closing of the American Mind,* p. 54.

50. Richard Slotkin, *Gunfighter Nation: The Myth of the Frontier in Twentieth-Century America* (New York: Atheneum, 1992), pp. 526–27.

51. See Paul Edward Gottfried, *Multiculturalism and the Politics of Guilt: Toward a Secular Theocracy* (Columbia, MO: University of Missouri Press, 2002).

52. See Andrew Pollack, "Cyberspace's War of Words," *The Globe and Mail,* 10 August 1995, p. A15.

53. Biagi, pp. 45–49.

54. Gottfried, *Multiculturalism and the Politics of Guilt.*

55. Tunstall, p. 274.

56. Tunstall, p. 104; Vipond, pp. 24–29.

57. Arthur Kroker, *Technology and the Canadian Mind: Innis/McLuhan/Grant* (Montreal: New World Perspectives, 1984).

58. See George Grant, *Lament for a Nation: The Defeat of Canadian Nationalism* (Ottawa: Carleton University Press, 1965), pp. 76–87.

59. Innis, *Empire and Communications.*

60. See Neil Postman and Steve Powers, *How to Watch TV News* (New York: Penguin, 1992).

61. Marshall McLuhan and Bruce R. Powers, *The Global Village: Transformations in World Life and Media in the 21st Century* (New York: Oxford University Press, 1989), pp. 88, 165; Leo Strauss, *On Tyranny* (Chicago: University of Chicago Press, 1991), p. 211.

62. Conrad Philip Kottak, *Prime-Time Society* (Belmont, CA: Wadsworth, 1990), p. 12.

63. Kottak, p. 93.

64. Derrick De Kerckhove, *The Skin of Culture: Investigating the New Electronic Reality* (Toronto: Somerville House, 1995).

CHAPTER 12

Literature: The Voice of Diversity

Paula Jessop

But still, the fates will leave me my voice, and by my voice I shall be known.
—Ovid's *Metamorphoses*

. . . this rock was the very rock she had failed to drive tent pegs into three thousand miles away in Ontario . . . it was part of the great Canadian Shield, a connection that ran deep and underfoot . . .
—Elizabeth Hay, in *Late Nights on Air*

Objectives

....

After reading this chapter, you should be able to

- appreciate and recognize how story is a distinct voice and mirror of a culture

- identify the complexities of the relationship between voice and power in literature and your world

- recognize and describe how literature artfully portrays and describes diversity and our societal responses through narrative, language, and symbols

- express an appreciation for literature's unique role in learning about and accepting, allowing and admitting others, and expressing our true lives

INTRODUCTION

Diversity in Paradise

In Wayson Choy's first novel, *The Jade Peony*, we come to know a multigenerational family, new to 1930s Canada. It is made up of a domineering grandmother consumed by ancient superstitions, a nervous new wife for a stressed father and step-mother to his grieving children, a gay, adopted son orphaned by a murder/suicide, and a young girl who dies following an illegal abortion. Considering this cast of characters alone, we know immediately that Choy will use his story to present the most common elements and consequences of social diversity: tensions in an immigrant population, **intergenerational** conflicts over the values of the elderly, the secret confusions of a gay child, the pressures felt by a new step-parent. With each character and through the distinctive voices of children, Choy exposes the costs, pressures, and growth diversity forces in the individual, the family, the community, and thus the nation.

In this passage using the **voice** of an innocent but all-seeing child narrator, Choy gives us a stunning picture of what diversity looks like at recess and what tolerance feels like in Miss Doyle's classroom:

> At recess, our dialects and accents conflicted, our clothes, heights and handicaps betrayed us, our skin colours and backgrounds clashed, but inside Miss E. Doyle's tightly disciplined kingdom we were all—lions or lambs—equals. We had glimpsed Paradise.[1]

The child narrator understands how their illusion of belonging, their childish belief they can be accepted as another one of many is "betrayed" by their all too obvious differences that 'conflict' and 'clash.' Choy's deliberate use of the word "betrayed" carries many meanings that need to be recognized if we are to appreciate his subtle expression of diversity and all it suggests. For a child to know 'betrayed' and its implications, for a child to recognize at such an early age how each of them is different, allows Choy to tell us much about their society. At this young age, why do they see their differences first? Who taught them to see only their differences? What other hurts, repeated rejections, and snubs have each experienced and endured to be able to recognize the familiar sting of their difference? What other hurtful and hateful environments do they move in to be able to recognize and feel by contrast the paradise of a classroom where all are undeniably, unconditionally equal?

An author's singular choice of word is vital to understand and appreciate if we are to recognize how stories show us about ourselves and our world. It is literature's job, its role in culture and society to show us what authors see. In this particular passage, Choy is showing us a world of diversity where even young children have been initiated into the ways of intolerance and already seek and relish a paradisal retreat from its pain and consequences. Choy has given us a memorable picture of despair and hope in one paragraph, with the added poignancy that it is a child showing us something many adults choose to ignore.

The Jade Peony, first published in 1995, continues to earn awards, attract national attention, and international recognition. It is taught on course outlines in high schools, colleges, and universities, from Yellowknife to Charlottetown, from Ottawa to Hong Kong, from Oxford University to the Sorbonne. Why? Because Choy's very human voices tell very human stories that carry meaning for us all. The pictures of diversity and their intimate detailing combined with the power of a rich and varied story reflect who we are as individuals as communities and as nations. Without judgment, Choy portrays the consequences of tolerance and intolerance. This is what great literature can do—provide each of us with a mirror reflecting our own image and the image of the world in which we live so we can better see it and create better paths into the future. Paradoxically literature can reassure us that we are all uniquely different thus uniquely and universally the same as those with whom we share our planet.

In this chapter, we will look at several seminal Canadian stories and how their authors express diversity through theme, language, and symbols. We will consider how these literary elements artfully reveal the many subtleties of diversity while engaging and entertaining us. We will study how everyone living and working in our diversified society needs to know our country's stories because each provides a unique reflection and expression of ourselves and our world that can be found nowhere else.

CRITICAL THINKING OUTSIDE THE BOX 12.1

Re-read the quote from *The Jade Peony*. The child narrator refers to Miss Doyle's classroom as her "kingdom" where all were equal whether they were lions or lambs—weak or strong students. Consider your classmates in any course in which you are enrolled. How does this population express the community in which your school is located? Does your class reflect the diversity you find in restaurants, shops, and your workplace? Is your class a real microcosm of the wider community? Do you believe your class has achieved equality? Do you believe every individual present feels safe and accepted? What is your role in ensuring that all feel and know they are "undeniably, unconditionally equals?"

THE IMPORTANCE OF LANGUAGE

Much of what will be considered in this chapter is based on the power of language: the power and role of words in living with diversity, explaining its value and its nature, and in defending it. Often, individuals witness the cruelty of discrimination and intolerance of the 'different' or of 'the other' and do not know how to respond even though they find it distressing and want to take action. Perhaps they are caught off guard or, they experience such a strong emotional response they cannot form a rational verbal response. Often it is only some time following the experience that a strong and valid response can be formed and expressed. By then the moment has passed, often the perpetrator has disappeared and we are left with a sense of frustration and guilt. We have all experienced that "I should have said . . ." moment. So where do we look for help? Can we prepare ourselves for those moments when we know we must challenge cruelty but simply lack the words? Where can we look for just the right words so we are not scrambling at the moment and are able to respond with fairness and firmness?

Literature is a very good resource here. The telling of stories, the language used by authors and their characters revealing varied human experiences can serve as templates, models, or guides for us. The stories or narratives that describe human struggle and triumph can give us ideas about how to *use words* to respond to many human dilemmas. When we are confident in our language, our voice changes to one of power, individuality, and independence. Individual voice is one of the most necessary elements of a democracy, a society that is fair, inclusive, and courageous. See Have You Heard? 12.1.

Just as we recall and learn from the experiences of friends, remembering their stories from lunch or texts, the experiences we glean from reading great literature can also stay with us and teach us. Thus, in this chapter we will look at several novels and consider the language—the actual words—the author uses to express, reflect, and describe situations

---

CRITICAL THINKING OUTSIDE THE BOX 12.2

Consider a time when you witnessed some human behaviour that in your thinking was discriminatory in some manner. Perhaps you heard somebody refer abusively to the colour of an individual's skin, or refer in a disparaging manner to their presumed faith or sexual preference. Describe the event. Then, describe how being a witness to this left you feeling. Record your thoughts now as you recall the event and what you would or would not have done differently in response to the incident?

HAVE YOU HEARD? 12.1

Etymology (e – ti – mol- o- gy) The Story of a Word

....

Speaking of language, let's take a look at the history of the word 'diversity.' Every word has a life of its own, its own story, a past—its origin, its original country, or language of use, its original use in writing; a present—its most current form with phrases and sentences demonstrating its use. This history is called 'etymology' and it traces the 'story' of every word in any language. The *Oxford English Dictionary* (OED) is a good source for learning about the history of an English word, for learning the story of every English word in current use.

where diversity and difference are part of characters' lives. We will look at how these differences are met by the larger community. We will ask what the author means or suggests or shows us about *acceptance* of the different, *admission* of the other and *allowing* diversity into your life and how that is all achieved.

First, A Little History

Diversity is one of the oldest words in the English language. It originated, like many English words in another language, French, Old French to be exact. It then 'migrated' into Old English, probably during wars and the dislocation of conquered peoples. The OED states as its definition: "different or varied, unlikeness."

Of course, from one definition can come many uses, and this is another feature of etymology—it traces the different *ways* the word is used and provides examples.

A Very, Very Old Idea

The first use of the word *diversity* is recorded as being 1300 and the very famous poet Chaucer used it in his poem *The Man of Laws* in 1386. The OED next records its use in 1882 by the British philosopher and historian Frederick William Farrar. It is his use that is of particular interest to us. Farrar wrote "Unity does not exclude diversity . . . without diversity there can be no true and perfect unity. . . . without diversity there is death."[2]

But what does that mean? What actual use is this history to us as we think about diversity? Perhaps the most important thing to learn from the 'etymology' of our word *diversity* is that it is a very old *idea* because it is the job of words to represent, communicate, and express *ideas* and *concepts*. Thus, we see from the etymology of *diversity* that the concept is not new. Neither is the attitude that the unity or wholeness of a society, a culture, and a nation depends on diversity. It depends on difference and diversity if it is to thrive and succeed as a peaceful and tolerant place where many different and varied individuals may grow and prosper by living their true lives and using their voice to express the truth of their existence.

With this definition in mind and considering Farrar's use as our template, let us move to our first novel and explore how the author has created fictional (not true) characters who live with diversity, how they experience it, and how their world responds to their difference.

We Are All Versions of One Another and of Ourselves

In her 2003 work *Deafening* author Frances Itani presents Grania O'Neill, the third daughter of Irish immigrants who own a hotel in small town Ontario. The year the story opens is 1902 and Grania is five years old, having recovered from a serious bout of scarlet fever that has left her profoundly deaf. It has also left her different from everybody else in her world—her mother, her father, her brother, her sister, her playmates, the hotel guests—with her profound deafness she is seen as profoundly different. Suddenly a bright future becomes different too. School will be different. Marriage possibilities will be different—not a small consideration for a female child in 1902.

How does her world—her family, her town—respond to her new status, her new self, her difference? How is her world managing this new diversity, this 'other' Grania? Her mother refuses to accept it: "Twice a week, she goes to the Catholic church and prays that Grania's hearing will come back. Even though the priest shakes his head, Mother has not given up hope." Her father ". . . tries to keep his sorrow at bay. He knows that the child will never hear."[3]

It is Grania's Grandmother, affectionately called Mamo, who breaks through the family's denial and fears and says out loud what needs to be done, how they must face their new reality. She loudly proclaims that the family will allow it and allow it to make no difference. "Don't treat her differently . . . talk to her the way you did before . . . Don't leave her out. . . . Include her in everything . . . never stop speaking to her, whether she understands or not. . . ."[4] For Mamo, this 'other' Grania is simply that, another version of Grania's self. Mamo clearly understands that we are each, every day, different versions of ourselves. She realizes that this understanding of ourselves keeps the changes life forces upon us in perspective.

Itani's Mamo offers the world a way to manage diversity, to accept difference, and to allow all the various dimension we find in any individual, all the versions of the individual. "Don't treat her differently" and "include her" and "never stop speaking. . . ." This is sound counsel for anybody working with a colleague of a different race, living with a

---

CRITICAL THINKING OUTSIDE THE BOX 12.3

Trying Out Itani's Universal Rules

What is your opinion of Mamo's instructions as universal rules as suggested above? Do you believe they are or would be effective and useful as guidelines in helping an individual navigate a diverse workplace, learning place, or diverse city? Do they serve as good guides to working and living happily in a multicultural society such as ours? Such as yours? Or, are they only a good place to start, or, are they overly optimistic, simplistic?

---

neighbour of a different faith, or accepting a relative of a different sexual preference. The same words apply: "Don't treat them any differently," "include them," and "never stop speaking to them." These are universal rules by which to live in unity and fairness with our fellow humans.

Grania, who at the age of five, pictures her new and different life as living under water, will not be left to drown or drift. Because of Mamo's extraordinary understanding and her extraordinary will, she will not allow the family to deny the reality of Grania's new needs and new abilities and thus set Grania adrift within the family. The fact of her difference makes no difference to Mamo and so that becomes her creed. At every turn, Mamo models courage and strength to make certain Grania believes she is the *same* as she was before the onset of deafness: the *same* intelligent child who is loved and capable of love. The *same* child who will connect with family and the world and who will continue to learn. The opening lines of the novel perfectly express Mamo's goal for her granddaughter, "Your name . . . This is the important word. If you can say your name, you can tell the world who you are."[5] Nothing has changed for Mamo because she has the strength to accept that everything has changed for Grania. There is no denying that Grania is now different. Yet, more important than her difference is the essential version of Grania. The essential qualities and characteristics of Grania have been unaltered. She remains vibrant, smart, curious, loving, happy, eager, and longing to be loved, just like those around her. The same as the people in her world. She will simply learn in a different way. A small difference, a minor variance when set beside and compared with all her qualities that are unchanged.

Indeed Mamo is correct. Grania does learn how to tell the world who she is, how to sign, and how to communicate with fluency and intelligence. She learns that she is worthy of love and loving. Grania falls in love and is deeply loved by a young man working at the school where she teaches. They are married days before he is shipped to Europe as a medic in World War I. Between signing and lip reading, they openly and easily communicate, making jokes, telling their stories, and making plans; just as do other couples in love and newly married. Their parting words, expressed on the platform of the crowded Belleville train station are from the heart, no different from all the others who were expressing the same goodbyes, the same love and the same longing for those leaving for war.

> Jim searched . . . until he was certain they had eye contact. His right hand reached to the left side of his chest and made her name-sign, the private G between finger and thumb plucking at the tunic that covered his heart. He grinned and dropped his arms to his sides. . . . Grania made the C, his own name-sign the last thing he saw."[6]

Just like all individuals, just like each of us, Grania's world continues to change. Life continues to challenge her; nothing remains stagnant; her life is constantly in a state of flux with every change bringing loss and gain. Life itself is full of diversity and difference and Grania's and our best way to manage it happily is to accept, admit, and allow it knowing that simply because we are human, we have the capacity to integrate, encompass, and include the new and different and the other into our own lives.

Diverse Faces

A novel is complex by its nature. Critics generalize by saying a novel is about family and poetry is about the individual. And nothing is more complex than a family. For Itani diversity within a family is important to accept and allow and it is also complicated. Her inclusion of World War I as one of her major settings (where the story takes place) allows her to bring another complication to Grania's family and her life. When her sister Tress's very handsome husband Kenan is sent home from the war he arrives home with an 'other' face and an 'other' body, deeply disfigured. He describes how he remembers it happened:

> My arm wouldn't move. I was holding my other hand to my face. I didn't know how badly my cheek was blown apart. I could barely see. . . . My hand couldn't hold my face together any more.[7]

Tress and Kenan are too frightened to name their fears. This 'other' newly figured Kenan slips into a silent depression, lurking in shadowy rooms and refusing to visit his family, rejecting his wife through his fear and shame. Tress has no skills to deal with her fear, her disappointment, or her overwhelming pity for Kenan. She has no language with which to describe or tell of her turmoil and is daily growing more isolated and sad which in turn diminishes Kenan: ". . . Tress, who stood in the middle of the room looking like sorrow itself. . . . In seconds, he'd managed to shrink inside Tress's palpable gloom."[8] Ironically, unexpectedly, it is Grania who teaches them to say how they feel and what they fear about all the differences in their lives. She feels the fear in the little house and starts there, "'Both afraid.' The words blurted out . . . her hand shook out the sign for *both* . . . Kenan's right hand lifted and again he mimicked her sign, this time the sign for *both*. His lips moved. . . . His head nodded slightly, just barely."[9] It is the first time he has spoken in weeks and it is the beginning of a long and steep road to his different and new life.

THE THREE A'S OF DIVERSITY

If we can accept that our life may take different turns than we want; if we can admit into our lives people who seem so very different than ourselves; if we can allow that those closest to us will change profoundly over the long years we share with them—then we are well on the way to using difference to learn. Accepting, admitting, allowing—these are the words that let us embrace diversity and difference within our own private worlds. In *Deafening* Frances Itani weaves a story of men and women who model for us all as they turn the shock of the extraordinary—disability and deformity—into the sure and ordinary nuances of a normal life. Itani presents families and individuals who are strong enough to accept, admit, and allow difference in their lives, something other than what they had planned. After great struggle they overcome their fears because it is the only way for a human to live a full life, with all its 'other' faces.

Just as there are versions of ourselves so too are there versions of what each of us believe in. And logically versions of the names we give to what we believe. When people

---

CRITICAL THINKING OUTSIDE THE BOX 12.4

Record a story from your life. This might be a story from your childhood that your parents love to tell. Or, a memory you have from your early school days. It might be the telling of a great game you played in or watched—a surprising win or a near loss or just a great game. Whatever you select from your life, be certain you are the main character and that you achieve something. Once your story is written, re-read it and consider what it predicted or foreshadowed about you now. What can you see of yourself today in the story from your past? What does the story reveal about you now?

---

believe in 'something greater than themselves' it suggests they believe that a greater power is at work in some manner in their life. It may take the form of fate, it may take the form of the natural world or nature or Mother Nature. It may take the form of an individual, distant and mysterious like Mohammad, God, Allah, Buddha, Tara, Christ, Gitchi Manitou. These versions of faith and belief, these diverse ways to name a 'greater power in my life' have many things in common. They are mysterious and often possess extraordinary powers. For example, Allah is believed to be capable of seeing into our minds and knowing what we are thinking. Gitchi Manitou is capable of setting life in balance with nature which is his great creation. Fate is believed to possess the power of seeing into our futures and deciding what will happen next to us. Tara is believed to save. Christ is thought to be capable of creating 'miracles,' extraordinary incidents that have no logical explanation. All these 'powers' inspire individuals in mysterious and various ways: one power may inspire the individual to behave in a right manner, to treat others with kindness, to think of others first. These powers, often very distant and physically invisible to us, lived in some human form many generations ago.

For all their minor differences and variations, their role in our lives is the same: to offer solace, to listen to our thoughts, prayers, and meditations, and to guide us to live in tolerant unity, fairness, and inner peace. For many individuals, belief systems or religion or faith provide the familiar comfort of rituals and human-like figures, which act as invisible companions, keeping us company in lonely or difficult times.

Joseph Boyden's first novel *Three Day Road* presents an unconventional family: two loyal friends, Xavier and Elijah, both young men who meet in a northern Ontario Residential School. They are rescued by Niska, Xavier's aunt who acts on her suspicions of how Elijah is being treated at the school. She takes both Xavier and Elijah into her life and cares and loves them as a deeply devoted mother. She sees no difference between her nephew and his friend and treats Elijah no differently than Xavier. In her mind they are two children who need love, caring and security and thus are her family, she theirs.

Niska chooses to live away from urban civilization. She feels more secure and balanced living in the natural civilization of the woods, rivers, and open skies. She teaches Elijah and Xavier how to live in this world and she teaches them to show tolerance of those that live elsewhere. Most importantly she teaches the boys to live true lives with strength and pride. See Have You Heard? 12.2.

The Natural World as a Template for Diversity

Boyden's Niska is a character who lives in unity with the diverse elements of the natural world. She accepts, admits, and allows the various powers of the natural world and thus learns from nature and its creator Gitchi Manitou. She believes in Gitchi Manitou, the

---

HAVE YOU HEARD? 12.2

Symbols in Literature and Becoming an Ideal Employee

· ·

In literature there are many tools or ways authors have to describe and express the story they are telling. It is often description that makes a book very pleasurable to read and allows us, the reader, to picture another world in great detail or to feel very close to a character. A very subtle tool an author has to describe his characters and express their characteristics is by using symbols. A symbol will be very subtly used by an author. It is like a clue and a cue, signalling the reader to consider what the symbol might be suggesting, what other meanings the author hopes the reader will discover. Names of characters are often symbolic. The name Niska is Cree for "Canadian Geese." The reader is required to ask "why Niska? Why did the author select that name? Why Elijah? What is the author trying to tell me by his very purposeful use of these names? This is where literature makes demands of its reader, demands to think as you read. To look beyond the obvious and find meaning that can give you information that the author really wants you to have but chooses to tell you with only clues. Why Xavier? Why Niska? When you are alert to these details and their meanings; when you find yourself questioning ideas like this, you have become a critical reader, which is very good practice for making you a critical thinker, an employer's ideal employee.

creator and the power that sustains the balance of her world. She also believes Gitchi Manitou has given her the seizures she experiences and does not fear their onset nor the visions that accompany them. Indeed she finds meaning in them and uses them for her comfort.

The tolerance that Niska lives by and teaches Xavier and Elijah was not learned at the institutions of the community in which she lived, the residential school.

They kept me away from my sister. . . . When I was caught speaking my tongue, they'd force lye soap into my mouth and not give me anything to eat for days . . . younger children were beaten . . . forced to eat food from the floor like dogs. . . . Sister Agnes . . . cut my hair, making it shorter than the rest of the girls' . . . they were going to remove the black hair that reached to my waist as a symbol of . . . our defeat. . . . I sat and smiled serenely as . . . my scalp ached.[10]

At the age of twelve, from where does Niska get the strength to respond to unfairness and intolerance with dignity and calm? From her association with the natural world and its maker; from her belief in the goodness of her soul that feeds on the balance Gitchi Manitou has modelled for her in the woods she hunts and the waters she paddles. When she is viciously punished, she moves into her mind and her visions accompanied by her belief in the Great Spirit.

> I saw the bush once more, summertime . . . autumn, with the sun high. A beaver dam that had not been abandoned, a new lodge of freshly woven branches. I sat in a canoe with a young man paddling ahead of me. On a bend in the river, a large moose, a bull, stood on the shore. The same excitement that always comes with spotting one, especially one so large, swelled in me. We drifted silently by with the current . . . I waited and dreamed . . .[11]

Understanding the Other

When Xavier is lying in a muck-oozing trench surrounded by body parts and he is assigned rest, his thoughts turn to the teachings of Niska and reveal how their faith helps them find meaning in their lives, even when desperation and desolation surround them. He muses over the military's use of the number three and tries to understand how the white men may possess some knowledge that could be of help to him:.

> . . . my life has been divided into three for me by these *wemistikoshiw*. There was my life before them and their army, there is my life in their army, and, if I live, there will be my life after . . . home. They must have some magic in their number of three. I know that you, Niska, taught me that we will all someday walk the three-day road, and now I'm left wondering what connection there might be between their world and mine. I need to find out if we share something, some magic. Maybe it will help get me through. . . .[12]

Unthreatened by the differences between the two cultures, Xavier's faith has taught him to search for connections and commonalities rather than differences and dissimilarities. He remains open to what he can learn from these differences and how allowing them in his world, may help. Understanding does not always come, yet he does not condemn or shun, simply accepts the difference:

> Their big holiday approaches . . . Christmas that celebrates the birth of their *Gitchi Manitou* . . . but me, I don't see much of their god in it. Their god is a fighter *Manitou*, I assume, although this is not how their holy men talk of him. When they talk . . . they use words like *forgiveness, virgins, children*. But I believe their god must be a warrior, for he is the one they all pray to before they go over the top. I will never understand this god, these people.[13]

Meaning in Belief and Ritual

Without condemning or judging the other, Boyden's Xavier continues to find strength and meaning in the practice of his faith and its rituals. When he is battle weary, fearful, and needs to master the pain of watching the moral deterioration of Elijah and feels his helplessness to arrest Elijah's slide into inhumanity, he knows what he must do: build a sweat lodge that will restore his balance, console his spirit while lifting his prayers to Gitchi Manitou, the creator of all balance:

> . . . I search for good rocks and borrow old canvas . . . I search the sparse woods . . . then construct a *matatosowin* and build a hot fire . . . heating the rocks all day . . . I strip down . . . crawl into the lodge with a pail of water, . . . I want the steam to release the prayers from inside my head so that I may send them up into the sky. . . . I think of you, Niska. I think of home. . . . I begin a simple prayer. . . . *I want to hear. I want to see . . . I want to see what I should do.* I pour more water . . . I pray until I have left my body and float over this place . . . .[14]

By the end of the war, Xavier is severely injured, morphine addicted, and wracked by exhaustion and depression. Each believing the other to be dead, Niska meets Xavier at the train station. They are both, in each other's eyes, reborn: "Nephew . . . you are home. You are home . . . I was told you were dead, Auntie,. . . And I was told you were, too,"[15]

And so begins their three-day road together, a journey that will demand all Niska's faith, strength, and will to bring Xavier back to life because she paddles with the dead weight of her greatest fear, "that he has come home only to die."[16] She begins paddling his ravaged body and splintered spirit back to their home in the woods.

From where does this 60 year old woman get the strength and the power to even attempt to slowly, tenderly pull Xavier back from the brink of death and soulless destruction? She will find all she requires within her own strengths, cultivated over a lifetime and nourished by her belief in herself, her faith, and its rituals.

On the third day, Niska builds a sweat lodge for Xavier and herself so Gitchi Manitou will hear her prayers and allow Xavier the forgiveness he craves and renew his life. When she carries Xavier's unconscious body with its fevered mind into their sweat lodge, she begins to tell him his story. She will not give up. She has faith that "If I choose my words right, and speak from that place inside that tells no lies, he will hear"[17]

Looking Beyond Difference

These remarkable characters that Joseph Boyden has created in *Three Day Road,* reveal the power of belief and tolerance. Niska, Xavier, and Elijah show us how, if we learn to admit into our lives the mystery and power surrounding us, diverse and foreign some of it may be, we can learn from other voices and be strengthened. When we look beyond the differences

---

CRITICAL THINKING OUTSIDE THE BOX 12.5

A Different Language . . . A Different Opportunity

Cree language is expressed throughout the excerpts selected from *Three Day Road* in this section. Did the use of Cree expressions significantly interfere with your understanding of the ideas being presented? Did it frustrate you? Could you infer from the surrounding descriptions and words the meaning of the Cree word? Has this been the first time you are reading Cree? Has it added something to your learning? Did you attempt to pronounce it. Visit the many websites available for more information on the Cree language and its growth in Canada. If you understand Cree, comment on how you feel to see it written in a text like this?

CRITICAL THINKING OUTSIDE THE BOX 12.6

Consider the faith in which you were raised. Think about a good friend and her or his faith. Record the similarities you recognize. Describe parallel seasons of celebration. Explain how special holidays in each coincide with certain seasons or times of the year. If you were not raised in any particular faith, describe what 'greater power' is active in your life. Or, describe what significant beliefs you have formed about nature, a 'greater power,' the creation of life, the existence of life after death. Describe what you think about when you are in a difficult situation, what comforts you when you are feeling worn out and exhausted by life. Why do these thoughts ease your struggle or pain? How?

---

and seek to understand and admit the similarities of various faiths and belief systems and accept their capacity to comfort regardless of their dissimilarities, we have taken a bold step into a world that is diversely rich and **restorative**, positive, and constructive.

Human Story

Human beings are hardwired to tell stories, to listen to stories, to create stories, and to learn from stories. Regardless of the language you first spoke, you learned that language through the telling of stories. You learned the structure and grammar of your languages through the telling and repetition of stories. That is why parents are so strongly encouraged to read to children. It is a natural way for a child to learn language, learn about others, to learn all the complex dimensions of their language. It is a way for children to learn about themselves.

The idea of telling *your story,* an idea we see Joseph Boyden's Niska express is an ancient one that is part of every culture on the planet. Stories are one of the most human of all human activities. Regardless of how they are shared—read from a book, told in texts or e-mail or around a dinner table, acted out on a stage or on a movie screen, sung or played with musical instruments in concerts, recited in poetry, shown in photographs and on canvases—stories are the intellectual and emotional and physical expression of the truth. They form every culture's and nation's history (his*tory*) and are told repeatedly over and over from one friend to another, from one generation to the next, from one nation to the next. Humans love stories and love storytelling.

It is estimated that a Canadian tells about seven stories a day in their conversations at work, with friends and during family time, over the phone, on the computer, in bed, walking to school. They could be stories of what happened at work, they could be stories of a friend's tragedy, a story of a winning goal—any human activity, any human experience, and any human desire are the stuff of stories. Sometimes stories use examples: they may feature animals instead of humans. Sometimes they are set in faraway places in extraterrestrial settings with characters that are not human, but their meaning will always communicate something of what it is to be human and what it is to struggle and win and love and lose. Because stories are all created by humans, they will naturally express the range of human experience and emotions: deep loss, profound sadness, pain, guilt, remorse, exhilaration, joy, love, whatever feeling can be experienced, whatever world can be imagined by humans, they will be found in our stories.

Without stories we cannot know ourselves. What does that mean? The experiences that are contained in stories have been felt and experienced by some human at some time at some place in our world. And so, stories let us get to know what others have experienced; help us understand what is important to some humans and not important to others. Thus, stories let us share our different lives with others who are different from us. Stories let us describe our experiences be they painful or joyous, sad or happy; the human experience is recognized and acknowledged in stories. When we recognize our stories are being heard, that someone is listening, it empowers our voice and affirms the worth of our voice and our selves.

Why would we want to know all this about other human beings? Because we share a relatively small space with them. Because to know others is how we stay connected with our world, how we understand others who *appear* on the surface to be very different.

To know others we often understand that our differences may be insignificant, for beneath that surface is the true person, their true life and what it truly feels like to live that life.

When you know somebody's 'story' it gives new eyes with which to view an individual. It gives us *human understanding,* an understanding that is vital to not only admitting difference and allowing the 'other' but also the understanding that gives us the capacity to look within and accept ourselves too.

The Twins of Discrimination

One of the most important stories that reveals the true life of a character while revealing the true nature of a culture and what it feels like to exist with racism and gender discrimination, comes from the Canadian writer Austin Clarke. His masterpiece, *The Polished Hoe,* traces the story of a plantation slave Mary-Mathilda, in a Carribean island nation between the two world wars. It is told by Mary-Mathilda to a police officer in the form of her confession after killing her owner, her father, and the father of her son.

Clarke sets Mary-Mathilda's tale in a world of pure physical beauty with its warm and sparkling ocean, its rich and sun-drenched fields and wide blue skies. A world, upon closer view that is in a state of deadly decline with a degenerate leadership and a dying culture filled with despairing individuals.

It is a world strictly organized by class, gender, and colour; a world where men, both black and white, both lowly and high born define women as sexual objects for their use. "I was a girl . . . the prey . . . to take advantage of. They could. And did. Take advantage of this girl. I was there. To have, and to discard, to have, at a whim and a will."[18] Clarke creates a world where the identity of women is reduced and confined to sexual use, a concept still present in our world today. In Clarke's setting, Mary-Mathilda's story becomes everyone's story: "This is my history in confession, better late than never . . . and as I sit here . . . giving you this history of my personal life, and the history of this Island of Bimshire, altogether, wrap-up in one."[19]

As anxious as Mary-Mathilda is to begin her statement to Officer Percy. "From the beginning and work towards the end."[20] Percy, who has been in love with Mary-Mathilda since boyhood, does not want to hear her story. Percy a proud representative of the law, the judiciary, the first and last place for justice, does not want to know Mary-Mathilda's story: Mary-Mathilda must fight to have her story heard, because in her world, silence and suppression are key to maintaining the status quo, the state of discrimination and suffering. A woman's story is of no importance. As a woman, she is barely considered human, thus how could her story be believed, be recognized as true, credible or important in this world that routinely condemns and convicts women simply because they are different gender from white men who hold the reins of power. Percy tries hard to convince her nobody wants to hear her story, including him, even though he confesses to loving her:

> . . . I don't really want to hear it. The powers-that-be don't. The public don't and the Village don't . . . *nobody*, not the Plantation, the Vicar, the Solicitor-General, nor the Commissioner o' Police himself . . . Not the Church . . . Not the School Systems . . . not a member of the Board o'Governances . . . I don't want to know what your act is, neither. You haven't tell me what is the act and I don't want to know.[21]

But Mary-Mathilda's days of silent endurance have ended. She now understands the value of telling her story; the value of voice, her voice, her stories, and the value of her life. It is of no consequence to Mary-Mathilda that society doesn't want to 'know.' She is resolved: they *will* know: her life and what it is like, how it feels, how it simply *is* for every woman to live in this life. "I wanted you to know what life was like for a woman growing up in this Island. . . . In all stores where men . . . hire young girls . . . All o' them wanted a piece."[22]

Mary-Mathilda is also driven to have her story heard for another reason, "I still have to tell my story . . . I still have to leave the history for Wilberforce, and one to be left back to the people of this Village and people coming after me so they would know what happened. And I still have to save my soul."[23]

Stories as Endings and Beginnings

Why is it important that the generations that follow us 'know what happened' in our lives? Know our stories? How does telling a story 'save your soul'?

CRITICAL THINKING OUTSIDE THE BOX 12.7

Everybody's life story begins before they were born. It begins with your parents and their parents and their parents, like a Russian doll, one story revealing another and another. How your parents met, for example, is an example of how your story began before you were born. If, before you were born, your parents immigrated to Canada, separately or together, that story is part of your story that began before you were born. Think of a story that is part of your life but began before you were born. Think about its main characters—parents, grandparents, older siblings—and what characteristics the story reveals about them. Do you see, are you aware of those qualities in you? Do you see traits revealed by their story, present in you today?

In a society where discrimination is the organizing principal and the order of justice, secrets abound. Until one person uses his/her voice to turn one secret into one story, nothing will change. The 'powers that be' know the inherent danger of stories: one story naturally breeds another story and another story and so on. When the air is filled with voices telling their diverse stories, when the voices explode society's secrets with stories, the rules of racial and gender discrimination are weakened, their foundation cracks, and their walls crumble.

Wilberforce's story begins with Mary-Mathilda's story, and her story begins with her Mother's story: "I found myself in the next room. Partitioned from me and Gran . . . there, on the cot was Ma. With Mr. Bellfeels on top of her . . . Seeing my mother, Ma, underneat . . . shaking her head as if each *huhn* was a knife driving-in her heart."[24]

If Wilberforce is not given the story of these women's endurance, their strengths, and their capacity to love their children; if he does not know what will and resolve they demonstrated in their own ways, what humiliations and degradations they knew, how will Wilberforce ever know what strengths they passed on to him? How will he know all the power and strength that flows and beats invisibly in his veins? How will he know himself, the chapters of his story, his life, that began, as do all our stories, before being born or as his mother says ". . . knowing the history of himself."[25] How will he pay homage to their suffering by creating change?

As vile and vicious as Mary-Mathilda's story is, as corrupt and condemning, she will tell it in her own voice and in her own time. She *will* have it heard because "my act brought a end to its history . . ."[26]

She closed her eyes, measuring the distance of his fly and the size of the opening and the length of the handle of the hoe; she closed her eyes, and delivered the first swing. A noise came from him. And two seconds passed—her eyes were now open—before the blood came spurting from his instrument. . . . The head was still left . . . she swung the hoe a second time, and a third and a fourth . . . countless in her madness . . . it was not murder. It was a sacrifice.[27]

Stories Disregard Difference

Like all human choices and acts, Mary-Mathilda's murderous act does not float, isolated as an island in her life, disconnected from other people, other places, other feelings and experiences. There are other people involved, there are other places, other roles and settings that are part of Mary-Mathilda's story and hers, part of their stories. Mary-Mathilda's own story not only reveals her life, but also serves to reveal the story of the island and the lives of all women on the plantation, of all great grandmothers, grandmothers, mothers, and daughters.

It reveals how their profound poverty, their perfect powerlessness, their stunned silences, and their denied deaths roar and crash through every generation with the same relentlessness as the ocean waves beating on their island beaches. Mary-Mathilda's and the other women's stories reveal the basest level of morality in a deeply corrupted and deeply corrupting world. A morality whose roots are unmistakably entwined with racism, misogyny and class—the sign posts of human indifference to difference.

Twin Roots

In a society where racial and gender discrimination are the rule, every story begins in the same place: a place where individuals have lost their humanity, grown incapable of human dignity, become blind to suffering and apathetic to the steady decline of their society and their own futures.

> . . . driver, overseer, bookkeeper, manager, any one . . . even the man-leader of a field gang, anybody in the scheme of things, in a more higher position, could grab your hand, and lead you in a cane field; pull down your bloomers, put you to lay down on a pile of cane trash; and after he unbutton his fly, and pull out his dickey . . . he could lay down 'pon top o'you, *bam-bam-bam!* and jerk off. And that was that. Yes. . . .That is the history of life on a Plantation. In this Island. On any Plantation. . . I am not talking fiction.[28]

This degradation of females is key to maintaining many kinds of discrimination: disregard for a woman's most basic rights and privileges needs to be repeated and sustained, one generation after the next after another in order that discrimination is to continue its stranglehold,

> I hear this from my gran-mother. They made a calypso on Clotelle . . . it climb to number one on the hit parade. It was a sweet calypso, too . . . They found Clotelle henging from the tamarind tree in the Plantation yard . . . Ma . . . saw Clotelle laying down in the cane-brake, with her face washed in tears; and bleeding; and that it was later the same night . . . that Clotelle climbed up the tamarind tree; and how Clotelle had-use pieces of cloth that she rip-off from her own dress, with all the blood and all the man's semen staining it; and how Clotelle make a rope outta her own dress, and wrap-it-round the highest branch she could reach in the tarmarind tree . . . henging . . . in broad daylight . . . she was five months in the family way . . .[29]

The Needs of Brutality

The secret tragedies not to be spoken, are eulogized in song. But nothing changes for the women. To understand why the war continues unabated between males and females, Clarke reveals the roots of this horrific gender war by telling the men's stories. Their stories carry their own brand of brutality that begets brutality that begets more brutality.

Paradoxically, but not surprisingly, the black males, **emasculated** by their white owners because they are not paid, cannot feed their own families, have no chance of owning their own home or growing their own food. Over time they become paralyzed and powerless to act out against the omnipotence of the all-controlling whites and their class, "One day my gran-mother say, they henged a slave, after they give him forty lashes, with a balata, for stealing a fowl; and they henged from the same tamarind tree as Clotelle . . ."[30]

> Golbourne was a model of manhood . . . but twenty-something years ago, walking . . . holding hands with the nursemaid . . . walking her home, . . . Lord! . . . Bellfeels lay-wait for Golbourne . . . when Mr. Bellfeels stop beating Golbourne with his riding-crop, followed-up with kicks from his brown leather Wellingtons, in Golbourne's two groins, what you see today . . . is the direct result of the venom in the beating administered by Mr. Bellfeels on Golbourne.[31]

The racial war where white men brutalize black men, becomes part of the women's stories because it is the women in turn who are brutalized by broken and bowed men, becoming the physical repository for the men's powerlessness and impotency. The only way men existing in such barbaric societies believe they can take back power is to practice the same brutality on those more vulnerable than themselves and in their eyes that is women. There is no logic in this spiral of violence and vehement hatred. There is no logic in any war.

Clarke shows us that to fight the white dominating class is futile. It will lead to more desperate violence against them. So, instead the men **project** their desire for revenge and their rage onto those they know will not fight back, cannot fight back—women—those with no protection, no rights, and no voice. Rape is the most satisfying of these revenges because it is the ultimate way to exert power over anybody—it is humiliating, degrading, and it is most often, secret. It lets bent and beaten men prove, at least in their own eyes, they still possess some authority and potency in their lives.

Societies like Clarke's island, where race and gender discrimination are systemic, men regardless of their colour, will grow only to view women as the passive recipients of their emasculated rage. They cannot conceive of women as living diverse lives, rich in intellect, emotion, and experience. They cannot perceive women as individuals with plans, dreams, and desires; as individuals independent of the control of men. Racist and **misogynistic** dominators need their victims' identities to be rooted in silence, poverty, and physical vulnerability. They need the female identity reduced to a single plane: an object for the sexual satisfaction of the male. This is how such societies maintain their power.

Blindness Breeds Stories

With the intolerance of racism and misogyny comes a very particular kind of blindness, a blindness that allows stories to thrive and fulfill their purpose. This blindness does not admit the strength of women to survive, endure and, to one day, tell their stories. This blindness does not allow for the capacity of women to speak the truth of life, everyone's life, and release the secrets of their world through story, into the light of day. This blindness knows the power of stories, thus will not allow them for this blindness sees that silence breeds fear and fear breeds submission and that cycle sustains the hold of the unjust and dominating forces.

Once a story is told and heard, suddenly there is ground for growth, imagination, and dreams. It is in that fertile ground where real change begins. Those who dominate with intolerance *will* lose their way because they are blind, giving rise to secrets-cum-stories. Mary-Mathilda proves how the crude blindness of intolerance, racism, and misogyny allows her story that will change history.

WHAT IS THE GOOD OF A STORY

Today, newspapers, news broadcasts, educational, political, social websites, and documentaries decry the lack of human rights for women around the world: lack of education, lack of dominion over their bodies and the care of their bodies, lack of choice in a life partner, lack of financial independence, the list is endlessly long and dark. Racism still rages around the world, intolerance and bigotry based on the colour of skin, the choice of faith thrive. On and on and on. How can a story like Clarke's *The Polished Hoe* take on these worldwide forces of discrimination that not only destroy the lives of women and families, but also the futures of nations and governments. For any society that does not accept, admit, and allow rights to every individual who lives within its borders with equanimity and justice, is a society facing decline and isolation in a world increasingly in need of unity.

What is the good of a *story*, simple words, phrases, plots, characters, symbols, and settings, regardless of how artistically arranged and expressed? How does a story stand up against the deeply damaging and entrenched attitudes and behaviours of systemically sustained gender and race discrimination? What is the human value of a story when compared to the ancient values of gender and race intolerance?

Secrets-cum-Stories

The value is in the telling, as Austin Clarke's Mary-Mathilda knows. The value is in being heard. For when we tell our stories, when we hear our own words vibrating in our own voices, being released into the world beyond the vaults of our minds, we are opening ourselves to human understanding. Our secrets, our societies' secrets become stories, thereby losing some of their dark and fearful edges, when spoken out loud in the light of day. Stories are, after all, only made up of words and images that carry our deepest held fears, loves, losses, and dreams. It is in the revealing of them that we connect with others and learn that they too have their secrets-cum-stories completely different and exactly the same as ours. Stories show us, confirm for us, that we are not alone in our unhappiness, our hopes, or in the lives we want.

Author, poet and essayist Carole Shields says,

> . . . getting what we want requires being able to articulate that sentence, "I want"—what? Women have not been able to make those kinds of demands on society. What women tend to say is, "This is good for the family," "This is good for all of us." But what I want is something that is forbidden—the very idea of the "I" wanting . . . Women in the twenty-first century haven't had much practice at expressing our wants. I think we can hardly do it as women. It's only recently we've known what we can do as far as work in the world goes, how narrow the options were for our mothers or even for us as young women. There really wasn't a lot offered to us and certainly not an invitation to want more.[32]

By My Voice

But still, is it enough? As Clarke has shown us, one story leads to another, to another and so on until the air, the culture is filled with the energetic chatter of storytelling that becomes a blooming confidence taking root and growing, sustained by the sound of many diverse voices. A flowering of language, language different from the language that spins relentlessly in the confines or our minds—language that can be heard by even one, then another, and another. Carole Shields said, "It seems to me that people are always changing, and changing quite dramatically, and that what changes them is access to language and the ability to expand their expressions of themselves through language . . . through fiction we can undertake those journeys and yet remain at home and enormously expand our comprehension of the universe. . . . My own life isn't enough for me."[33]

Mary-Mathilda wanted more. Her own life was not enough for her. Nor are the lives being lived by women in societies, cultures, and countries where gender and race wars rage secretly or publicly; where females take the brunt of systemized discrimination and are victimized, brutalized, isolated, and silenced.

Stories alone will not solve universal and dangerous discriminations. Yet, all change begins with one individual's voice. One individual who tells the story of her life in her own voice, possesses universal powers beyond measure when compared to the silence broken by her voice. The ancient poet Ovid wrote of an ageless priestess, Sibyl, who declared: "But still, the fates will leave me my voice, and by my voice I shall be known."[34]

Beyond Our Own

On Austin Clarke's island of Bimini, small and isolated though it may be, there are still regions of the island, the north side, the west beach, the south plain, that carry subtle differences and distinctions for the people who live in each region. Every nation feels this same need to impress order on their homeland by naming or even just imagining their *place*, their homeland as being diverse and shaded by differences. The smallest village will have its distinctions: downtown area, east end, north neighbourhood. It is a natural inclination for humans to identify with their immediate most familiar surroundings and distinguish them from those streets or neighbourhoods that they don't know as well or do not frequent as often. Paradoxically, it is a way of embracing the whole by creating parts.

One of the defining distinctions of Canada for its own people and for the world is our regions. Across and around the world, Canada's regions are very familiar: the Atlantic Region, the Prairies, the Far North, the West Coast, and Central Canada. Each carries in the global imagination a physical image: the Atlantic Region—fishing villages and red beaches, Central Canada—big bustling cities or old villages tucked into bright ski runs, the Far North—snowy, windswept vistas, the West Coast—mountains against winding coast lines and, the Prairies, of course, golden wheat bending beneath big blue skies. For much of the world, these regional sun-filled, blue-skied panoramic pictures *are* Canada. That is true. But we are more.

While we hold the same visuals as the rest of the world, we also hold the up-close details that make vast vistas diminish. We have learned some of these details from our own family vacations, our old geography homework, or from our own stories.

NATIONAL SELF-KNOWLEDGE

Why is it important to know about our own country and all its distinctions? Why is this kind of national self-knowledge important? Because knowing, understanding, and accepting distinctions and variants lets us appreciate how rich Canada is as a brilliant social experiment in diversity, not always successful, not always positive, but always interesting.

A country as physically diverse as Canada, sprawling spectacularly across every world map, will naturally create a society that *must* raise a people with varying, diverse ways of living, of growing, and of expressing themselves. The very geography and landscape of our everyday lives demand diversity if we are to thrive and prosper. Diversity is our natural state. Like any country, our geography very much determined how we settled the land, how we moved about, and how we described our terrain.

Tree: Human Ratio

Margaret Atwood writes in her classic examination of Canadian literature *Survival*, that ". . . with such a high ratio of trees, lakes and rocks to people . . ."[35] our landscape is going to play a major part in our stories of how it is to live a life in this landscape. Some have even suggested that our stories' geographic settings become characters themselves in our tales.

Late Nights on Air is such a story—a novel where the setting becomes a vital character. It is portrayed as a living breathing creature with whom others fall in and out of love, embrace, and escape. Author Elizabeth Hay brings three women together in Yellowknife each escaping a heart broken in various ways then befriending each other while working at the local national broadcaster's radio station where Harry is their boss. Leaving their original home 'lands' they have arrived in the north because it has been a part of their imaginations since childhood.

Elizabeth Hay's character Gwen first fell in love with the idea of the far north when she heard a radio documentary from her bed while recovering from a typical case of Ontario poison ivy. Eleanor escaped an emotionally paralyzing marriage of six months and came north from Ottawa because her father kept books about the far north and read them to her as a child. Dido, from Sweden, is escaping a love affair begun with her young husband's father. The Canadian far north was as far away from him as she thought she could get and from which she could test his love. Harry is in Yellowknife because he knew it was his last chance in radio, having sabotaged his own career in Toronto with drink and derision.

It is Gwen's childhood memory of radio that propels these characters to follow the journey made by the explorer and adventurer John Hornby, a wealthy, professional adventurer who made several trips to the far north. On his last trip, he, his young nephew, and a third traveller, discovered the upper reaches of the Thelon River, now one of the largest conservation parks in the world. He and his companions planned to overwinter in the

---

CRITICAL THINKING OUTSIDE THE BOX 12.8

If you have not travelled to the far north, describe your picture of this region. How have you formed this mental picture of the north? Consider another region of the country and your mental images of that region. How would you describe these two regions' differences and similarities to an individual visiting Canada for the first time?

CRITICAL THINKING OUTSIDE THE BOX 12.9

Just as in real life a journey in literature always predicts and foreshadows personal change for the characters involved. If the author decides to write their journey along rivers it is usually symbolic of personal growth. Travel of any kind—a weekend getaway, a summer road trip, a winter southern escape—always alters the traveller. Moving our bodies, minds, and imaginations into another, different place, changes the individual. Why? Record a memorable journey you took: perhaps one from childhood, during high school for a sports tournament or more recently. Detail where you travelled, with whom, and one or two impressions you still carry from that time away. Reflecting on it now, did it change you in any way? Did you see something, someone differently. Did you see you differently?

fall of 1904 but "had not laid in his winter's meat by September," so they froze as they starved to death.

THE POWER OF JOURNEY

As we all do when we pack our bags to travel, we pack ourselves too, bringing along all the complications we have taken from every home, every relationship, every experience. Into two canoes went not only Harry's and Eleanor's, Gwen's and Ralph's gear: backpacks, tents and scotch and food supplies but also their losses, fears, attitudes, differences, likes, and similarities, along with their dreams and their hopes of fulfilling that dream, each in their individual way. It didn't matter where each was from, it was where they were travelling that became important.

They were to "fly to the eastern arm of Great Slave Lake and in a few weeks they would reach the Thelon River and view the remains of John Hornby's cabin . . . where his body had lain undiscovered for more than a year in the wooded oasis in the Barrens."[36] The travellers have a different picture in their imaginations of the risks being taken, varying views of their adventure and different reasons for their journey.

As Hay's **narration** unfolds we learn of this place, this singular region of Canada "the big of Canada"[37]—the far north and the farther north. Just as the characters are struggling with the territory of their own hearts, having shared it with a stranger and lost it, so too are there other territorial wars underway. The Berger Inquiry looking into the construction of the Mackenzie Valley Pipe Line was in full swing at the time. Berger was charged with exploring the consequences of constructing an 800-mile pipeline across the Mackenzie Valley to bring oil and gas into southern Canada. A Dene woman, Teresa who once was a nun, tells Gwen that the dispute is not complicated,

> If someone is sitting across from you and says, 'I want your land.' And you say no, I happen to like it here and I've been here forever, then they should respect what you've said, and that's an end to it. They shouldn't try to get around you. They shouldn't read something else into what you've said. They should *respect* you.[38]

Berger's 'ugly consequences' are enumerated by many who Berger listens to with grace and generosity he considers part of his job. Gwen listens and learns as Dene, scientists, old people, young people take the stand and express the wonder of the region and how losing or diminishing this 'eighth wonder' is unimaginable:

Snow geese in late August gathered in the thousand on the arctic coast, feeding for several weeks . . . before flying eight hundred miles non-stop to northern Alberta . . . On these August staging grounds . . . the birds were easily frightened by planes overhead and activity on the ground—was enough to flush them into the air. .. the white whales of the Beaufort Sea were wary of man, yet increasingly exposed. To give birth they came into the warmer, shallow waters of Mackenzie Bay, now the site, . . . of offshore drilling for oil and gas. Then there were the caribou . . . the post calving-aggregation, the gathering en masse in July that forms the sight over which everyone marvels, a spectacle equal to the long lost . . . massing of buffalo . . . disturb . . . with drastic results.[39]

Detailed Pictures

In every reflection on the Berger Inquiry, Hay draws a more detailed picture of the far north, and a fuller picture of Canada. The far north defines Canada as surely as do its big cities. Hay subtly presents why changes to one part of the country—one region—affect us all. The massive and vast dynamics of the natural world reach unseen via interconnections and **interdependencies**, beyond the unmapped boundaries of any region, or every region.

When Justice Berger moved the inquiry into the south, to involve the Canadian public in the debate, he hoped to impress on the rest of the country the uniqueness of the region and how indifference to its difference would alter Canada as a whole. He asked repeatedly,

> what gave them the right to exploit the north, to subject its shifting terrain of sea coast, tundra, boreal forest, rocky hills and marshy plains, permanently frozen ground and discontinuous permafrost to a development project that scientists were saying couldn't be completed without ugly consequences, . . . Berger had

spoken of the arctic wilderness as the 'last of North America, the eighth wonder of the world.'[40]

CONSEQUENCES OF INDIFFERENCE

In a region where there are four races speaking seven languages a variety of voices spoke their stories and their truths and Justice Berger listened to all with grace and composure. Their voices were heard across the airwaves as radio picked up the proceedings and the life of all in Canada was changed to hear the stories of another region often forgotten or disregarded because of great distances and many differences,

> . . . voices that had never been on the radio had their chance . . . plain spoken, same-spoken, tentative yet clear, young and old, in translation or speaking English, usually soft, sometimes strident, native people were convincing . . . that the land gave them life, it was their flesh and blood, they were born and raised on it, they lived and survived by it, they loved and respected and belonged to it, as had their ancestors for thousands of years . . . the past had never gone away, had no intention of going away.[41]

Not only were voices raised from across the spectrum of ecological, sociological, political and historic points of view, there was also the recognizable voice of racism, growing from the indifference that comes with distance and boils over into ignorance and finally intolerance, and accepted unfairness, "There's very, very few white people who will be friends with native people. Any of these white people that are friends with native people, it's like a pearl in a pile of gravel."[42]

We Are More Than Distance

Long distances leave a regionalized country vulnerable to an endless cycle of assumptions and misunderstandings that can too often grow into resentments and conflict. If individuals do not remain vigilant and aware of their fellow Canadians, we will slip into a fossilized interpretation of our regions, leaving us with few connections other than the most general terms of geography and citizenship.

The Very Rock

It is our responsibility as Canadians to know Canada, to see with our own eyes our many differences: our places, our many faces and to seek out our many stories. Elizabeth Hay writes ". . . it was a privilege to be here, to see the vast tundra landscape that produced one-inch flowers and immeasurable skies."[43] It is our privilege to live in a land, to have as our birthright, an endless horizon of varying life forms, landscapes, and experiences,

---

CRITICAL THINKING OUTSIDE THE BOX 12.10

Think of another region of Canada that perhaps has interested you or that you hope to visit. What would you like somebody from that area of Canada to know about your life? What assumptions do you believe they hold about your life?

---

waiting to be known by us. It is a privilege to understand and accept every region of Canada and come to understand each of our region's subtle differences and, more importantly, our remarkable similarities.

> . . . this rock was the very rock she had failed to drive tent pegs into three thousand miles away in Ontario, on an ill-conceived camping trip . . . it was part of the great Canadian Shield, a connection that ran deep and underfoot, though on the surface it failed to bring even two quarrelsome people together.[44]

It is our most essential role as Canadians to understand we are, each and all, more than we think we know.

CANADA'S NATURAL CONDITION

As Elizabeth Hay reveals in *Late Nights on Air* diversity is the natural condition of Canada, regardless of what we speak: regions, flora, fauna, wildlife, landscape, language, geography, climate, Canada is a deeply diversified place. Not surprisingly then this also applies to Canadians themselves—endlessly diverse and opposing yet so relentlessly the same in our hopes for our families and our personal aspirations. It follows then that such uniqueness is shaped by the uniqueness of every family.

FAMILY TIES

Shani Mootoo's profound novel *Valmiki's Daughter* opens with a searing picture of two young women from two apparently conventional upper-middle class Trinidadian families. Vashti, the younger daughter of Valmiki Krishnu and his wife Devika, walking home from school one day, is approached by a former classmate, Merle Bedi. At first she does not recognize Merle who she knew as a brilliant student and peer of her elder sister Viveka: a passionate pianist, a spirited girl bound for the concert stages of the world. "The woman is thin with the depleted meagerness of the alcoholic. Her long black hair is oily and clumped. She wears what was once a white shirt, a school shirt from not too long ago . . . and the trousers . . . men's trousers, are covered in dirt, dust, urine . . . She is barefoot."[45]

Vashti stands and in a moment recalls gossipy rumours and secrets that revolved around Merle.

> But if she is doing this sort of thing, what they say about her can't be true then. It can't be so that she is a buller. If is woman she like, how come she doing it with man? Well, maybe is not a bad thing, then. That might cure her . . . from such a family. . . . No wonder they shut she out the house."[46]

Viveka hands her the pita sandwich she has just purchased from a street vendor and is anxious to be away, not wanting to be seen by her school mates or neighbours.

This haunting image sets the stage for Mootoo's novel, which explores the cost of living a true life, living with secrets, and living in emotional isolation, because your sexual preference goes against societal and familial norms. The scene eerily predicts what will become of any man or woman in this world should he or she chooses to live their life loving a same-sex partner rather than a **heterosexual** partner.

Two Faces of One Life

Valmiki, a prosperous, popular and famous doctor is accepted by the community as a devilish womanizer. But this vaguely admired and flagrant behaviour is merely a façade for his true self, a man who prefers male sexual companionship.

> . . . philandering had been for him a sword, it was a doubled-edged kind. On the one hand, it was a suggestion of his more-than-okay status with the ladies (not one, but many) and so worked against suspicions of who and what he was at heart[47]

His first lover as a young man, Tony, remains with him as a strong and stringent memory. Near the end of their university days, when Valmiki's girlfriend announced her pregnancy, he was relieved and regretful, "Valmiki had been determined to return home and to fall into whatever role was expected of him, or at least to adopt some form of numbing complacency. People talked . . . men he knew, . . . lived a double life."[48] And so over the years he has secretly taken and abandoned a trail of male lovers. His most current is Saul with whom he hunts and spends weekends away under the guise of sporting fellows' masculine weekend forays into the forest. See Have You Heard? 12.3.

Valmiki watches his daughter Viveka with growing anxiety as he recognizes her maturing sexuality. Her interests, her talk, and her behaviours all reveal to him alone what he fears most for her: a **duplicitous** future, like his own life, lived in shadows and

---

HAVE YOU HEARD? 12.3

Forest as Symbol

....

Mootoo often uses the forest as a symbol throughout *Valmiki's Daughter*. In western art, the forest is used to suggest the subconscious. It is dark, mysterious, and the closeted energy of nature all create a picture of what our subconscious might look like if we could see it physically. In Mootoo's work, the forest is a place where characters go to hunt, to walk, and to explore. Each enters the forest anxious, frightful, and tense and looking or hunting for something. They find respite, discover new things about themselves and learn new ways of living. When we enter our subconscious either through meditation, prayer, or reflection, we find it is a place of mystery, a place of discovery, and we often emerge rested and restored with our most private questions answered.

---

shame: a life of sexual difference that will not be accepted by the rest of the family, their community, or the world. Her younger sister reflects her, ". . . face it Vik, you're not like other girls. You walk so fast, and you don't stay still, and you don't dress up or wear makeup. You don't even talk about boys."[49] Her sexual awakening confirms Vashti's ruminations when she meets Anick at a party. The new French wife of a long time friend and neighbour, Anick is homesick for Parisian life and friendships of ideas and interests: opera, live theatre, symphony concerts, literary events, and discussions. She is also finding the other sacrifices she has made for marriage becoming untenable. Having told her husband Nayan about her bisexual past she marries him believing her love for him will usher in a new phase for her. But she is wrong, "He told Anick he hated that part of her life, that he was appalled, even tormented, by the idea that she had once loved women. Since then, she had dreaded the day he would throw all that she had so recklessly told him back at her. . . . She had to fight the breaking of her heart at what she had sacrificed in herself by marrying him . . . this man . . . whose presence bent her spirit and heart . . ."[50]

Anick and Viveka meet and allow their attraction to grow into a passionate and loving affair, realizing it will need to always be a secret between them. But Viveka believes that every choice has its cost, "everything comes with a price. People often only give something if they stand to gain."[51] However, she is too young to know the sum to be exacted.

When Nayan and Anick announce the pending arrival of their first baby at a party with Viveka and her family, Valmiki recognizes immediately the root of Viveka's distress:

> She looked as if she would faint. Valmiki retreated quickly toward her. He took her glass and draped an arm around her shoulders. He turned her away from the revelling, . . . and ushered her to the veranda. Viveka was trembling. Valmiki whispered, "Catch your breath, Vik, stay calm and catch your breath . . ." Valmiki was suddenly determined. He would . . . try to give her some morsel of happiness by being more present for her. Perhaps, he reasoned, the universe would then be kinder and in some miraculous turnabout allow his daughter the freedom to love in any way she wanted, and in so doing spare her the double life he was forced to live . . . there were so many casualties in these pretenses . . . he did not want this for his daughter . . . he would make a deal with the universe.[52]

Shani Mootoo has presented a gripping picture of a conventional family hiding their true lives because of their culture's inability to allow, accept, and admit sexual preference and sexual diversity; a society unable to allow one the most basic of freedoms: to love with truth. Crippled by shame and cultural taboos, their only hope is to first move to an honest and open place within the family. The parents are too far gone in their duplicity to achieve this, but the father's love and devotion to his daughters drives him to want something different and true for Viveka. It requires deep and sustained courage on all sides—courage taught by love and known by the self—to effect such change in human attitudes and behaviours.

AN ETHIC OF FAIRNESS

In his work *A Fair Country*, John Ralston Saul suggests that the successful future of Canada's experiment in diversity depends on fairness and inclusion. He concludes that Canadian ideas of fairness and inclusion originate with Aboriginal Peoples. He writes that a welcoming community builds a circle around its diverse newcomers, a circle encompassing and expressing our founding ideals: egalitarianism, inclusion, fairness, and patience. He refers to it as the "**ethic** of fairness." It takes courage, discipline, and time. Saul says there are many Canadians willing to invest those values. Surely Canada is worth courage and discipline. Surely we are. Surely you are.

DIVERSITY IN PARADISE

Think of all that is lost when one person is afraid to accept, allow, and admit difference of any kind into their lives. Think of the stories that are silenced, the lives bent, and the spirits suffocated.

Instead, let us follow the finest characters we have met here and have the courage and discipline to deal with our own fears, then the fears of our families, our neighbours, and our community. Let us learn from our own true stories like those offered here. Let us take lessons from the trials and triumphs of the characters you have met; listen carefully to their language and resolve to develop the discipline required to apply these life lessons to your every day ordinary lives. Stories teach us we cannot know one another until we know each others' stories.

Each story maps the rise of courage and voice required to create and share an extraordinary life in an extraordinary country: a place where new stories will be told and shared, stories in *your* voice, authentic stories of your truths, expressed, heard, and lived out loud with pride and dignity. Stories of individuals just like you who have the voice, the intellect, the ethic, and the power to turn an experiment in diversity into diversity in paradise.

CHAPTER SUMMARY

Canada's literature is a mark of our civilized society, our inclusive culture, and a people who value the lives of others. The stories that shape our literature voice our diverse and distinctive experiences, so we may all listen and learn: about ourselves, about others, and about our place in the world.

Our literature **organically** recognizes and recounts our very particular experiences as a society living daily with the privileges and responsibilities only available in a society that values and defends difference. When we appreciate and recognize how story expresses a range of voices, we hold in our imaginations an authentic reflection of our country and of our best selves.

While engaging and entertaining us, our finest writers explore and identify the complexities of the relationship between voice, power, and change. Our novelists and poets create compelling plots and descriptive images to inspire individuals to forever alter everything in their world by having the courage to voice the authentic story of their true lives. As a student of diversity, it is your responsibility to appreciate and understand narrative, its language and symbols and the extraordinary experiences of the ordinary Canadians it all reveals.

Literature details the power of expressing and sharing our true lives so we may know and understand one another a little better; so we may know and understand ourselves a little better and thus grow to accept, admit, and allow diversity. To know we are so much more.

KEY TERMS

duplicitous, p. 369

emasculated, p. 360

ethic, p. 371

heterosexual, p. 369

interdependencies, p. 366

intergenerational, p. 342

misogynistic, p. 360

narration, p. 365

organically, p. 372

project, p. 360

restorative, p. 354

voice, p. 342

DISCUSSION QUESTIONS

1. How does literature help us all accept, admit, and allow difference in our lives?

2. Review the "universal rules" offered by Francis Itani's character Mamo. Now, select two other characters you have met in this chapter. Would Itani's rules work to help them?

3. How do the stories of our ancestors inform us with the strength to grow and face challenges?

4. Throughout this chapter you have read excerpts from literature that integrate different languages and dialects. How did you initially respond to this and what is the significance of it to you as a student of diversity?

5. What are three or four discoveries you have made about Canada while reading this chapter: its people, its history, its places?

NOTES

1. Wayson Choy, *The Jade Peony* (Vancouver: Douglas & McIntyre Ltd., 1995), p. 84.
2. *OED, Compact Edition of the OED*, Volume I, p. 775, entry 550.
3. Frances Itani, *Deafening* (Toronto: Harper *Flamingo* Canada, 2003), p. xiv.
4. Ibid., p. xiv.
5. Ibid., p. xiii.
6. Ibid., pp. 150–151.
7. Ibid., p. 306.
8. Ibid., p. 294.
9. Ibid., p. 296.
10. Joseph Boyden, *Three Day Road* (Toronto: Penguin Canada, 2005), p. 92.
11. Ibid., p. 94.
12. Ibid., p. 246.
13. Ibid., p. 306.

14. Ibid., p. 319.
15. Ibid., p. 6.
16. Ibid., p. 9.
17. Ibid., p. 354.
18. Austin Clarke, *The Polished Hoe* (Toronto: Thomas Allen Publishers, 2002), p. 103.
19. Ibid., p. 20.
20. Ibid., p. 99.
21. Ibid., p. 100.
22. Ibid., p. 244.
23. Ibid., p. 100.
24. Ibid., p. 207.
25. Ibid., p. 191.
26. Ibid., p. 103.
27. Ibid., p. 461.
28. Ibid., p. 104.
29. Ibid., pp. 14–15.
30. Ibid., p. 15.
31. Ibid., p. 16.
32. Quoted in Eleanor Wachtel, *Random Illuminations: Conversations with Carole Shields* (Toronto: Goose Lane Editions, 2007), p. 161.
33. Ibid., p. 94.
34. Ovid, *Metamorphoses*, Mary Innes (transl.) (London: Penguin, 1955), p. 315.
35. Margaret Atwood, *Survival, A Thematic Guide to Canadian Literature* (Toronto: House of Anansi, 2004), p. 39.
36. Elizabeth Hay, *Late Nights on Air* (Toronto: McClelland & Stewart Ltd., 2007), p. 244.
37. Ibid., p. 271.
38. Ibid., p. 145.
39. Ibid., p. 160.
40. Ibid., p. 160.
41. Ibid., p. 84.
42. Ibid., p. 84.
43. Ibid., p. 267.
44. Ibid., p. 47.
45. Shani Mootoo, *Valmiki's Daughter* (Toronto: House of Anansi Canada, 2008), p. 22.
46. Ibid., p. 23.
47. Ibid., p. 42.
48. Ibid., p. 67.
49. Ibid., p. 87.
50. Ibid., p. 233.
51. Ibid., p. 311.
52. Ibid., pp. 354–355.

GLOSSARY

age at first marriage: The average age at which men and women marry for the first time. (p. 42)

age-specific marriage rate: The number of people marrying in different age groups. (p. 42)

age-specific mortality rate: The number of people dying in different age groups. (p. 44)

aggregating: Summarizing demographic observations or information. (p. 52)

***anomie*:** Etymologically the word means an absence, breakdown, or conflict over "norms" within a particular society or culture. Durkheim uses the word to describe what is almost an individual psychological state consisting of disorder, chaos, and subsequent feelings of meaninglessness (French, from Greek). (p. 174)

antidiscriminatory: Said of legislation or actions that attempt to ensure individuals or groups are not disadvantaged because of their **gender**, age, **disabilities**, **race**, or ethnicity. (p. 203)

ascribed status: A characteristic that people are born with and over which they have little or no control. An ascribed status, such as **race**, **sex**, social class, and age, significantly influences people's lives, affecting their chances of achieving educational, occupational, and financial success. (p. 73)

assimilation: The process whereby immigrants adopt the language, values, norms, and worldview of the host culture at the expense of their heritage culture. (p. 115)

band: A native political entity, ultimately defined by the federal government. (p. 141)

Beringia: A continent-sized landmass that linked Siberia and Alaska (also called the Bering Land Bridge). (p. 57)

"big R" religion: The type of religion one often reads about in introductory texts, as defined by either the religious specialist or the academic for a general audience. It ignores the specifics of the wide variety of religious traditions present at the local level. See also **"little r" religion**. (p. 170)

Bill C-31: An amendment to the ***Indian Act***, passed in 1985, which enabled people who had lost their Indian status through marriage or through the marriage of their mothers to apply to be reinstated as **registered Indians**. (p. 132)

capitalist class: Karl Marx's term for those who own the **means of production**—the land, machinery, factories, and so on—required for the production of goods and services. (p. 81)

celibacy: The state of being unmarried. (p. 42)

census: A list compiled by the government of every person who is in a **population** at a given point in time. (p. 51)

civil registry: A list, compiled by a government, of births, deaths, or marriages. (p. 50)

civil unions: See **civil partnerships**. (p. 263)

the closet: The practice of lesbians and gay who maintained their sexual identities as secret; also refers to complex web of legislation, laws, and social practices that kept homosexuality a secret. (p. 267)

"coming out" A public declaration that one is gay or lesbian. (p. 267)

comparative method: A method used to evaluate the quality of demographic sources; it involves calculating trends of vital events based on information from adjacent districts. (p. 52)

compulsory heteronormativity: The institutionalized belief that everyone must be heterosexual. (p. 251)

conflict theory: The perspective that sees society as consisting of many groups whose interests often conflict. The theory proposes that inequality stems from the **exploitation** and oppression of one section of society by another. Therefore, inequality should be reduced or abolished. (pp. 81, 230, 286)

conjugal family: A family whose members are linked by blood ties. (p. 284)

conservative ideology: The belief that things are best left as they are. An example is the belief that biological causes determine male and female behaviour and, therefore, that attempts to change traditional **gender spheres** are futile. (p. 228)

crosschecking: A process used to evaluate the quality of demographic information; it involves using a variety of sources linked to people in order to verify the information obtained about them. (p. 51)

cross-sectional analysis: A method used to examine demographic patterns over the life cycle, involving dividing people into nonoverlapping age categories. Demographic patterns are then generalized to describe the demographic experience over a lifetime. (p. 53)

Crow's Index of Selection: A method used to measure the potential for **natural selection** in human **populations**; it takes into account both deaths and births (**mortality** and **fertility**). (p. 55)

crude birth rate: The number of **live births** for every 1000 people in a **population**. (p. 41)

crude death rate: The number of deaths for every 1000 people in a **population**. (p. 44)

crude marriage rate: The number of marriages for every 1000 people in a **population**. (p. 42)

cults: Non-traditional religious movements, a "subspecies" of religion centred on a single person or principle. They can either be positive or negative organizations. (p. 174)

cultural frames: The assumptions within a culture that set the parameters about how a concept is defined. (p. 243)

culture industry: A 20th-century phenomenon that refers to the means by which mass media corporations manufacture a "culture" for the sake of profit and entertainment; this artificial version of "culture" reinforces the interests of these corporations, since their idea of "culture" reflects their own interests and biases. (p. 328)

decennial census: The **census** recorded once every ten years. (p. 51)

deinstitutionalization: A movement to discharge people from institutional settings and to place them in the **community**. (p. 208)

demography: The scientific study of human **populations**. (p. 40)

Department of Indian Affairs (DIA): The federal ministry or branch of the federal ministry responsible for Native people. (p. 141)

dependency ratio: The ratio of the number of people aged less than 15 and over 64 years to the number of people aged 15 to 64 years. (p. 47)

developmental disabilities: Intellectual development that has been delayed; formerly referred to as "mental retardation." See also **disability**. (p. 203)

dialect: A version of a language that is distinct from a standard version in terms of grammar, pronunciation, and vocabulary; it is usually restricted to a specific geographical area of a nation or territory whose regions share the same language. (p. 320)

dialectical process: The ongoing process of social discourse and negotiation between members of that society. (p. 171)

disability: According to the World Health Organization, "Any limitation (resulting from an **impairment**) in the ability to perform any activity considered normal for a human being or required for some recognized social role or occupation" (International Classification of Impairments, Disabilities and Handicaps [WHO, 1980]). In Canada, it has become common to use the term to represent the notion of disability, **handicap**, and impairment, and adjectives such as mental, intellectual, and physical are used with the word to denote which body part and/or function is affected. (p. 198)

discrimination: The unequal or unfavourable treatment of people because of their perceived or actual membership in a particular **ethnic group** that restricts their full participation in the social, economic, and political life. (p. 109)

disposable income: **Income** above that required for basic necessities, such as food, clothing, and accommodation. (p. 71)

documentary method: A method of evaluating the quality of demographic sources by using the opinions of informed colleagues to assess the accuracy and completeness of the records. (p. 52)

domestic labour: Work related to home and family maintenance. From feminist perspectives, usually associated with women's work in the home. (p. 294)

duplicitous: The often complex act of convincing others of something that is not true; behaving deceitfully. (p. 369)

ecclesiastical registries: A list of births, deaths, or marriages compiled by religious groups. (p. 50)

economy of rights: A hierarchy of rights, within which specific rights can be ranked among others. (p. 265)

emasculated: To deprive of strength, vigour, or power usually pertaining to men. (p. 360)

emigration: The movement of people out of a specific geographical area. (p. 47)

emigration rate: The number of people leaving an area for every 1000 people in the **population**. (p. 48)

empowerment: Obtaining the resources, such as physical or financial means, to take control of one's own life. (p. 206)

empty nesters: Parents whose children have left home to live on their own. (p. 283)

the Enlightenment: A period usually dated to 18th-century Europe, spanning approximately 1687–1789, and marks a movement when philosophy sought to use human reason and the scientific method to explain phenomenon instead of religious beliefs and/or superstitions. (p. 246)

equality of opportunity: The condition that exists when all citizens, regardless of their **ascribed status**, have the chance to succeed educationally, occupationally, and financially. (p. 80)

essentialize: To attempt to reduce a phenomenon to some single common "essence" or universal definition. Most scholars now recognize that all descriptions and knowledge are conditional, and that definitions therefore cannot be compressed into one single explanation or classification. (p. 163)

ethic: A set of principles, morals, for right behaviour. (p. 371)

ethnic group: A group of people who share norms, values, traditions, and ancestry, and thus are considered distinct. (p. 104)

ethnocentrism: Viewing or judging the world from the point of view of one's own culture. Two variations are the assumption that what is true of one's culture is true of other cultures and the belief that one's culture is superior to other cultures. (pp. 112, 330)

evolution: A change either in physical form or in the frequency of certain genes over time. (p. 55)

executive federalism: What exists when important and far-reaching political decisions are made by the prime minister, provincial premiers, federal and provincial Cabinet ministers, and senior bureaucrats. Some believe this method of decision making runs counter to democracy, or to the belief that citizens should be involved in government decision making. (p. 13) See also **federalism**.

expectation method: A method used to evaluate the quality of demographic sources, which involves calculating expected proportions of vital events on the basis of such factors as economic conditions, marriages, and **migration**. (p. 52)

exploitation: Karl Marx's term for the situation in which the **capitalist class** pays workers less than the real value of their work. (p. 82)

extended family: A family that comprises two or more nuclear families joined through blood ties. The classic example is a husband and wife, their unmarried children, their married children, and the spouses and children of their married children. (p. 280)

externalization: What occurs when human perceptions and understanding of the universe become externally manifest as representations in both the things that we make (objects, tools, art, music, institutions, culture, etc.) and the things we do with those "products" within the public sphere. (p. 171)

external migrants: Migrants who move from outside a specific area. The area can be defined at many different levels, such as the neighbourhood, province, or nation. (p. 49)

failed states, system of: According to fundamentalists, the nation-state of the modernist ideal, which is seen as morally bankrupt due to its secularization and the resulting corruption, social chaos, and meaninglessness. (p. 178)

familia: The total number of slaves in a **household** (Latin). (p. 287)

familism: An ideology that promotes the traditional view of the family as the norm: working father, stay-at-home mother, and children. (p. 289)

fecundity: The maximum number of children a woman can produce during her lifetime. (p. 40)

federalism: A system of governing a country that divides responsibilities between two levels of government. Each level is responsible for the same **population** and cannot abolish the other level. (p. 13)

feminist theory: The view that women are disadvantaged in society and therefore must seek equality with men. (p. 288)

feminization of poverty: A trend characterized by growth in the percentage of women living in poverty. (p. 76)

fertility: The number of **live births** in a **population**. (p. 40)

fertility rate: The number of **live births** per 1000 women aged 15 to 44. (p. 41)

fundamentalism: Generally, a description of a religious movement of those who return their focus to what they believe to be the fundamental truths and practices of a religion. (p. 177)

gay bashing: Physical or verbal assaults, ranging from insults to lethal violence, inflicted on men or women who are taken to be homosexual. (p. 267)

gay gene: The Xq28 gene that some have suggested causes homosexuality in men. (p. 245)

gay liberation: A social movement that emerged after the Stonewall riots. Gay liberation affirms gay men's ways of organizing sexual and social relationships outside of compulsory heterosexuality. (p. 267)

Gay Pride parade: An annual event that celebrates and affirms the diversity of sexual identities, but also serves as a vehicle to protest ongoing inequality of sexual minorities. (p. 271)

gays: Men whose sense of self and self-presentation is based on the sexual attraction to men and on a desire to be connected to other such men. (p. 243)

gender: The cultural aspect of masculinity and femininity. (p. 218)

gender identity: The social role a person assumes, which is usually but not always masculine for men and feminine for women. (p. 218)

gender spheres: Areas of work, school, or recreation that are dominated by one or the other **gender** (e.g., engineering for men and secretarial work for women). (p. 222)

gender stereotypes: Generalizations about how men and women should behave, what their strengths are, and where they are best suited to work, learn, and play in society. (p. 219)

genealogical analysis: Recreation of family histories. Can be used to calculate the amount of relatedness (inbreeding) among people in the **population**. (p. 54)

genealogies: Family histories or trees. (p. 51)

general systems theory: A sociological approach that studies the family as a self-contained unit. (p. 284)

glass ceiling: The invisible **gender** barrier that keeps women at the bottom of the occupational hierarchy and prevents them from winning promotions to positions of power. (p. 222)

global village: A condition in which every part of the world is electronically connected to every other part, creating a feeling that every culture is involved in the affairs of all other cultures. (p. 321)

Golden Horseshoe: The narrow stretch of cities along Lake Ontario from Niagara Falls to Oshawa. (p. 6)

gross migration rate: The number of people who enter and leave an area for every 1000 people in the **population**. (p. 48)

"handicap": "Any resulting disadvantage for an individual that limits the fulfilment of a normal role or occupation" (International Classification of Impairments, Disabilities and Handicaps [WHO, 1980]). See also **disability**. (p. 201)

heterosexism: Privileging of heterosexual ways of organizing social relations to exclusion of other ways. (p. 251)

heterosexuality: Sexual attraction to the opposite sex. This term also denotes the institutionalization and normalization of such attraction. (pp. 244)

hieroglyphics: The pictographic system used by the ancient Egyptians. (p. 316)

homophobia: Literally fear of homosexuals, but also refers to reactions that suggest anxiety or hatred of homosexuals or homosexuality. (p. 245)

homosexuality: Sexual attraction to the same sex. (p. 244)

household: A group of people who live together. (p. 51)

identity: A sense of self and how that is presented to others. (p. 245)

ideological legitimation: An assumption or set of assumptions that attempts to justify a political, economic, or social relationship or system. (p. 289)

ideology of the family: (p. 289) See **familism**.

immigration: The movement of people into a specific geographical area. (p. 46)

immigration rate: The number of people entering an area for every 1000 people in the population. (p. 48)

impairment: "Any abnormality of physiological or anatomical structure or function" (International Classification of Impairments, Disabilities and Handicaps [WHO, 1980]). (p. 204)

inclusive societies: Societies characterized by the involvement and participation of all of its members. (p. 198)

income: The flow of money received over a specified period. (p. 67)

Indian Act: An act through which the federal government gave itself tremendous power over Native people in Canada. (p. 128)

individual discrimination: Acts of **discrimination** carried out by individuals. (p. 109)

infant mortality rate: The number of children dying under one year of age. (p. 44)

institutional discrimination: Discrimination that limits the full participation of minority groups in the social, political, economic, and educational institutions of Canada. May or may not be intentional. (p. 111)

interdependencies: Dependence between two or more people or parties for mutual benefit. (p. 366)

intergenerational: Between generations. (p. 342)

internalization: Occurs when an individual or society creates objects of culture to represent an understanding of reality, then internalizes or reabsorbs into consciousness the objectified world in such a way that the structures of this world or culture come to determine the subjective structures of consciousness. (p. 171)

internal migrants: Those migrants who move within a specific area. The area can be defined at many different levels, such as the neighbourhood, province, or nation. (p. 49)

intersexed: A person who has intermediate or atypical sexual or reproductive characteristics, which usually differentiate male from female. (p. 271)

isonomy: A method used to estimate inbreeding by examining the frequency of marriages occurring between people who share a surname. (p. 54)

jiva: From the Sanskrit, "soul." Often used by the Jain tradition to describe the thing that differentiates living from non-living entities. (p. 168)

karma: The principle of universal causality resulting from action. It is the accumulated sum of all actions in which an individual has participated, and the subsequent results of those actions that "bear fruit" in some future existence. (p. 164)

kinship coefficients: A method used to estimate inbreeding by examining the proportion of surnames within a **population**. (p. 54)

language families: Groups of related languages. (p. 130)

language isolate: A language that has no known related language. (p. 130)

Lavender Scare: This refers to persecution of homosexuals in mid-20th century the United States federal government. (p. 256)

learning disability: A comprehensive term that describes limitations in one's capacity to learn. (p. 209) See also **disability.**

lesbian: A term for a woman whose sense of self and self-presentation is based on a sexual attraction to other women and a desire to connect with other such women. In some cases, this identity is political. (p. 243)

lesbian continuum: The spectrum of women's experiences that are identified as necessarily women's. Rich does not argue that all women are lesbians in terms of female/female sexuality, but that their experiences are antithetical to patriarchy. (p. 251)

LGBTTIQ: An acronym for the lesbian, gay, bi-sexual, transgendered, two-spirited, intersexed, and queer community. (p. 264)

liberal feminism: A form of feminism that pursues equality between men and women, most often through social and political reform. (p. 250)

liberation theories: Approaches to the study of family that see conflict as an essential characteristic of families and change and diversity as a means of freeing some family members from an oppressive family environment. (p. 286)

life expectancy: The age to which most humans can expect to live (average age at death). (p. 43)

life span: The maximum age that a human has ever lived. (p. 43)

lingua franca: The common language used among cultures with different languages to communicate with each other. (p. 331)

"little r" religion: The specific forms of religion passed from grandmother to mother to daughter, or from grandfather to father to son. (p. 171) See also **"big R" religion**.

live births: Babies born alive. (p. 40)

longitudinal analysis: A method used to examine demographic patterns over the life cycle that involves following a birth or marriage cohort through time. (p. 53)

male homosexual panic: A feeling of anxiety that is aroused when individuals fear that a relationship may appear to be homosexual when it is in fact non-sexual, in its worse case, it results in violence. (p. 267)

mass medium: A medium available to and used by most people in the world. (p. 314)

matriarchy: A type of family in which authority is vested primarily in the female. (p. 287) See also **patriarchy**.

means of production: The land, machinery, factories, and other resources required for the production of goods and services. In a capitalist society, the means of production are owned by a small percentage of the **population**. (p. 81)

media think: In the terminology of James Winter, a professor at the University of Windsor, the way media owners, managers, and workers think, see, and represent the world around us. (p. 327)

medical discourses: Ways of thinking/knowing that are institutionalized in and through the medical field. (p. 254)

Meech Lake Accord (1987): The constitutional accord agreed to by the Prime Minister and the ten provincial premiers. The name of the Accord was taken from the Meech Lake cottage where the meeting took place. It died when it failed to receive the appropriate approval from the Manitoba legislature. (p. 13)

"mentally deficient": A term used in the past to describe a person whose intellectual development was limited. (p. 200)

meritocracy: A social system that rewards people in direct proportion to their merits (skills, talents, and abilities) rather than to their **gender**, **race**, or social connections. A meritocracy would remove all **systemic barriers** that block men and women from entering nontraditional spheres. (p. 232)

Métis: A person who is a descendant of a particular people of French-Cree heritage. (p. 134)

middle class: Those who own a small amount of **wealth** and are employed in relatively secure and high-paying occupations. (p. 87)

migration: The movement of people into and out of specific geographical areas. (p. 46)

misogynistic: attitudes and behaviors demonstrating individual or systemic hatred of women, refusal of their rights and the restriction of their identities. (p. 360)

mode of production: The means by which goods are produced in society; in Marxist theory, the defining characteristic of a society. (p. 286)

moksha: A primarily Hindu and Jain term from the Sanskrit language that means liberation or "release" from the cycles of birth and death in the traditions of South Asia. (p. 170)

Mollyhouse: An establishment in the 1700s where men—and occasionally women—met and dressed in clothes of the opposite gender, sometimes to meet others attracted to the same sex. (p. 268)

moral panic: An intense feeling of anxiety that the social order is threatened, often because a group is perceived to be a threat. (p. 256)

morbidity: The number of people with a specific disease in a **population**. (p. 46)

mortality: The number of people in a **population** dying in a given period. (p. 43)

multiculturalism: The federal government's official commitment to furthering national unity by promoting the positive aspects of cultural differences and the English and French languages. (p. 114)

Multiculturalism Act: A federal act that officially sanctioned multiculturalism; became law on 21 July 1988. (p. 116)

narration: A way of expressing, telling, voicing an experience; a method or style of organizing a story into a pattern with beginning, middle, and end for the purpose of sharing. (p. 365)

National Policy (1879): A conscious attempt by the government of John A. Macdonald to build an economy based on manufacturing and to lessen Canada's dependence on resource exports. (p. 20)

natural selection: The preferential survival and reproduction of individuals in a **population** by virtue of possessing a genetic characteristic that gives them an advantage. (p. 55)

nature/nurture: These are a series of arguments over whether biology or environment plays a larger role in the person we become. (pp. 228, 244)

net migration rate: The increase or decrease in the size of a **population** for every 1000 people based on the number of people who enter an area minus those who leave. (p. 48)

nirvana: From the Sanskrit, "extinction." Primarily a Buddhist term to indicate a departure from the cycle of rebirths, and entry into a different mode of existence. (p. 170)

nominative records: In **demography**, sources of demographic information that list a person's name. (p. 51)

nomos: According to Peter Berger, the stable social environment that occurs when individuals freely identify and participate within the "social project" and feel they are not being forced to participate in a particular role. (p. 172)

nonrandom mate selection: A distinct preference in the choice of a mate or marriage partner. (p. 54)

normalization: This is a process through which certain neutral actions become constructed as normal or abnormal. (pp. 207, 247)

nuclear family: A **household** that includes a married couple and their children. (p. 279)

nuptiality: The demographic **variable** that measures the incidence, rate, and other aspects of marriage in society. (p. 41)

objectivation: Occurs when the **products of the human cultural project** become the primary objects of our consideration and attention—that is, when we begin to interact with the representations we have created of reality as if they were the real universe itself. (p. 171)

Omnibus Bill: A government bill containing many separate items. This was the Canadian *Criminal Law Amendment Act,* 1968–1969, which legalized homosexual sex acts in private. It was also known as Bill C-150. (p. 263)

oppressed: To have experienced marginalization, exploitation, and feelings of powerlessness. (p. 215)

orality: The technique of communication that relies solely on the spoken or gestured word. (p. 316)

organically: A natural process of growth and change; a recognition of the natural state of ideas. (p. 372)

pack journalism: A term used to describe the occupation of reporters who feed off one another, move in unison, and rush to be the first to receive accolades for "breaking" a story. (p. 327)

paleodemography: The study of prehistoric **populations** on the basis of their physical remains. (p. 56)

parchment: The dried skin of sheep and goats, used by the ancient Greeks for writing material. (p. 318)

patriarchal: Pertaining to a family type where authority is vested in the male. (p. 287) See also **matriarchal**.

pedophilia: A person who feels sexual attraction for prepubescent children. (p. 256)

pictograph: A symbol or picture used in some writing systems to represent entire words or utterances, as opposed to a letter of an alphabet representing a vocal sound. (p. 316)

pluralism: The belief that ethnic conflict will always be a central part of modern, industrial societies and that ethnicity will always be a vital component of individual and group identity. (p. 115)

political power: The degree to which a person or a group can enforce its demands. (p. 85)

population: A group of people who live within a specific geographical or political boundary, who are genetically similar (i.e., they interbreed), and who share a cultural heritage during a certain time frame. (p. 52)

post-operative transsexuals: Individuals who have undergone gender reassignment surgery. (p. 270)

pre-operative transsexuals: Individuals who are undergoing hormonal treatments to bring their gender identity into alignment with their physical bodies. (p. 270)

Powley test: A set of ten main considerations that must be taken into account in order for the courts to determine whether a **Métis** hunting without a provincial licence was doing so in accordance with his or her proper Aboriginal right. After Steve Powley, who with his son killed a bull moose in Sault Ste. Marie in 1993 (the court ruled in their favour). (p. 135)

prejudice: The attitude of judging people on the basis of statements, ideas, and beliefs that do not hold up under scrutiny. (p. 107)

products of the human cultural project: Things we make, such as objects, tools, art, music, institutions, culture, etc., to represent our understanding of the world we live in. Human beings project meaning into the universe by creating both a material and an institutional culture that reflects that meaning, and these products become the primary objects (**objectivation**) of our attention. (p. 172)

progressive ideology: The belief in using social change to improve society. For example, under the assumption that social causes determine male and female behaviour, changing how society raises children will liberate people from restrictive **gender spheres**. (p. 229)

project: To throw, or cast forward, to push onto another in mental or emotional sense. (p. 360)

race: An arbitrary system of classification that divides humans into different categories (races) based on differing physical characteristics, such as skin colour and eye shape. Biologically, humans are all of the same species or race; but sociologically, physical traits are important symbols. (p. 104)

racial profiling: Any action undertaken for reasons of safety, security or public protection, that relies on **stereotypes** about **race**, colour, ethnicity, ancestry, religion, or place of origin, or a combination of these, rather than on reasonable suspicion, to single out an individual for greater scrutiny or different treatment. (p. 113)

racism: Discrimination based on **race** and assumed behavioural and mental similarities or deficiencies. Racism usually takes the form of the belief in the superiority of one race to another. (p. 109)

radical feminism: A type of feminist thought that argues that patriarchy is a necessary part of our current social order, so a major envisioning of our social institutions is necessary to challenge women's oppression. (p. 251)

regionalism: An attitude of the citizens of a certain region that they have not been given adequate recognition for their part in building Canada and have been penalized by the federal government in favour of another region. (p. 4)

registered Indian: Someone who is "legally" an Indian, according to the federal *Indian Act*. (p. 133)

rehabilitation medicine: A field of medicine that aims to return or to restore people to a former state of health or well-being. The term now also refers to helping people to participate to their fullest potential in society by achieving the highest level of well-being possible. (p. 201)

rehabilitation team: A group approach to **rehabilitation medicine**, developed to combat the many physical, mental, or intellectual **disabilities** facing returning veterans after World War II, involving team conferences and team planning. The approach recognizes that treating the effects of disabilities includes social aspects such as education, vocational training, housing, and employment and that professional expertise and access to a variety of services are needed. (p. 201)

representation by population: The principle that allocates seats in the House of Commons to each province according to its share of the national population. For example, a province that has 10 percent of the population receives 10 percent of the seats. (p. 14)

reserve: An area of land that has been reserved for Native peoples' use. (p. 137)

residential schools: Church-run boarding schools for Native children that existed from 1910 to the 1960s. (p. 151)

restorative: Something which returns or gives back strength, vitality, courage. (p. 354)

royal commission: An information-gathering device used by the federal government to investigate issues deemed important to Canada. The commission travels across Canada, headed by people appointed by the federal government. A royal commission can only advise government; it cannot implement policy. (p. 28)

sacred canopy: Within the "social project" (the project of building a society) religion can be used to protect its cultural institutions from assault from within by its members. Religion can give authority and legitimacy to social institutions. (p. 173)

same-sex marriage: The legal bonding of same-sex partners with the same legal rights and responsibilities as opposite-sex marriage. (p. 304)

samsara: A word from the Jain religion used to describe the transient world and the cycles of birth and rebirth (reincarnation). (p. 170)

script: A system of combined symbols for words, as opposed to **pictographs** or an alphabet. (p. 318)

self-determination: Making free choices and acting without outside interference. (p. 209)

sentencing circle: An innovative Native justice forum based on traditional concepts of restorative justice that involves **community** members and not just legal professionals, and that provides ways of dealing with people charged with crimes that are alternatives to the choices usually available in the Canadian legal system. (p. 147)

sex: A man or a woman's biological sexual characteristics, as indicated by the reproductive organs and the hormonal system a person is born with. (p. 218)

sexology: The sustained scientific study of sexuality. (p. 247)

sexual identity: A sense of self that is shaped by how one is sexually attracted to others. (p. 244)

sexual inversion: A reversal of gender traits, in which a person of a specific sex performs the gender of someone from a different sex. In 19th-century sexology, it was a term for homosexuality. (p. 247)

sexual orientation: The direction or pattern of attraction to others based on sexual, gender characteristics; used to suggest that there are physiological as opposed to sociological forces at work; replaced gender preference. (p. 244)

smudging: The burning of herbs, such as sweetgrass, to create a smoke bath. It is used for purifying people and ceremonial space, tools, and objects, much as incense is used by Catholics, Hindus, Jews and Buddhists. Smudging is a daily morning ritual for some. (p. 149)

social controls: The means society uses to ensure that men and women behave in **gender**-appropriate ways. May include laws, ridicule, and **discrimination**. (p. 219)

social inequality: The degree to which people have access to and control over valued resources, such as money, **wealth**, status, and power. (p. 66)

Socialist/Marxist feminism: A variety of feminism that seeks to liberate women through the dismantling of capitalism. (p. 251)

social movements: Major historical changes in the day-to-day lives of groups resulting from concerted social action. Examples include the women's movement and the civil rights movement. (p. 202)

sociopsychological dimension to regionalism: Concerned with how people living in different regions feel and act toward each other, their **community**, and the federal government. (p. 30) See **regionalism.**

sodomy: While this originally referred to sexual intercourse that was decided to be 'unnatural,' in the context of Canadian legal history, it refers to anal intercourse. (p. 258)

space-oriented media: Said of media that facilitate delivery and communication of information across vast distances of territory or space. (p. 318) See also **time-oriented media.**

stereotype: A collection of generalizations about a group of people, which are negative, exaggerated, and unable to be maintained when subjected to critical analysis. (p. 108)

Stonewall: A reference to the Stonewall Inn where riots erupted following the resistance of the patrons, many of whom were gay or transgendered, to a police raid in 1969. (p. 269)

stratification: The state of a society when it is made up of groups of people who have differing degrees of access to and control over valued resources. (p. 66)

structural–functionalism: 1. A theory proposing that inequality serves a positive function by ensuring that the most functionally important occupations are carried out by the most talented people, thus preserving the stability and proper functioning of society. An example is the idea that strict divisions of labour between men and women reduce role confusion and ensure that necessary jobs are done by those best equipped to do them. 2. A sociological approach that views the family as a stabilizing force for its members and for society as a whole. (pp. 79, 230, 282)

sweat lodge: A ritual "sauna" used by First Nations or Native Peoples, in which a sauna-like sweat bath is prepared by pouring water on heated rocks. Also refers to a tradition-based practice in which people physically and spiritually cleanse themselves, often as part of their healing path and of (re)connecting themselves to their Native identity. (p. 145)

systemic barriers: Laws, discriminatory practices, and psychological roadblocks that prevent men and women from entering non-traditional spheres. (p. 233)

telegraph: A device invented in 1844 that transmits messages across distances using electric wire. (p. 320)

television imperialism: The power of television over other media; its tendency to be the dominant medium in a culture. (p. 328)

time-oriented media: Said of media sufficiently durable to preserve the history and tradition of cultures across vast amounts of time. (p. 318) See also **space-oriented media.**

transcendent God: A divine being existing above and independently of the material world. (p. 164)

transfer payments: The name given to the billions of dollars that the federal government gives to the provinces and territories to help them deliver services to their populations. Key types of transfer payments are the Canada Assistance Plan (CAP), Equalization, and Territorial Formula Financing. (p. 10)

transgender: A term that refers to those whose gender identity is not aligned with their physical bodies. (p. 255)

transsexual: A person who experiences an incompatibility between his or her anatomical **sex** and his or her psychological **sex**. Most transsexual people seek to alter their bodies through hormone therapy and/or gender reassignment surgery. (p. 220)

transvestite: A man or woman who adopts the dress and the behaviour of the opposite **sex**. (p. 220)

treaty: In the context of Canada, a legal agreement signed between either the British or the Canadian government and one or more Native nations. (p. 137)

tribalism: The condition in which people are encouraged to act as members of a group rather than as individuals. (p. 321)

"Ultimate Reality": An all-pervasive force that is representative of the "Supreme Experience," the effulgent and universal Awareness, the ultimate and absolute that permeates the universe. This force is impersonal and transcends all ideas or concepts of personality; one cannot have a personal relationship with it. (p. 164)

unification theories: Approaches to the study of family that see families as adaptive units that mediate between individuals and society. (p. 282)

upper class: Those who own a considerable amount of **income** and **wealth**. In Canada, the upper class constitutes about 5 percent of the population. (p. 86)

urban reserves: A new type of **reserve** being created in Saskatchewan, consisting of lands located in a municipality or Northern Administrative District whose main function is to provide central urban locations for Aboriginal businesses. (p. 143)

variable: A characteristic that differs or varies among groups. (p. 40)

vernacular: A form of speech or a **dialect** that is characteristic of a particular region or nation. (p. 320)

vital event: A demographic term referring to births, marriages, or deaths. (p. 52)

voice: The expression of one's opinion and experience in the spoken or written word, the opinion itself, or the right to express an opinion; the right, ability, and power to express opinions, perceptions, ideas, feelings, experiences, stories. (p. 342)

wealth: An accumulation of assets, such as a house, savings, or a car. (p. 71)

working class: Karl Marx's term for the vast majority of the population who must sell their labour in order to survive. (p. 81)

SELECTED BIBLIOGRAPHY

Chapter 1

Adamec, Robert. *Memorial Gazette* 37(9) (27 January 2005).

Archer, Keith, Roger Gibbins, Rainer Knopff, and Lesie A. Pal, eds. *Parameters of Power: Canada's Political Institutions*. Toronto: Nelson, 1995.

Black, Errol, and Jim Silver. *Equalization: Financing Canadians' Commitment to Sharing and Social Solidarity*. Canadian Centre for Policy Alternatives, March 2004.

Bowker, Marjorie Montogomery. *The Meech Lake Accord: What It Will Mean to You and to Canada*. Gloucester, ON: Voyageur Publishing, 1990.

Bradfield, Michael. *Regional Economics: Analysis and Policies in Canada*. Toronto: McGraw-Hill Ryerson, 1988.

Brodie, Janine. *The Political Economy of Canadian Regionalism*. Toronto: HBJ, 1990.

Brym, Robert. "Canada's Regions and Agrarian Radicalism." In James Curtis and Lorne Tepperman, eds., *Images of Canada: The Sociological Tradition*. Scarborough, ON: Prentice-Hall, 1990.

Conway, J.F. "Western Alienation: A Legacy of Confederation." In John A. Fry, ed., *Contradictions in Canadian Society*. Toronto: Wiley, 1984.

Davis, Jo, ed. *Not a Sentimental Journey: What's Behind the Via Rail Cuts, What You Can Do About It*. Toronto: Gunbyfield Publishing, 1990.

Dyck, Rand. *Canadian Politics: Critical Approaches*. Scarborough, ON: Nelson, 1993.

Gibbins, Roger. *Conflict and Unity: An Introduction to Canadian Political Life*, 3rd ed. Scarborough, ON: Nelson, 1994.

Harmer, Harry. *The Longman Companion to Slavery, Emancipation and Civil Rights*. Toronto: Pearson Education Ltd., 2001.

Hiller, Harry S. *Canadian Society: A Macro Analysis*. Toronto: Pearson, 2000.

Hurtig, Mel. *The Betrayal of Canada*. Toronto: Stoddart, 1990.

Johnston, Donald J., ed. *With a Bang, Not a Whimper: Pierre Trudeau Speaks Out*. Toronto: Stoddart, 1988.

Kilgour, David. *Inside Outer Canada*. Edmonton: Lone Pine Publishing, 1990.

Lithwick, N.H. "Is Federalism Good for Regionalism?" In Garth Stevenson, ed., *Federalism in Canada*. Toronto: McClelland and Stewart, 1989.

"Maritimes Kept Poor by Ontario." *The Hamilton Spectator*, 30 July 2001.

Mathews, Ralph. *The Creation of Regional Dependency*. Toronto: University of Toronto Press, 1983.

McQuaig, Linda. "Just One Sponsor, but Canadians Love CBC *People's History*." 21 December 2000. Straight Goods.com <http://goods.perfectvision.ca/ViewFeature.cfm?REF=23>. Accessed 8 February 2002.

Morton, Desmond. *A Short History of Canada*. Edmonton: Hurtig, 1983.

Phillips, Paul. *Regional Disparities*. Toronto: Lorimer, 1978.

Qualman, Darrin. *The Farm Crisis and Corporate Power*. Ottawa: Canadian Centre for Policy Alternatives, 2001.

Savoie, Donald J. *The Canadian Economy: A Regional Perspective*. Toronto: Methuen, 1986.

Statistics Canada. *The Daily*, 27 January 2005.

Statistics Canada. *The Daily*, 4 May 2005.

Swan, Neil, and John Serjak. "Analysing Regional Disparities." In James Curtis, Edward Grabb, and Neil Guppy, eds., *Social Inequality in Canada: Patterns, Problems, Policies*, 2nd ed. Scarborough, ON: Prentice-Hall, 1993.

"Top 300 Private Companies," Globeinvestor.com <www.globeinvestor.com/series/top1000/ tables/private/2005>. Accessed 29 April 2006.

Trudeau, Pierre E. *A Mess That Deserves a Big NO*. Toronto: Roberston Davies Publishing, 1992.

Wien, Fred. "Regional Inequality: Explanations and Policy Issues." In James Curtis, Edward Grabb, and Neil Guppy, eds., *Social Inequality in Canada: Patterns, Problems, Policies*, 2nd ed. Scarborough, ON: Prentice Hall, 1993.

Young, Lisa and Archer Keith eds. *Regionalism and Party Politics in Canada*. Toronto: Oxford University Press, 2001.

Chapter 2

Abu-Laban, B. "Arab Immigration to Canada." In J.L. Elliott, ed., *Two Nations, Many Cultures: Ethnic Groups in Canada*. Scarborough, ON: Prentice-Hall, 1979.

Bilson, G. *A Darkened House: Cholera in Nineteenth-Century Canada*. Toronto: University of Toronto Press, 1980.

Bourbeau, R., and J. Légaré. *Évolution de la mortalité au Canada et au Québec, 1831–1931. Essai de mésure par génération*. Montreal: Les Presses de l'Université de Montréal, 1982.

Brookes, A.A. "The Golden Age and the Exodus: The Case of Canning, Kings County." *Acadiensis* 11 (1981): 57–82.

Brunger, A.G. "Geographical Propinquity Among Pre-famine Catholic Irish Settlers in Upper Canada." *Journal of Historical Geography*, 8 (1982): 265–82.

Cavalli-Sforza, L.L., and W.F. Bodmer. *The Genetics of Human Populations*. San Francisco: W.H. Freeman, 1971.

Charbonneau, H. "Jeunes femmes et vieux maris: la fécondité des mariages précoces." *Population*, 35 (1980): 1101–22.

Charbonneau, H., and A. LaRose, eds. *The Great Mortalities: Methodological Studies of Demographic Crises in the Past*. Liege: Ordina Editions, 1979.

Connell, K.H. *The Population of Ireland 1750–1845*. Oxford: Clarendon Press, 1950.

Crawley, R. "Off to Sydney: Newfoundlanders Emigrate to Industrial Cape Breton 1890–1914." *Acadiensis* 17 (1988): 27–51.

Cressy, D. "The Seasonality of Marriage in Old and New England." *Journal of Interdisciplinary History* 16 (1985): 1–21.

Crow, J.F. "Some Possibilities for Measuring Selection Intensities in Man." *Human Biology* 30 (1958): 1–13.

Crow, J.F., and A.P. Mange. "Measurement of Inbreeding from the Frequency of Marriages Between Persons of the Same Surname." *Eugenics Quarterly* 12 (1965): 199–203.

Darroch, A.G., and M.D. Ornstein. "Family and Household in Nineteenth-Century Canada: Regional Patterns and Regional Economies." *Journal of Family History* 9 (1984): 158–77.

Dixon, R.B. "Explaining Cross-Cultural Variation in Age at Marriage and Proportions Never Marrying." *Population Studies* 25 (1971): 215–33.

Dobzhansky, T. "Natural Selection in Mankind." In G.A. Harrison and A.J. Boyce, eds., *The Structure of Human Populations*. Oxford: Clarendon Press, 1972.

Donnelly, F.K. "Occupational and Household Structures of a New Brunswick Fishing Settlement: Campobello Island, 1851." In R. Chanteloup, ed., *Labour in Atlantic Canada*. Saint John: University of New Brunswick, 1981.

Elder, G.H., and R.C. Rockwell. "Marital Timing in Women's Life Patterns." *Journal of Family History* 1 (1976): 34–53.

Elliott, J.L. "Canadian Immigration: A Historical Assessment." In J.L. Elliott, ed., *Two Nations, Many Cultures: Ethnic Groups in Canada*. Scarborough, ON: Prentice-Hall, 1979.

Fogel, R.W., S.L. Engerman, J. Trussel, R. Floud, C.L. Pope, and L.T. Wimmer. "The Economics of Mortality in North America, 1659–1910: A Description of a Research Project." *Historical Methods* 11 (1978): 75–108.

Gaffield, C.M. "Boom and Bust: The Demography and Economy of the Lower Ottawa Valley in the Nineteenth Century." *Canadian Historical Association, Historical Papers*, 1982: 172–95.

Gee, E.M.T. "Early Canadian Fertility Transition: A Components Analysis of Census Data." *Canadian Studies in Population* 6 (1979): 23–32.

Gibson, J.R. "Smallpox on the Northwest Coast, 1835–1838." *BC Studies* 56 (1982): 61–81.

Gossage, P. "Absorbing Junior: The Use of Patent Medicines as Abortificants in Nineteenth-Century Montreal." *The Register* 3 (1982): 1–13.

Hajnal, J. "Age at Marriage and Proportions Marrying." *Population Studies* 7 (1953): 111–36.

Harney, R.F. "Men Without Women: Italian Migrants in Canada 1885–1930." *Canadian Ethnic Studies* 11 (1979): 29–47.

Harrison, G.A., and A.J. Boyce., eds. *The Structure of Human Populations*. Oxford: Clarendon Press, 1972.

Henry, L. *Population: Analysis and Models*. New York: Academic Press, 1976.

Kaprielian, I. "Immigration and Settlement of Armenians in Southern Ontario: The First Wave." *Polyphony* 4 (1982): 14–27.

Katz, M.B., M.J. Doucet, and M.J. Stern. "Population Persistence and Early Industrialization in a Canadian City: Hamilton, Ontario, 1851–1971." *Social Science History* 2 (1978): 208–29.

Kaye, V.J., and C.W. Hobart. "Origins and Characteristics of the Ukrainian Migration to Canada." In C.W. Hobart, W.E. Kalbach, J.T. Borhek, and A.P. Jacoby, eds., *Persistence and Change: A Study of Ukrainians in Alberta*. Toronto: Ukrainian Canadian Research Foundation, 1978.

Keyes, J. "Marriage Patterns Among Early Quakers." *Nova Scotia Historical Quarterly* 8 (1978): 299–307.

Kussmaul, A. "Time and Space, Hoofs and Grain: The Seasonality of Marriage in England." *Journal of Interdisciplinary History* 15 (1985): 755–79.

Landry, Y. "Mortalité, nuptialité et canadianisation des troupes française de la guerre de Sept Ans." *Social History* 12 (1979): 298–315.

Lavoie, Y. *L'Émigration des Québécois aux États-Unis de 1840 à 1930*. Quebec: Éditeur officiel du Québec, 1979.

Li, P.S. "Immigration Laws and Family Patterns: Some Demographic Changes Among Chinese Families in Canada, 1885–1971." *Canadian Ethnic Studies* 13 (1980): 58–73.

Li, P.S. "Chinese Immigrants in the Canadian Prairie, 1910–1947." *Canadian Review of Sociology and Anthropology* 19 (1982): 527–40.

Lloyd, S. "The Ottawa Typhoid Epidemics of 1911 and 1912: A Case Study of Disease as a Catalyst for Urban Reform." *Urban History Review* 8 (1979): 66–89.

Matwijiw, P. "Ethnicity and Urban Residence: Winnipeg, 1941–1971." *Canadian Geographer* 23 (1979): 45–61.

McGinnis, J.D.P. "The Impact of Epidemic Influenza: Canada, 1918–1919." *Canadian Historical Association, Historical Papers* (1977): 121–40.

McKeown, T. *The Modern Rise of Population*. London: Edward Arnold, 1976.

McLaren, A. "Birth Control and Abortion in Canada, 1870–1920." *The Canadian Historical Review* 59 (1978): 319–40.

McQuillan, K. "Economic Structure, Religion, and Age at Marriage: Some Evidence from Alsace." *Journal of Family History* 14 (1989): 331–46.

Medjuck, S. "The Social Consequences of Economic Cycles on Nineteenth-Century Households and Family Life." *Social Indicators Research* 18 (1986): 233–61.

Model, J. "The Timing of Marriage in the Transition to Adulthood: Continuity and Change, 1860–1975." In J. Demos and S. Boocock, eds., *Turning Points: Historical and Sociological Essays on the Family*. Chicago: University of Chicago Press, 1978.

Nam, C.B., and S.O. Gustavus. *Population: The Dynamics of Demographic Change*. Boston: Houghton Mifflin, 1976.

Norris, D.A. "Household and Transiency in a Loyalist Township: The People of Adolphustown, 1784–1822." *Social History* 13 (1980): 399–415.

Osborne, B. "The Cemeteries of the Midland District of Upper Canada: A Note on Mortality in a Frontier Society." *Pioneer America* 6 (1974): 46–55.

Parker, W. "The Canadas." In A. Lemon and N. Pollock, eds., *Studies in Overseas Settlement and Population*. New York: Longman, 1980.

Roth, E. "Historic Fertility Differentials in a Northern Athapaskan Community." *Culture* 2 (1982): 63–75.

Roychoudhury, A.K., and M. Nei. *Human Polymorphic Genes: World Distribution*. Oxford: Oxford University Press, 1988.

Sharna, R.D. "Premarital and Ex-nuptial Fertility (Illegitimacy) in Canada 1921–1972." *Canadian Studies in Population* 9 (1982): 1–15.

Shryock, H.S., and J.S. Siegel. *The Methods and Materials of Demography*. San Diego: Academic Press, 1976.

Statistics Canada. Internet site <www.statcan.ca>.

Statistics Canada. *2001 Census Handbook*. Ottawa: Minister of Industry, 2003.

Statistics Canada. *2001 Census of Canada*.

Statistics Canada. *Births, 2001*. Ottawa: Health Statistics Division, 2003.

Statistics Canada. *Deaths, 2000*. Ottawa: Health Statistics Division, 2003.

Statistics Canada. *Marriages, 2001*. Ottawa: Health Statistics Division, 2003.

Swedlund, A.C. "Historical Demography: Applications in Anthropological Genetics." In J.H. Mielke, and M.H. Crawford, eds., *Current Developments in Anthropological Genetics*, vol. 1. New York: Plenum Press, 1980.

Veevers, J.E. "Age Discrepant Marriages: Cross-national Comparisons of Canadian-American Trends." *Social Biology* 31 (1984): 118–26.

Weaver, J.C. "Hamilton and the Immigration Tide." *Families* 20 (1981): 197–208.

Willigan, J.D., and K.A. Lynch. *Sources and Methods of Historical Demography*. New York: Academic Press, 1982.

Wrigley, E.A. "Family Limitation in Pre-industrial England." *Economic History Review* 19 (1966): 82–109.

Wynn, G. "Ethnic Migrations and Atlantic Canada: Geographical Perspectives." *Canadian Ethnic Studies* 18 (1986): 1–15.

Chapter 3

Allahar, Anton L. and James E. Cote. *The Structure of Inequality in Canada*. Toronto: James Lorimer and Company Ltd., 1998.

Badets, Jane, and Tina W.L. Chui. "Focus on Canada's Changing Immigrant Population." Statistics Canada, Catalogue No. 96-311E. Ottawa and Scarborough, ON: Statistics Canada and Prentice Hall, 1994.

Clement, Wallace. *The Canadian Corporate Elite: An Analysis of Economic Power*. Ottawa: Carleton University Press, 1986.

Cooke-Reynolds, Melissa, and Nancy Zukewich. "The Feminization of Work." *Canadian Social Trends*, 72 (Spring 2004): 27. Statistics Canada, Catalogue No. 11-008.

Creese, Gillian, Neil Guppy, and Martin Meissner. *Ups and Downs on the Ladder of Success*. Ottawa: Statistics Canada, 1991.

Crompton, Susan. "Left Behind: Lone Mothers in the Labour Market." *Perspectives*, Summer 1994: 23.

Davies, James B. "The Distribution of Wealth and Economic Inequality." In James Curtis, Edward Grabb, and Neil Guppy, eds., *Social Inequality in Canada: Patterns, Problems, Policies*, 3rd ed. Scarborough, ON: Prentice Hall Allyn and Bacon Canada, 1999.

Gee, E., and S. Prus, "Income Inequality in Canada: A Racial Divide." In M. Kalbach and W. Kalbach, eds., *Perspectives on Ethnicity in Canada*. Toronto: Harcourt Brace, 2000.

Grabb, Edward G. *Theories of Social Inequality: Classical and Contemporary Perspectives*. Toronto: Holt, Rinehart, and Winston, 1990.

Hou, Feng, and T.R. Balakrishnan. "The Economic Integration of Visible Minorities in Contemporary Canadian Society." In James Curtis, Edward Grabb, and Neil Guppy, eds., *Social Inequality in Canada: Patterns, Problems, Policies*, 3rd ed. Scarborough, ON: Prentice Hall Allyn and Bacon Canada, 1999.

Hunter, Alfred A. *Class Tells: On Social Inequality in Canada*. Toronto: Butterworths, 1981.

"Likelihood of Saving Increase with Income." *Infomat: A Weekly Review*, 20 July 2001, Cat. No. 11-002E.

Macionis, John J., Juanne Nancarrow Clarke, and Linda M. Gerber. *Sociology*. New Jersey: Prentice-Hall, 1993.

Marx, Karl. *Critique of the Gotha Programme*. Moscow: Progress Publishers, 1970.

Naiman, Joanne. *How Societies Work: Class, Power, and Change in a Canadian Context*, 2nd ed. Toronto: Irwin Publishing, 2000.

Picot, G., and A. Heisz. "The Labour Market in the 1990s." *Canadian Economic Observer*, February 2000. Statistics Canada, Catalogue No. 11-010-XPB.

Roy, F. "Social Assistance by Province, 1993–2003." *Canadian Economic Observer*, November 2004. Statistics Canada, Catalogue No. 11-010.

Statistics Canada. "Income Distributions by Size in Canada, 1997." Catalogue No. 13-207-XPB, 1999.

Turner, Bryan S. *Equality*. London: Tavistock Publications, 1986.

Chapter 4

Abella, Rosalie. *Report of the Commission on Equality in Employment*. Ottawa: Supply and Services Canada, 1984.

Barrett, Ralph V. "Pedagogy, Racism and the 'Postmodern Turn.'" *The College Quarterly* 1 (Fall 1994).

Berger, Peter, and Brigitte Berger. *Sociology: A Biographical Approach*. New York: Basic Books, 1972.

Berton, Pierre. *Why We Act Like Canadians*. Markham, ON: Penguin, 1987.

Bissoondath, Neil. *Selling Illusions: The Cult of Multiculturalism in Canada*. Markham, ON: Penguin Books, 2003.

Brodie, Janine, and Linda Trimble. *Reinventing Canada: Politics of the 21st Century*. Toronto: Pearson Education Canada, 2003.

Canadian Policy Research Network. "Populations Projections for 2017." Available <www.cprn.org/en/diversity-2017.cfm>. Accessed 29 April 2006.

Driedger, Leo. *Race and Ethnicity: Finding Identities and Equalities*, 2nd ed. Don Mills, ON: Oxford University Press, 2003.

Elliott, Jean Leonard, and Augie Fleras. *Engaging Diversity: Multiculturalism in Canada*. Scarborough, ON: Nelson, 2002.

Elliott, Jean Leonard, and Augie Fleras. *Unequal Relations: An Introduction to Race and Ethnic Dynamics in Canada*. Scarborough, ON: Prentice-Hall, 1992.

Fleras, Augie, and Jean L. Kunz. *Media and Minorities: Representing Diversity in a Multicultural Canada*. Toronto: TEP, 2001.

Fleras, Augie, and Jean Leonard Elliott. *Multiculturalism in Canada: The Challenge of Diversity*. Scarborough, ON: Nelson, 1992.

Gould, S.J. *The Mismeasure of Man*. New York: W.W. Norton, 1981.

Government of Canada. *The Canadian Multiculturalism Act: A Guide for Canadians*. Ottawa, 1990.

Haas, Jack, and William Shaffir. *Shaping Identity in Canadian Society*. Scarborough, ON: Prentice-Hall, 1978.

Hawkins, Freda. *Canada and Immigration: Public Policy and Public Concern*. Kingston, ON and Montreal: McGill-Queen's University Press, 1988.

Heisz, Andrew. Statistics Canada. "Ten Things to Know About Canadian Metropolitan Areas: A Synthesis of Statistics Canada's Trends and Conditions in Census Metropolitan Areas Series." Ministry of Industry, 2005.

Henry, Frances. *The Caribbean Diaspora in Toronto: Learning to Live with Race*. Toronto: UTP, 1994.

Henry, Frances, Carol Tator, Winston Mattis, and Tim Rees. *The Colour of Democracy: Racism in Canadian Society*, 2nd ed. Toronto: Harcourt Brace, 2000.

Hill, Daniel G. *Human Rights in Canada: A Focus on Racism*. Ottawa: Canadian Labour Congress, 1977.

Hiller, Harry H. *Canadian Society: A Macro Analysis*. Toronto: Prentice-Hall, 2000.

James, Carl E. *Seeing Ourselves: Exploring Race, Ethnicity and Culture*, 3rd ed. Toronto: TEP, 2003.

Johnson, Walter. *The Challenge of Diversity*. Montreal: Black Rose Books, 2006.

Kalbach, Madeline A., and Warren E. Kalbach. *Perspectives on Ethnicity In Canada: A Reader*. Toronto: Harcourt Brace, 2000.

Kelley, Ninette, and Michael Trebilcock. *The Making of the Mosaic: A History of Canadian Immigration Policy*. Toronto: UTP, 1998.

Kennedy, K.A.R. *Human Variation in Space and Time*. Dubuque, IA: Brown, 1976.

Li, Peter S. *Destination Canada: Immigration Debates and Issues*. Don Mills: Oxford University Press, 2003.

Li, Peter S. *Ethnic Inequality in a Class Society*. Toronto: Wall and Thompson, 1988.

Montagu, A., ed. *The Concept of Race*. London: Collier-Macmillan, 1964.

Ontario Human Rights Commission. "Paying the Price: The Human Cost of Racial Profiling: Inquiry Report," 2004. Available <www.ohrc.on.ca/english/consultations/racial-profiling-report.shtml>. Accessed 29 April 2006.

Palmer, Howard. *Immigration and the Rise of Multiculturalism*. Toronto: Copp Clark, 1975.

Smith, Charles C. "Crisis, Conflict and Accountability: The Impact and Implications of Police Racial Profiling." *African Canadian Community Coalition on Racial Profiling*. March 2004.

Stoffman, Daniel. *Who Gets In? What's Wrong with Canada's Immigration Program and How to Fix It*. Toronto: Macfarlane Walter and Ross, 2002.

Wise, Tom. "Racial Profiling and Its Apologists." *Z Magazine*, March 2002.

Chapter 5

A good place to begin a search for information on Native culture is the local Native Friendship Centre. These are found in most Canadian cities. Other good sources of information are the Native Studies departments found in some community colleges and a few universities.

Barman, Jean. "Aboriginal Education at the Crossroads: The Legacy of Residential Schools and the Way Ahead." In D.A. Long and O.P. Dickason, eds., *Visions of the Heart: Canadian Aboriginal Issues*. Toronto: Harcourt Brace, 1996.

Bergman, Brian. "Dark Days for the Inuit." *Maclean's*, 4 March 1996, p. 67.

Dickason, Olive P. *Canada's First Nations: A History of Founding Peoples from Earliest Times*. Toronto: McClelland and Stewart, 1997.

Francis, Daniel. *The Imaginary Indian: The Image of the Indian in Canadian Culture*. Vancouver: Arsenal Pulp Press, 1992.

Frideres, James S., and Rene Gadacz. *Aboriginal People in Canada: Contemporary Conflicts*, 6th ed. Toronto: Prentice-Hall, 2001.

Henslin, James, Dan Glenday, Ann Duffy, and Norene Pupo. *Sociology: Canadian Edition: A Down-to-Earth Approach*. Toronto: Allyn and Bacon, 2001.

Indian Treaties and Surrenders, vol. 1. Toronto: Coles Publishing, 1971. Reprint of federal government publication.

Knockwood, Isabelle. *Out of the Depths*. Lockeport, NS: Roseway Publishers, 1992.

LaRoque, Emma. "Three Conventional Approaches to Native People." In Brett Balon and Peter Resch, eds., *Survival of the Imagination: the Mary Donaldson Memorial Lectures*. Regina: Coteau Books, 1993. Pp. 209–18.

Lawrence, Bonita. *"Real Indians" and Others: Mixed-Blood Urban Native Peoples and Indigenous Nationhood*. Vancouver: UBC Press.

Purich, Donald. *The Métis*. Toronto: Lorimer, 1988.

Rice, Brian, and John Steckley. "Lifelong Learning and Cultural Identity: Canada's Native People." In Michael J. Hatton, ed., *Lifelong Learning: Policies, Practices, and Programs* (APEC pub. #97-HR01.5). Toronto: School of Media Studies, Humber College, 1997. Pp. 216–29.

Robinson, Angela. *Ta'n teli-ktlamsi Tasit (Ways of Believing): Mi'kmaw Religion in Eskasoni, Nova Scotia*. Canadian Ethnography Series, vol. 3. Toronto: Pearson Education Canada, 2005.

Smith, Donald. *Le Sauvage*. Ottawa: National Museum of Man, 1974.

Steckley, John. *Aboriginal Voices and the Politics of Representation in Canadian Introductory Sociology Textbooks*. Toronto: Canadian Scholars Press.

Steckley, John, and Bryan Cummins. *Full Circle: Canada's First Nations*. Toronto: Prentice-Hall, 2001.

Chapter 6

Berger, Peter L. *The Sacred Canopy: Elements of a Sociological Theory of Religion*. New York: Doubleday, 1967.

Buchignani, Norman. "South Asians in Canada: Accommodation and Adaptation." In R.N. Kanungo, ed., *South Asians in a Canadian Mosaic*. Montreal: Kala Bharati, 1984, pp. 157–180.

Buchignani, Norman. "Research on South Asians in Canada: Retrospect and Prospect." In Milton Israel, ed., *The South Asian Diaspora in Canada: Six Essays*. Toronto: The Multicultural History Society of Ontario (in cooperation with Centre for South Asian Studies, University of Toronto), 1987. Pp. 113–140.

Buchignani, Norman, Dorren Indra, and Ram Srivastava. *Continuous Journey: A Social History of South Asians in Canada*. Toronto: McClelland and Stewart, 1985.

Canadian Multiculturalism Act, R.S., 1985, c. 24 (4th Supp.). Available Canadian Heritage site <www.canadianheritage.gc.ca/progs/multi/policy/act_e.cfm>. Accessed 4 April 2006.

"A Tale of Perseverance: Chinese Immigration to Canada." *Life and Society*, CBC Archives, 2006. Available <http://archives.cbc.ca/IDD-1-69-1433/life_society/chinese_immigration>. Accessed 4 April 2006.

Chinese Immigration Act, S.C. 1900, c.32 S.6 and S.C. 1903, c.8 S.6.

Choquette, Robert. *Canada's Religions*. Ottawa: University of Ottawa Press, 2004. P. 145.

Citizenship and Immigration Canada. Archives. Available <www.cic.gc.ca/english>.

Clifford, James. *Routes: Travel and Translation in the late Twentieth Century*. Cambridge, MA: Harvard University Press, 1997.

Coward, Harold, and David Goa. "Religious Experience of the South Asian Diaspora in Canada." In Milton Israel, ed., *The South Asian Diaspora in Canada: Six Essays*. Toronto: The Multicultural History Society of Ontario (in cooperation with Centre for South Asian Studies, University of Toronto), 1987. Pp. 73–86.

Daniels, Roger. "The History of Indian Immigration to the United States: An Interpretive Essay." In Jagat Motwani, Mahin Gosine, and Jyoti Barot-Motwani, eds. *Global Indian Diaspora: Yesterday, Today and Tomorrow*. New York: Global Organization of People of Indian Origin, 1993. Pp. 439–445.

Dawson, Lorne L. *Comprehending Cults*. Toronto: Oxford University Press, 1998. Pp. 52–53.

Department of Justice of Canada website. <http://canada.justice.gc.ca/en/justice2000/libmin00.html>. Accessed 2005.

Durkheim, Emile. *The Elementary Forms of Religious Life*. New York: Free Press, 1995. P. 44.

Geertz, Clifford. *The Interpretation of Cultures*. New York: Basic Books, 1973. P. 90.

Johnson, Hugh. *The Voyage of the Komagata Maru*. University of British Columbia Press, 1989.

Kupferschmid-Moy, Denise. *Across the Generations: A History of the Chinese in Canada*. <http://collections.ic.gc.ca/generations/index2.html>. Accessed 29 April 2006.

Petros, C.I. "Indo-Canadians." In J. Motwani, M. Gosine, J. Barot-Motwani, eds. *Global Indian Diaspora: Yesterday, Today and Tomorrow*. New York: Global Organization of People of Indian Origin, 1993. Pp. 475–484.

Ramcharan, Subash. "South Asian Immigration: Current Status and Adaptation Modes." In R.N. Kanungo, ed., *South Asians in a Canadian Mosaic*. Montreal: Kala Bharati, 1984. Pp. 33–48.

Sampat-Mehta, R. "First Fifty Years of South Asian Immigration: A Historical Perspective." In R.N. Kanungo, ed., *South Asians in a Canadian Mosaic*. Montreal: Kala Bharati, 1984. Pp. 13–32.

Shohat, Ella. *Talking Visions: Multicultural Feminism in a Transnational Age*. Cambridge: MIT Press, 1998.

Sinclair, K. "Women and Religion." In M.I. Dudley and M.I. Edwards, eds., *The Cross-Cultural Study of Women: A Comprehensive Guide*. New York: City University of New York (The Feminist Press), 1986. Pp. 107–124.

Smart, Ninian. *The World's Religions*. Cambridge: Cambridge University Press, 1998. p. 10.

Smith, Huston. *Why Religion Matters*. New York: HarperSanFrancisco, 2001.

Statistics Canada. *The Daily*, February 17, 1998. Available <www.statcan.ca/Daily/English/980217/d980217.htm>. Accessed 26 April 2006.

Thomas, David. *Transcultural Space and Transcultural Beings*. Boulder, CO: Westview Press, 1996.

Wagle, Iabal. "South Asians in Canada, 1905–1920." In Milton Israel and N.K. Wagle, eds., *Ethnicity, Identity, Migration: The South Asian Context*. Toronto: University of Toronto Centre for South Asian Studies, 1993. Pp. 196–216.

Weber, Max. *The Protestant Ethic and the Spirit of Capitalism*. New York: Charles Scribner's Sons, 1958.

Weber, Max. *The Sociology of Religion*. Boston: Beacon Press, 1964. P. 1.

Chapter 7

Accessibility for Ontarians with Disabilities Act. June 14, 2005.

Alford, Glen, ed. *The Advocate*. Toronto: Ontario March of Dimes.

Bickenbach, Jerome. *Physical Disability and Social Policy*. Toronto: University of Toronto Press, 1993.

Bowland, A., C. Nakatsu, and J. O'Reilly, eds. *The 1995 Annotated Ontario Human Rights Code*. Toronto: Carswell, 1995.

Canadian Human Rights Act, R.S.C., 1985.

Driedger, Diane, and Susan Gray, eds. *Imprinting Our Image: An International Anthology of Women's Disabilities*. Charlottetown: Gynergy, 1992.

Eisenberg, Myron G., Cynthia Griggins, and Richard J. Duval, eds. *Spring Series on Rehabilitation: Vol. 2. Disabled People as Second-Class Citizens*. New York: Springer, 1982.

Findley, Timothy. *The Piano Man's Daughter*. Toronto: Harper Collins, 1995.

Goar, Carol. "Historic Moment for Nation's Disabled." *Toronto Star*, 17 March 2010, p. A15.

Goar, Carol. "Tories Earn Mixed Grades at Best from Disabled." *Toronto Star*, 24 March 2010, p. A23.

Higgens, Paul. *Masking Disability: Exploring the Social Transformation of Human Variation*. Springfield: Charles C. Thomas, 1992.

Hornberger, Chris and Peter Milley. *Final Report, Diversity Planning for Inclusive Employment*. Halifax, Nova Scotia: Halifax Global Incorporated, 2005.

Human Rights Legislation: An Office Consolidation. Toronto: Butterworths, 1991.

Ministry of National Health and Welfare: Disabled Persons in Canada. Ottawa: Ministry of National Health and Welfare, 1981.

Kinsey, A.C., W.B. Pomeroy, and C.E. Martin. *Sexual Behavior in the Human Male*. Philadelphia: Saunders, 1948. Reproduced with permission of the Kinsey Institute for Research in Sex, Gender, and Reproduction, Inc.

Office for the Disabled Persons. *The Needs and Attitudes of Disabled Ontarians*. Toronto: Environics Research Group, 1989.

Ontario Ministry of Health and Long-Term Care, Advisory Group. Every Door is the Right Door Towards a 10-Year Mental Health and Addictions Strategy: A Discussion Paper, July 2009.

Rioux, Marcia, and Michael Bach, eds. Disability Is Not Measles: New Research Paradigms in Disability. North York, ON: Roeher Institute, 1994.

Rogers, Patricia. "Atlanta Olympics Take Aim at Barriers to the Disabled." Toronto Star, 16 July 1996.

Rubin, Josh. "Wheelchair Racers Preview Olympic Dash." Toronto Star, 14 July 1996.

Special Committee on the Disabled and Handicapped, First Report (Obstacles). Ottawa: 1980.

Speech by the President of the Treasury Board of Canada to the Disabled People's International Summit. September 10, 2004.

Statistics Canada. Participations and Activity Limitations Survey 2006: Tables. Ottawa: Statistics Canada, 2007, Catalogue No. 89-628-xie-no.003.

Statistics Canada. People with Disabilities. Available <www.hrsdc.gc.ca/.3indiclt.4r@-eng.jsp?iid=40>.

United Nations Convention on the Rights of Persons with Disabilities 2007. Available <www.un.org/disabilities/document/Convention/convotptprot-e.pdf>.

Chapter 8

Baker, Maureen. "Gender and Gender Relations." In R. Jack Richardson and Lorne Tepperman, eds., *An Introduction to the Social World*. Toronto: McGraw-Hill Ryerson, 1987.

Bly, Robert. *Iron John: A Book About Men*. Reading, MA: Addison-Wesley, 1990.

Carey, Elaine. "Women Still Two Steps Behind Men." *Toronto Star*, 9 August 1995, p. A15.

Colombo, Robert. *The 1994 Canadian Global Almanac*. Toronto: Macmillan Canada, 1994.

Fillion, Kate. *Lip Service: Challenging the Sexual Script of the Modern Woman*. Toronto: HarperCollins, 1995.

Friedan, Betty. *The Feminine Mystique*. New York: Dell, 1974.

Jones, Charles, Lorna Marsden, and Lorne Tepperman. *Lives of Their Own: The Individualization of Women's Lives*. Toronto: Oxford University Press, 1990.

Lorenz, Konrad. *On Aggression*. New York: Harcourt Brace and World, 1966.

Mackie, Marlene. *Exploring Gender Relations: A Canadian Perspective*. Toronto: Butterworths, 1982.

Miles, Rosalind. *The Women's History of the World*. Paladin: London, 1989.

Tannen, Deborah. *You Just Don't Understand: Men and Women in Conversation*. New York: Ballantine, 1990.

Wolf, Naomi. *The Beauty Myth*. Toronto: Random House, 1990.

"Women's Ranks Thin in Politics." *Toronto Star*, 28 August, 1995, p. A3.

Chapter 9

Alexander, Jacqui. "Not Just (Any) Body can be a Citizen: The Politics of Law, Sexuality and Postcoloniality in Trinidad and Tobago and the Bahamas." *Feminist Review* 48 (1994): 5–23.

Allman, Dan. *M is for Mutual, A is for Acts: Male Sex Workers and AIDS in Canada*. Ottawa: Health Canada, 1999.

Bergling, Tim. *Sissyphobia: Gay Men and Effeminate Behaviour*. New York: The Haworth Press, 2001.

Canadian Blood Services, "Ministers of Health." <www.sang.ca/CentreApps/Internet/UW_V502_MainEngine.nsf/page/Ministers%20of%20Health?OpenDocument&CloseMenu>. Accessed 26 May 2010.

Chauncey, George. *Gay New York: Gender, Urban Culture and the Making of the Gay Male World, 1890–1940*. New York: Basic Books, 1994.

D'Emilio, John. "Capitalism and Gay Identity." In Ann Snitow, Christine Stansell, and Sharan Thompson, eds., *Powers of Desire: The Politics of Sexuality*. New York: Monthly Review Press, 1983.

Hall, Kira. "Go Suck Your Husband's Sugarcane! Hijras and the Use of Sexual Insult." In Anna Livia and Kira Hall, eds., *Queerly Phrased: Language, Gender and Sexuality*. New York: Oxford University Press, 1997.

Infoism. "About LGBT Rights by Country or Territory," 2006. <http://infoism.net/wiki/LGBT_rights_by_country_or_territory>. Accessed 1 May 2010.

Johnson, David L. *The Lavender Scare: The Persecution of Gays and Lesbians in the Federal Government*. Chicago: University of Chicago Press, 2004.

Krajeski, James. "Homosexuality and the Mental Health Professions: A Contemporary History." In Robert P. Cabaj and Terry S. Stein, eds., *Textbook of Homosexuality and Mental Health*. Washington: American Psychiatric Press, 1996.

Lock, Margaret. "Perfecting Society: Reproductive Technologies, Genetic Testing, and the Planned Family in Japan." In Margaret Lock and Patricia A. Kaufert, eds., *Pragmatic Women in Body Politics*. Cambridge: Cambridge University Press, 1998.

Mackie, Vera. "The Trans-Sexual Citizen: Queering Sameness and Difference." *Australian Feminist Studies* 16 (2001): 185–92.

Nag, Mona. "Sexual Behaviour in India with Risk of HIV/AIDS Transmission." *Health Transition Review* 5 (1995): 293–305.

Olafson, Erna, David L. Corwin, and Roland C. Summit. "Modern History of Child Sexual Abuse Awareness: Cycles of Discovery and Suppression." *Child Abuse and Neglect* 17 (1993): 7–24.

Ottosson, Daniel. "Legal Survey on the Countries in the World having Legal Prohibitions on Sexual Activities between Consenting Adults in Private." 2006. <*http://ilga.org/Statehomophobia/LGBcriminallaws-Daniel_Ottoson.pdf*>. *Accessed* 9 November 2009.

Parliament of Canada. "Bill C-38: The Civil Marriage Act," 2005. <www2.parl.gc.ca/HousePublications/Publication.aspx?Docid=3293341&file=4>. Accessed 26 May 2010.

Pascoe, C.J. *Dude, You're a Fag: Masculinity and Sexuality in High School*. Berkeley: University of California Press, 2007.

Reddy, Gayatri. "'Men' Who would be Kings: Celibacy, Emasculation, and the Re-Production of Hijras in Contemporary Indian Politics—Gender Identity, Social Stigma, And Political Corruption." *Social Research* 70(1) (Spring 2003): 163–200.

Rich, Adrienne. "Compulsory Heterosexuality and Lesbian Existence." In Richard Parker and Peter Aggleton, eds., *Culture, Society and Sexuality: A Reader*, 2nd ed. New York: Routledge, 2007. Pp. 209–36.

Riddell, William Renwick. "Criminal Courts and Law in Early (Upper) Canada." *Journal of the American Institute of Criminal Law and Criminology* 9(2) (August 1918): 173–86.

Ross, Bekki. "Sex and (Evacuation from) the City." Paper at Engendering Social Justice Conference. University of British Columbia <www.wmst.ubc.ca/b_ross.html>. Accessed 29 May 2010.

Roughgarden, Joan. *Evolution's Rainbow: Diversity in Gender and Sexuality in Animals and People*. California: University of California Press, 2004.

Rubin, Gayle. "Thinking Sex: Notes for a Radical Theory of the Politics of Sexuality." In Richard Parker and Peter Aggleton, eds., *Culture, Society and Sexuality: A Reader*, 2nd ed. New York: Routledge, 2007. Pp. 150–87.

Sullivan, Nikki. *A Critical Introduction to Queer Theory*. New York: New York University Press, 2003.

Terry, Jennifer. "Anxious Slippages between 'Us' and 'Them': A Brief History of the Scientific Search for Homosexual Bodies." In Jennifer Terry and Jacqueline Urla, eds., *Deviant Bodies: Critical Perspectives on Difference in Science and Popular Culture*. Bloomington: Indiana University Press, 1995. Pp. 129–69.

Chapter 10

Anderson, Karen, et al. *Family Matters: Sociology and Contemporary Canadian Families*. Toronto: Methuen, 1987.

Baker, Maureen, ed. *Canada's Changing Families: Challenges to Public Policy*. Ottawa: Vanier Institute, 1994.

Baker, Maureen, ed. *Families: Changing Trends in Canada*, 2nd ed. Toronto: McGraw-Hill Ryerson, 1990.

Canadian Citizens to Defend Marriage, Defend Marriage [website], 2003 <www.defendmarriage.ca>.

Canadians for Equal Marriage. "House of Commons Adopts Equal Marriage Bill by Decisive Margin." Press release, June 28, 2005. Available <www.egale.ca/index.asp?lang=E&menu=20&item=1160>. Accessed 29 April 2006.

Cheal, David. *Family and the State of Theory*. Toronto: University of Toronto Press, 1993.

Crompton, Susan. "Always the Bridesmaid: People Who Don't Expect to Marry." *Canadian Social Trends*, Summer 2005. Available <www.statcan.ca/english/studies/11-008/feature/11-008-XIE20050017961.pdf>. Accessed 8 April 2006.

Eichler, Margrit. *Families in Canada Today*. Toronto: Gage, 1983.

Gannon, Maire. *Family Violence in Canada: A Statistical Profile*. Statistics Canada, Catalogue No. 85-224, 2004.

Hagedorn, Robert, ed. *Sociology*. Toronto: Harcourt Brace, 1994.

Mandell, Nancy, and Ann Duffy, eds. *Canadian Families*. Toronto: Harcourt Brace, 1995.

Montgomery, Jason, and Willard Fewer. *Family Systems and Beyond*. New York: Human Sciences Press, 1988.

Nett, Emily. *Canadian Families*. Vancouver: Butterworths, 1993.

"New Mega-Trends Reflect Family Decline." *Today's Family News*, 7 January 2005. Available FamilyFacts.ca <www.fotf.ca/familyfacts/tfn/2005/010705.html>. Accessed 8 April 2006.

Ramu, G., ed. *Marriage and the Family Today*, 2nd ed. Scarborough, ON: Prentice-Hall, 1991.

Reid, Dr. Darrel. "Crisis or Opportunity? Eleven Practical Steps for Strengthening the Family." *Commentaries*, November 1999. Available FamilyFacts.ca <www.fotf.ca/familyfacts/commentaries/110199.html>. Accessed 8 April 2006.

Sauvé, Roger. *Profiling Canada's Families III*. Ottawa: The Vanier Institute of the Family, 2004. Available <www.vifamily.ca/library/profiling3/sample2.html>. Accessed 8 April 2006.

Schlesinger, Rachel, and Benjamin Schlesinger. *Canadian Families in Transition*. Toronto: Canadian Scholar's Press, 1992.

Statistics Canada. *A Portrait of Families in Canada*. Ottawa: Minister of Industry, Science and Technology. Catalogue No. 89-523E, 1993.

Statistics Canada. "Family Violence in Canada: A Statistical Profile 2005." *The Daily*, 14 July 2005. Available <www.statcan.ca/Daily/English/050714/d050714a.htm>. Accessed 8 April 2006.

Statistics Canada. "Income of Canadian Families." Analysis Series, Catalogue No. 96F0030XIE2001014, 13 May 2003. Available <www12.statcan.ca/english/census01/products/analytic/companion/inc/contents.cfm>. Accessed 8 April 2006.

Statistics Canada. "Birth Rate at All-Time Low." *Informat: The Week in Review*. Ottawa: Health Statistics Division, April 27, 2004. Available <www.statcan.ca/english/freepub/11-002-XIE/2004/04/11804/11804_02p.htm>. Accessed 29 April 2006.

Statistics Canada. *Women in Canada 2000*. Ottawa: Minister of Industry, 1995.

Statistics Canada. *The Daily*. 20 May 2004.

Statistics Canada. "Births." *The Daily*, July 12, 2005. Available <www.statcan.ca/Daily/ English/050712/d050712a.htm>. Accessed 8 April 2006.

Statistics Canada. "Divorces." *The Daily*, March 9, 2005. Available <www.statcan.ca/Daily/ English/050309/d050309b.htm>. Accessed 8 April 2006.

Statistics Canada. "Lone-Parent Families as a Proportion of All Census Families Living in Private Households, Canada, Provinces, Territories, Health Regions and Peer Groups, 2001." November 26, 2003. Available <www.statcan.gc.ca/english/freepub/82-221-XIE/01103/ tables/html/49_01.htm>. Accessed 8 April 2006.

Statistics Canada. "Profile of Canadian Families and Households: Diversification Continues." *The Daily*, October 22, 2002. Available <www12.statcan.ca/english/census01/products/analytic/ companion/fam/contents.cfm>. Accessed 8 April 2006.

Thorne, Barrie, and Marilyn Yalom, eds. *Rethinking the Family*. Boston: Northeastern University Press, 1992.

Tucker, Robert, ed. *The Marx–Engels Reader*, 2nd ed. New York: W.W. Norton, 1978.

Chapter 11

Barlow, Maude. *Too Close for Comfort: Canada's Future within Fortress North America*. Toronto: McClelland and Stewart, 2005.

Biagi, Shirley. *Media/Impact: An Introduction to Mass Media*. Belmont, CA: Wadsworth, 1994.

Barber, Benjamin R. *Jihad vs. McWorld: How Globalism and Tribalism Are Reshaping the World*. New York: Ballantine Books, 1996.

De Kerckhove, Derrick. *The Skin of Culture: Investigating the New Electronic Reality*. Toronto: Somerville House, 1995.

Dyson, Rose A. *Mind Abuse: Media Violence In An Information Age*. Montreal: Black Rose Books, 2000.

Fleras, Augie and Jean Lock Kunz. *Media and Minorities: Representing Diversity in Multicultural Canada*. Toronto: Thompson Educational Publishing, 2001.

Fleras, Augie, and Jean Leonard Elliott. *Multiculturalism in Canada: The Challenge of Diversity*. Toronto: Nelson, 1992.

Herman, Edward and Noam Chomsky. *Manufacturing Consent: The Political Economy of the Mass Media*. New York: Pantheon Books, 2002.

Innis, Harold. *Empire and Communications*. Toronto: Press Procepic, 1986.

Klaehn, Jeffery ed. *Filtering the News: Essays on Herman and Chomsky's Propaganda Model*. Montreal: Black Rose Books, 2005.

Kottak, Conrad Philip. *Prime-Time Society: An Anthropological Analysis of Television and Culture*. Belmont, CA: Wadsworth, 1990.

Kroker, Arthur. *Technology and the Canadian Mind: Innis/McLuhan/Grant*. Montreal: New World Perspectives, 1984.

McLuhan, Eric, and Frank Zingrone, eds. *Essential McLuhan*. Concord, ON: Anansi Press, 1995.

McLuhan, Marshall. *The Mechanical Bride: Folklore of Industrial Man*. New York: Vanguard, 1951.

McLuhan, Marshall. *The Gutenberg Galaxy: The Making of Typographic Man*. Toronto: University of Toronto Press, 1962.

McLuhan, Marshall. *Understanding Media: The Extensions of Man*. New York: New American Library, 1964.

McLuhan, Marshall, and Quentin Fiore. *War and Peace in the Global Village*. New York: Bantam, 1968.

McLuhan, Marshall, and Bruce R. Powers. *The Global Village: Transformations in World Life and Media in the Twenty-First Century*. New York: Oxford University Press, 1989.

McQuaig, Linda. *All You Can Eat: Greed, Lust and the New Capitalism*. Toronto: Penguin Books, 2001.

McQuaig, Linda. *The Cult of Impotence: Selling the Myth of Powerlessness in the Global Economy*. Toronto: Penguin Books, 1998.

McQuaig, Linda. *Shooting the Hippo: Death by Deficit and Other Canadian Myths*. Toronto: Penguin Books, 1995.

McQuaig, Linda. *The Wealthy Banker's Wife*. Toronto: Penguin Books, 1993.

McQuaig, Linda. *The Quick and the Dead: Brian Mulroney, Big Business and the Seduction of Canada*. Toronto: Penguin Books, 1991.

Meyrowitz, Joshua. *No Sense of Place: The Impact of Electronic Media on Myths*. Toronto: Penguin Books, 1995.

Ong, Walter. *Orality and Literacy: The Technologizing of the Word*. New York: Routledge, 1988.

Parenti, Michael. *Inventing Reality: The Politics of News Media*. New York: St. Martin's Press, 1993.

Postman, Neil. *The Disappearance of Childhood*. New York: Delacorte Press, 1982.

Postman, Neil, and Steve Powers. *How to Watch TV News*. New York: Penguin, 1992.

Rodman, George. *Mass Media in a Changing World*. New York: McGraw Hill, 2006.

Sauvageau, Florian, David Schneiderman, and Davis Taras. *The Last Word: Media Coverage of the Supreme Court of Canada*. Toronto: UBC Press, 2006.

Tunstall, Jeremy. *The Media Are American: Anglo-American Media in the World*. London: Constable, 1977.

Vipond, Mary. *The Mass Media in Canada*. Toronto: Lorimer, 2000.

Winter, James. *Media Think*. Montreal: Black Rose Books, 2002.

Winter, James. *Democracy's Oxygen: How Corporations Control the News*. Montreal: Black Rose Books, 1997.

Chapter 12

Atwood, Margaret. *Survival, A Thematic Guide to Canadian Literature*. Toronto: House of Anansi, 2004.

Boyden, Joseph. *Three Day Road*. Toronto: Penguin Canada, 2005.

Carrier, Roch. *The Hockey Sweater*. Trans. Sheila Fischman. Toronto: House of Anansi, 1979.

Choy, Wayson. *The Jade Peony*. Vancouver: Douglas & McIntyre Ltd., 1995.

Clarke, Austin. *The Polished Hoe*. Toronto: Thomas Allen Publishers, 2002.

Dickner, Nicolas. *Nikolski*. Trans. Lazer Lederhendler. Toronto: Random House, 2008.

Fong Bates, Judy. *A Year of Finding Memory*. Toronto: Random House, 2010.

Fulford, Robert. *The Triumph of Narrative: Storytelling in the Age of Mass Culture*. Toronto: House of Anansi, 1999.

Hacket Fischer, David. *Champlain's Dream*. Toronto: Vintage Canada, 2009.

Hay, Elizabeth. *Late Nights on Air*. Toronto: McClelland & Stewart Ltd., 2007.

Hill, Lawrence. *The Book of Negroes*. Toronto: Harper Collins, 2007.

Itani, Frances. *Deafening*. Toronto: Harper *Flamingo* Canada, 2003.

Koyczan, Shane. "We Are More." Vancouver: House of Parlance, 2010.

Laurence, Margaret. *The Diviners*. Toronto: McClelland & Stewart, 1974.

Lyall Aitken, Johan. *Masques of Morality, Females in Fiction*. Toronto: The Women's Press, 1987.

Lyon, Annabel. *The Golden Mean*. Toronto: Random House, 2009.

Mootoo, Shani. *Valmiki's Daughter*. Toronto: House of Anansi Canada, 2008.

Munro, Alice. *Lives of Girls and Women*. Toronto: McGraw-Hill Ryerson Ltd. 1971.

Munro, Alice. *Too Much Happiness*. Toronto: McClelland & Stewart Ltd., 2009.

OED, Compact Edition of the OED, Volume I, p. 775, entry 550.

Ovid. *Metamorphoses*. Trans. Mary Innes. London: Penguin, 1955.

Painter, Nell Irvin. *The History of White People*. New York: W.W. Norton & Company Inc., 2010.

Saul, John Ralston. *A Fair Country, Telling Truths About Canada*. Toronto: Viking Canada, 2008.

Wachtel, Eleanor. *Random Illuminations: Conversations with Carole Shields*. Toronto: Goose Lane Editions, 2007.

BIOGRAPHIES

Paul U. Angelini teaches in the General Arts and Science program at Sheridan College Institute of Technology and Advanced Learning. He has developed and delivered curriculum at Sheridan since 1988 in the fields of politics, sociology, human diversity, philosophy, and social movements. Paul completed his Master's degree in political studies from Queen's University and his combined honours bachelor of arts in political science and sociology at McMaster University.

Michelle A. Broderick completed her Ph.D. in Biological Anthropology at the University of Toronto. Since graduating in 1994, she has taught a variety of courses at Sheridan College, McMaster University, and the University of Toronto. Michelle is currently working in Institutional Research at the University of Toronto.

Leslie Butler has been a community college professor for twenty-four years. She has taught English and general education courses, and currently coordinates the Journalism New Media program at Sheridan College. She received a master's degree in English from the University of Waterloo and a master's degree in journalism from the University of Western Ontario.

Lee Easton teaches in the Department of English at Mount Royal University. He teaches courses in literary and communication theory as well as film studies. He is interested in representation of sexualities in popular culture. He has a Ph.D. from the University of Toronto and is currently chair of the Department of English at MRU.

Shane Gannon is an assistant professor in the Department of Sociology & Anthropology at Mount Royal University, in Calgary, Alberta. His current research and teaching interests include queering (post-)colonial sexual histories of South Asia and exploring the role of citizenship in sexual governance.

Eddie Grattan is presently a vice-principal of a school in Dundas, Ontario. He has a master's degree in sociology from Queen's University. He is presently doing research on the relationship between social class and the media portrayal of sport.

Grant Havers is professor of Philosophy and chair of the Department of Philosophy (with a cross-appointment in the Department of Political Studies) at Trinity Western University. He has published and lectured widely on North American political thought, especially the conservative tradition. Havers' most recent book is *Lincoln and the Politics of Christian Love* (University of Missouri Press, 2009).

Paula Jessop, M.A., has developed Canadian literature curriculum for the Ontario Ministry of Education and promoted the study of Canadian literature at the secondary and tertiary levels of education across Canada. She currently is the founder and artistic director of the *Toronto Reading Series*, and *Conversations*, a series of uniquely paired dialogues featuring Canadian authors in conversation with leading Canadian executives, academics, and professionals.

Nancy Nicholls is a professor in the Social Service Worker program at Centennial College and was the recipient of the Board of Governor's Award for Excellence in Valuing Diversity. She holds a master's degree in social work from the University of British Columbia and an honours bachelor of arts from York University. She has taught in college for twenty years and during her social work career she has worked in the fields of mental health, developmental disabilities, immigration and refugee rights as a counsellor, family and group therapist, community developer, administrator, and advocate. She has written about inclusive college classrooms.

Geoff Ondercin-Bourne has taught communications, ESL, and a variety of social sciences courses at Mohawk College for the past eight years. Before that, he taught global issues, Canadian politics, sociology, literature, communications, and ESL at Sheridan College for fifteen years. Geoff received a master's degree from McMaster University and an honours B.A. from the University of Guelph.

Mikal Austin Radford is a professor of Philosophy and Religion in the School of Community and Liberal Studies at Sheridan College (Brampton, Ontario) and Wilfrid Laurier University (Waterloo, Ontario) where he teaches courses in Asian philosophy and South Asian traditions. His ongoing research specializes in religion, eastern philosophy, multiculturalism, and transnational identity formation, with a focus on the Jain community of Canada and the United States. His publications include "*Sallekhana, Ahimsa*, and the Western Paradox: The Jaina Ritual of Fasting to Death," "Role Models of Jaina Citzenship in the Western World," "Religion as Meaning and the Canadian Context," and "(Re)Creating Transnational Religious Identity with the Jaina Community of Toronto."

John Steckley has been teaching at Humber College since 1983, and has taught Anthropology at Memorial University of Newfoundland and at Trent University, and Native Studies and Anthropology at Laurentian University. His twelve published books include *Beyond Their Years: Five Native Women's Stories* (1999), *Aboriginal Voices and the Politics of Representation in Canadian Introductory Sociology Textbooks* (2003), *De Religione: Telling the Seventeenth-Century Jesuit Story in Huron to the Iroquois* (2004), *White Lies About the Inuit* (2006), *Words of the Huron* (2007). With Bryan Cummins, he has co-authored

Full Circle: Canada's Native People (2001) and *Aboriginal Policing: A Canadian Perspective* (2002). With Guy Letts, he has co-authored *Elements of Sociology: A Critical Canadian Introduction* (2nd edition, 2010). His areas of specialization are Aboriginal languages (primarily Huron) and Aboriginal history. John has a master's degree in anthropology from Memorial University of Newfoundland and a doctorate in postsecondary education from the Ontario Institute for Studies in Education (OISE) at the University of Toronto. He was adopted into the Wyandot tribe of Kansas in 1999 and given the name *Tehaondechoren* ("He splits the country in two").

INDEX